1200

Crystallography
and Crystal Perfection

Crystallography and Crystal Perfection

Proceedings of a Symposium held in Madras
14–18 January 1963 and organized by the
University of Madras

Edited by G. N. RAMACHANDRAN
Department of Physics, University of Madras, India

ACADEMIC PRESS
London and New York · *1963*

ACADEMIC PRESS INC. (LONDON) LTD.
Berkeley Square House, Berkeley Square
London, W.1

U.S. Edition published by
ACADEMIC PRESS INC.
111 Fifth Avenue
New York 3, New York

Library of Congress Catalog Card Number: 63–15032

Printed in Great Britain by
Spottiswoode, Ballantyne and Company Limited
London and Colchester

List of Contributors

AJIT RAM VERMA, *Banaras Hindu University, Varanasi, India* (p. 197)

K. ANZENHOFER, *Max-Planck-Institut für Eiweiss- und Lederforschung, München, West Germany* (p. 51)

L. V. AZÁROFF, *Illinois Institute of Technology, Chicago, Illinois, U.S.A.* (p. 109)

G. BEURSKENS-KERSSEN, *University of Utrecht, The Netherlands* (p. 225)

J. M. BIJVOET, *University of Utrecht, The Netherlands* (p. 225)

G. BORRMANN, *Fritz-Haber-Institut der Max-Planck-Gesellschaft, Berlin-Dahlem, West Germany* (p. 101)

M. J. BUERGER, *Massachusetts Institute of Technology, Cambridge, Massachusetts, U.S.A.* (p. 3)

S. CHANDRASEKHAR, *University of Mysore, Mysore, India* (p. 125)

W. COCHRAN, *Cavendish Laboratory, Cambridge, England* (p. 67)

D. DALE, *Chemical Crystallographic Laboratory, Oxford, England* (p. 237)

H. J. ENDEMAN, *University of Utrecht, The Netherlands* (p. 225)

F. FUJIMOTO, *University of Tokyo, Tokyo, Japan* (p. 259)

K. FUJIWARA, *University of Tokyo, Tokyo, Japan* (p. 259)

D. C. HODGKIN, *Chemical Crystallographic Laboratory, Oxford, England* (p. 237)

W. HOPPE, *Max-Planck-Institut für Eiweiss- und Lederforschung, München, West Germany* (p. 51)

R. HUBER, *Max-Planck-Institut für Eiweiss- und Lederforschung, München, West Germany* (p. 51)

P. K. IYENGAR, *Atomic Energy Establishment, Bombay, India* (p. 279)

H. JAGODZINSKI, *Max-Planck-Institut für Silikatforschung, Würzburg, West Germany* (p. 177)

N. KATO, *Nagoya University, Nagoya, Japan* (p. 153)

P. KRISHNA, *Banaras Hindu University, Varanasi, India* (p. 197)

R. S. KRISHNAN, *Indian Institute of Science, Bangalore, India* (p. 329)

J. KROON, *University of Utrecht, The Netherlands* (p. 225)

J. I. LANGFORD, *University College, Cardiff, Wales* (p. 207)

J. LAVAL, *College de France, Paris, France* (p. 319)

K. LEHMANN, *Fritz-Haber-Institut der Max-Planck-Gesellschaft, Berlin-Dahlem, West Germany* (p. 101)

W. N. LIPSCOMB, *Harvard University, Cambridge, Massachusetts, U.S.A.* (p. 79)

M. MALLIKARJUNAN, *University of Madras, Madras, India* (p. 133)

D. McLACHLAN, Jr., *University of Denver, Denver, Colorado, U.S.A.* (p. 15)

S. S. MITRA, *Armour Research Foundation, Chicago, U.S.A.* (p. 347)

S. MIYAKE, *University of Tokyo, Tokyo, Japan* (p. 259)

P. S. NARAYANAN, *Indian Institute of Science, Bangalore, India* (p. 329)

S. NAYA, *Kwansei Gakuin University, Nishinomiya, Japan* (p. 43)

I. NITTA, *Kwansei Gakuin University, Nishinomiya, Japan* (p. 43)

T. ODA, *Osaka University of Liberal Arts and Education, Osaka, Japan* (p. 43)

V. M. PADMANABHAN, *Atomic Energy Establishment, Bombay, India* (p. 269)

R. PARTHASARTHY, *University of Madras, Madras, India* (p. 133)

V. RAGHUPATHY SARMA, *University of Madras, Madras, India* (p. 85)

R. RAMACHANDRA AYYAR, *University of Madras, Madras, India* (p. 25)

G. N. RAMACHANDRAN, *University of Madras, Madras, India* (pp. 25, 85, 133)

S. RAMAN, *Harvard University, Cambridge, Massachusetts, U.S.A.* (p. 79)

S. RAMASESHAN, *Indian Institute of Technology, Madras, India* (pp. 243, 309)

M. RENNINGER, *Kristallographisches Institut der Universität, Marburg, West Germany* (p. 145)

J. SHANKAR, *Atomic Energy Establishment, Bombay, India* (p. 269)

A. K. SINGH, *Indian Institute of Technology, Madras, India* (p. 309)

R. SRINIVASAN, *University of Madras, Madras, India* (pp. 67, 85)

P. TOLLIN, *Cavendish Laboratory, Cambridge, England* (p. 67)

S. N. VAIDYA, *Indian Institute of Science, Bangalore, India* (p. 243)

J. VAN LAAR, *University of Utrecht, The Netherlands* (p. 225)

K. VENKATESAN, *Chemical Crystallographic Laboratory, Oxford, England* (p. 237)

I. WALLER, *Uppsala University, Uppsala, Sweden* (p. 189)

A. J. C. WILSON, *University College, Cardiff, Wales* (p. 207)

A. M. WOOSTER, *Crystal Structures Limited, Cambridge, England* (p. 295)

G. A. WOOSTER, *Crystal Structures Limited, Cambridge, England* (p. 295)

W. A. WOOSTER, *Crystal Structures Limited, Cambridge, England* (p. 295)

I. S. ZHELUDEV, *Institute of Crystallography, Moscow, U.S.S.R.* (p. 359)

Preface

An International Symposium on Protein Structure and Crystallography was organized by the Department of Physics, University of Madras, during the second half of January, 1963. This volume is a report of the papers presented at the Symposium on Crystallography, which formed a part of the Conference. The papers in the Symposium were concerned with various aspects of crystallographic techniques. A large number of them dealt with methods of crystal structure analysis, in particular with the phase problem and the use of anomalous dispersion. Another group of papers dealt with crystal perfection and crystal disorder and a third group with electron and neutron diffraction and instrumentation. A series of papers dealing with the application of X-ray diffraction to protein structure was also presented, and this, along with the Presidential Address of Professor Bragg, are published in a companion volume to this one, entitled "Aspects of Protein Structure".

The Symposium was made possible by grants provided by the University of Madras, The University Grants Commission and the Council of Scientific and Industrial Research, Government of India. The Organizing Committee is deeply grateful to these agencies for the generous support of the Symposium. The organizers would also like to acknowledge the continuous support and encouragement given to them by Dr. A. L. Mudaliar, Vice-Chancellor, University of Madras. The Editor wishes to thank the Academic Press for their considerable help, in various ways, in providing preprints and for speedy publication of this volume. His thanks are also due to Dr. R. Srinivasan, Dr. R. Parthasarathy and Mr. C. Ramakrishnan for their assistance in reading the proofs and recording the discussions.

G. N. RAMACHANDRAN

Department of Physics
University of Madras

May 1963

Contents

SECTION IV—Anomalous Dispersion

SECTION V—Electron and Neutron Diffraction

SECTION VI—Instrumentation

SECTION VII—Other Physical Studies

SECTION I
Phase Problem

Some Properties of Image Functions

M. J. BUERGER

*Massachusetts Institute of Technology,
Cambridge, Massachusetts, U.S.A.*

ABSTRACT

The Patterson function can be interpreted as the image of the electron density in itself. Thus the Patterson function can be described as a special kind of *image function*. It is evidently a specialization of a more general image function which can be set up to provide the image of one function f_2 in another function f_1. In this paper the properties of such image functions are surveyed. Certain significant properties can be studied by using an *image algebra*, which is first developed. The general geometrical features of images are first discussed, and then the symmetries of images. This study throws light on the loss of translation components of symmetry elements which occurs in Patterson functions. The relation of convolutions to image functions is considered, and it is suggested that there do not exist non-periodic functions with the same self-convolution unless the function is centrosymmetrical.

1. INTRODUCTION

In deriving the Patterson function, one first sets up the product of the values of the electron-density function at a particular difference in argument, and integrates this product over the desired volume, specifically

$$A(\mathbf{t}) = \frac{1}{V^2} \int \rho(\mathbf{r}) \rho(\mathbf{r}+\mathbf{t}) \, dV \qquad (1)$$

This function is evidently a special case of a more general one

$$A'(\mathbf{t}) = \frac{1}{V^2} \int \rho_1(\mathbf{r}) \rho_2(\mathbf{r}+\mathbf{t}) \, dV \qquad (2)$$

in which the two electron densities are different.

More generally, let the coefficient in (2) be omitted, and let ρ_1 and ρ_2 be more general functions; then one can devise a simple function having the general features of (2) as follows:

$$f_3(\mathbf{t}) = \int f_1(\mathbf{r}) f_2(\mathbf{r}+\mathbf{t}) \, dV \qquad (3)$$

3

This will be called an *image function* (Buerger, 1963), for reasons which will become evident. It is related to a convolution, which can be written

$$f_3(\mathbf{t}) = \int f_1(\mathbf{r}) f_2(-\mathbf{r}+\mathbf{t}) \, dV \qquad (4)$$

The image function and convolution are, however, distinct, and their properties are different (Buerger, 1962).

What are the properties of the image function? To examine some of these properties will be the subject of this discourse.

2. Examination by Means of Point Functions

There are several ways of examining the properties of image functions. Joel (1963) has examined them by converting them to convolutions of different arguments and then treating them as products in Fourier space. This is a treatment of very general validity, but it is more illuminating to examine the properties by simplifying the functions in (3) to sets of weighted points. Any function can be transformed into a set of points by sampling it with appropriate delta functions. The sum of all such possible delta functions is the original function, but the behaviour of a few representative points is sufficient to characterize the behaviour of the function. This method was used with success in the study of the properties of the Patterson function (Buerger, 1959).

If each of the functions in (3) is sampled by means of delta functions, the functions yield the following sets of points.

$$f_1(\mathbf{r}) \rightarrow S_1$$
$$f_2(\mathbf{r}+\mathbf{t}) \rightarrow S_2 \qquad (5)$$

S_1, for example, represents a set of points; each point of the set can be regarded as having a weight equal to the value of f_1 at the point sampled by that delta function. The function product in (3) thus becomes the product of point sets, that is

$$f_1(\mathbf{r}) f_2(\mathbf{r}+\mathbf{t}) \rightarrow S_1 S_2 \qquad (6)$$

To manipulate such products calls for discussing a simple algebra.

3. Image Algebra

A. *Representation of sets*

Let a set S be comprised of a collection of points denoted by a, b, c.... Let the sign " + " indicate adding a point to a set. Then the meaning of S can be represented by

$$S = a+b+c+\ldots \qquad (7)$$

Thus the two terms on the right of (6) can be expanded as

$$S_1 = a+b+c+\ldots$$
$$S_2 = p+q+r+\ldots$$

(8)

so that the product on the right of (6) becomes

$$S_1 S_2 = (a+b+c+\ldots)(p+q+r+\ldots)$$

(9)

This can be expanded into a matrix which is, in general, rectangular.

$$S_1 S_2 = \begin{bmatrix} ap & aq & ar & \cdot & \cdot & \cdot \\ bp & bq & br & \cdot & \cdot & \cdot \\ cp & cq & cr & \cdot & \cdot & \cdot \\ \cdot & \cdot & \cdot & & \cdot & \end{bmatrix}$$

(10)

B. *Interpretation of simple products*

What is the meaning of the individual products, like ap? To interpret this, it is desirable to relabel the vector for the argument of the second function as

$$\mathbf{r}+\mathbf{t} = \mathbf{s}$$

(11)

If $\mathbf{t}$ is eliminated by this means, (3) becomes

$$f_3(\mathbf{s}-\mathbf{r}) = \int f_1(\mathbf{r})\, f_2(\mathbf{s})\, \mathrm{d}V$$

(12)

Thus a is a point sample of f_1 located at the end of vector $\mathbf{r}$, and p is a point sample of f_2 located at the end of vector $\mathbf{s}$. The weight of ap is the product ap, and this occurs at a point located at the end of vector $\mathbf{s}-\mathbf{r}$.

This is the vector from point a to point p, so it can also be designated $\overrightarrow{ap}$. It is evident that the label ap can therefore be used to imply both a weight ap and a location at the end of a vector $\overrightarrow{ap}$.

With this explanation, it is evident that the right of (10) represents a collection of points at the ends of vectors $\overrightarrow{ap}, \overrightarrow{aq}, \overrightarrow{ar}\ldots$, whose respective weights are $ap, aq, ar\ldots$. This permits interpreting the right of (10) as a collection of weighted points whose weights are determined by the products on the right of (10) and whose locations are interpreted by vectors determined by these paired letters.

A simple physical interpretation can be given to a product like ap. The vector component $\overrightarrow{ap}$ involves both distance and direction from a to p, and can be regarded as the image of p as seen from a. This image has a weight proportional to the weight of the point seen, namely p, and to the weight of the viewing point, namely a; the net weight of the image is thus ap. Thus the designation ap is an image. An image has two components: a weight component and a location component. The algebra dealing with such images is called *image algebra* (Buerger, 1961–62).

In making use of a designation ap to imply not only a point whose weight is ap but a point whose location is at the end of vector $\overrightarrow{ap}$, it is important to note that, whereas the weight ap is a product which follows the rules of ordinary algebra, the location ap follows the rules of vectors; that is

$$\overrightarrow{pa} \neq \overrightarrow{ap} \tag{13}$$

rather
$$\overrightarrow{pa} = -\overrightarrow{ap} = \overrightarrow{(-a)(-p)} \tag{14}$$

Accordingly, in image algebra

$$pa \neq ap \tag{15}$$

rather
$$pa = \overline{ap} = \bar{a}\,\bar{p} \tag{16}$$

where the bar over ap implies that the term is negative with respect to location. Thus, if image point ap, at the end of vector $\overrightarrow{ap}$, has co-ordinates xyz, the image point pa is at the end of vector $-\overrightarrow{ap} = \overrightarrow{(-a)(-p)}$ and accordingly has co-ordinates $\bar{x}\bar{y}\bar{z}$. The left side of (15) is thus obtained from the right side by inversion in the origin. They are said to be *inverses* of one another.

The rules of image algebra are thus that products are non-commutative, but associative, whereas addition is both commutative and distributive. Whereas the sign "$+$" signifies adding a term to a collection, the sign "$+\langle-\rangle$" signifies removing a term.

C. *Properties of* I

To complete the algebra a term corresponding with unity is still needed. This can be supplied by symbolizing a unit point at the origin. Let the symbol for such a point be I. Then any point a can be regarded as an image as seen from a unit point at the origin, namely

$$a = Ia \tag{17}$$

The term I, used as a prefactor, can therefore be omitted at pleasure.

If a in (17) is assigned the particular value I, it follows that

$$I = II \tag{18}$$

If the order of the I's on the right of (18) is reversed, (16) indicates that

$$I = \bar{I}\bar{I} \tag{19}$$

If both sides of (19) are inverted there results

$$\bar{I} = II \tag{20}$$

Comparison of (18) and (20) shows that

$$I = \bar{I} \tag{21}$$

so that I is its own inverse.

When I is used as a postfactor it functions as an invertor for, according to (16),

$$aI = \bar{I}\bar{a}$$

$$= I\bar{a}$$

$$= \bar{a} \tag{22}$$

The inversion also occurs for a set, because

$$SI = (a+b+c+\ldots)\,I$$

$$= \bar{I}(\bar{a}+\bar{b}+\bar{c}+\ldots)$$

$$= \bar{I}\bar{S}$$

$$= \bar{S} \tag{23}$$

D. *Multiple products*

Let points be located at a, b, and c. Then bc is the image of c from b, and this image point is readily located: it occurs at the end of vector $\vec{bc} = \overrightarrow{I(bc)}$. It is also possible to draw a vector from point a to point bc. This more complicated image point is designated $a(bc)$. It occurs at the end of a vector $(\mathbf{c}-\mathbf{b})-\mathbf{a}$. Since this vector can be rewritten $\mathbf{c}-(\mathbf{b}+\mathbf{a})$, it follows that

$$a(bc) = (\bar{a}b)c \tag{24}$$

THEOREM: *The parenthesis of a multiple product can be moved one space in either direction provided the sign of the captured or released term (not the object term) is changed.*

Furthermore, the vector $(\mathbf{c}-\mathbf{b})-\mathbf{a}$ can be rewritten $(\mathbf{c}-\mathbf{a})-\mathbf{b}$; it follows that

$$a(bc) = b(ac) \tag{25}$$

This result can be obviously extended to the more general relation:

THEOREM: *All terms of a multiple product are permutable except the object term.*

E. *Coefficients*

It is often convenient to use coefficients in connection with elements of image algebra. For example

$$a + a + a = 3a \tag{26}$$

In this case the meaning of the coefficient is obvious; the right of (26) implies a point at the end of vector $\vec{Ia} = \vec{a}$ whose weight is $3a$. More generally a weight may be expressed by a symbol. To avoid confusion with a term of a product designating an image, the coefficient, which is a weight coefficient, may be placed within pointed brackets: $\langle\rangle$. Thus $\langle m \rangle a$ indicates m coincident points each of weight a, all located at the end of $\vec{a}$; this is equivalent to a point at the end of $\vec{a}$ of weight ma. Similarly, $\langle - \rangle a$ is a point of negative weight a at the end of vector $\vec{a}$, etc.

F. *Point at the origin*

Consider the image aa. This occurs at the end of the vector $\mathbf{a} - \mathbf{a}$, which is a null vector, i.e. aa is located at the origin, but its weight is $aa = a^2$. It follows that

$$aa = \langle a^2 \rangle I \tag{27}$$

or, alternatively,

$$\frac{1}{\langle a^2 \rangle} aa = I \tag{28}$$

G. *Cancellation*

Cancellation can be produced by premultiplying or postmultiplying by an appropriate term. Cancellation by postmultiplication occurs as follows.

$$pq = r$$

$$(pq)\, q = rq$$

$$\overline{p}(qq) = rq$$

Now, according to (27)

$$qq = \langle q^2 \rangle I$$

so

$$\overline{p}\langle q^2 \rangle I = rq$$

$$Ip\langle q^2 \rangle = rq$$

$$Ip = \frac{1}{\langle q^2 \rangle} rq$$

$$p = \frac{1}{\langle q^2 \rangle} rq$$

Cancellation by premultiplication proceeds differently.

$$pq = r$$

$$\overline{p}(pq) = \overline{p}r$$

$$(pp)q = \overline{p}r$$

$$\langle p^2 \rangle Iq = \overline{p}r$$

$$Iq = \frac{1}{\langle p^2 \rangle} \overline{p}r$$

$$q = \frac{1}{\langle p^2 \rangle} \overline{p}r$$

4. Basic Properties of Image Sets

A. *Image sets*

Let a set be decomposed into its component parts,

$$S_2 = p + q + r + \ldots \tag{29}$$

The image of this set in point a is the product

$$aS_2 = a(p + q + r + \ldots)$$
$$= ap + aq + ar + \ldots \tag{30}$$

If the order of terms on the left of (30) is reversed, the result is

$$S_2 a = (p + q + r + \ldots) a$$
$$= pa + qa + ra + \ldots$$
$$= \overline{a}\overline{p} + \overline{a}\overline{q} + \overline{a}\overline{r} + \ldots$$
$$= \overline{a}\overline{S}_2 \tag{31}$$

The sets in (30) and (31) are inverses, that is, all the co-ordinates of one are those of the other except that they are inverted through the origin.

B. *Geometrical features of image sets*

A product of two sets, such as $S_1 S_2$, can be given a simple geometric interpretation. If $S_1 S_2$ is expanded as in (10), a typical term like ap is seen to consist of a vector from point a to the origin, I, plus a vector from the origin to point p; more specifically,

$$\overrightarrow{ap} = \overrightarrow{aI} + \overrightarrow{Ip}$$
$$= \overrightarrow{Ia} + \overrightarrow{Ip} \tag{32}$$

Now let the symbol $\overrightarrow{S_1 S_2}$ represent the collection of vectors from the points of S_1 to the points of S_2. Each vector can be treated as (32), and the corresponding treatment of the collection of vectors can be symbolized by

$$\overrightarrow{S_1 S_2} = \overrightarrow{S_1 I} + \overrightarrow{I S_2}$$

$$= \overrightarrow{I \bar{S}_1} + \overrightarrow{I S_2} \tag{33}$$

This result can be interpreted as follows. The points of the image set $S_1 S_2$ can be located by constructing a set of vectors from the origin to the points of the inverse of S_1 and, taking each of these points as a separate new origin, constructing vectors to the points of S_2.

An alternative treatment of $\overrightarrow{S_1 S_2}$ is

$$\overrightarrow{S_1 S_2} = \overrightarrow{\bar{S}_2 \bar{S}_1}$$

$$= \overrightarrow{\bar{S}_2 I} + \overrightarrow{I \bar{S}_1}$$

$$= \overrightarrow{I S_2} + \overrightarrow{I \bar{S}_1} \tag{34}$$

This can be interpreted as follows. The points of the image $S_1 S_2$ can be located by constructing vectors to the points of S_2, and from each of these points constructing vectors to the inverse of $\bar{S}_1$.

These results can be recast into image language as follows:

THEOREM: *The set* $S_1 S_2$ *can be constructed by placing* S_2 *at each point of the inverse of* S_1 *and weighting it by the weight of that point.*

THEOREM: *The set* $S_1 S_2$ *can be constructed by placing the inverse of* S_1 *at each point of* S_2 *and weighting it by the weight of that point.*

These are the basic theorems of image theory.

C. *Vector sets*

A vector set is a special case of an image set in which both sets are the same, as in $S_1 S_1$. Such a set may be called a *self-image set*. For self-image sets the location theorems are the following.

THEOREM: *The self-image set* $S_1 S_1$ *can be resolved into images of the fundamental sets having the relative locations of the inverse of the fundamental set.*

THEOREM: *The self-image set* $S_1 S_1$ *can be resolved into images of the inverse of the fundamental set having the relative locations of the fundamental set.*

D. *Convolutions*

The convolution function has a form which can be reduced as follows.

$$\widehat{f_3}(\mathbf{t}) = \int f_1(\mathbf{r}) f_2(\mathbf{t}-\mathbf{r}) \, dV$$

$$= \int f_1(\mathbf{r}) f_2(-\mathbf{r}+\mathbf{t}) \, dV$$

$$= \int f_1(\mathbf{r}) \bar{f_2}(\mathbf{r}-\mathbf{t}) \, dV \tag{35}$$

Here $\bar{f_2}$ is the inverse of the function f_2. If $-\mathbf{t'} = \mathbf{t}$ is substituted in (35), it becomes

$$\widehat{f_3}(-\mathbf{t'}) = \int f_1(\mathbf{r}) \bar{f_2}(\mathbf{r}+\mathbf{t'}) \, dV \tag{36}$$

or

$$\overline{\widehat{f_3}}(\mathbf{t'}) = \int f_1(\mathbf{r}) \bar{f_2}(\mathbf{r}+\mathbf{t'}) \, dV \tag{37}$$

This is now in the form of an image function. The corresponding formulation for sets of discrete points is

$$\widehat{S_3} = S_1 \bar{S_2} \tag{38}$$

so that

$$\overline{\widehat{S_3}} = \bar{S_1} S_2 \tag{39}$$

Utilizing the basic theorem of image theory, it is evident that the convolution of two sets can be constructed as follows.

THEOREM: *The convolution of two sets can be constructed by placing the first set at each point of the second set and weighting it by the weight of that point.*

5. SYMMETRIES OF IMAGE SETS

The symmetries of image sets can be investigated by applying the foregoing theorem to symmetrical sets with the aid of the algebra of operations (Buerger, 1956). Consider two sets S_1 and S_2 having some symmetry in common, for example, parallel axes with a common angular component α. In particular, suppose S_1 has a screw axis one of whose operations can be represented (Buerger, 1956) by $^1A_{\alpha, \tau_1}$, while S_2 has a screw axis one of whose operations is $^2A_{\alpha, \tau_2}$. Let U_1 be a subset of one set of equivalent positions in S_1 and U_2 be a subset of one set of equivalent positions in S_2. To form $U_1 U_2$, U_2 is placed at each point of U_1. Any two of these images of U_2 are related by a translation T. Let T be decomposed into components of which $T_{\parallel}$ is parallel to the screw and $T_{\perp}$ is perpendicular to the screw. Here $T_{\parallel}$ is $-\tau_1$ because of the inverse character of

$\bar{U}_1$. Then, using the algebra of operations, the combination of $^2A_{\alpha,\tau_2}$ with T is

$$
\begin{aligned}
^2A_{\alpha,\tau_2}\cdot T &= A_{\alpha,\tau_2}\cdot T_{\parallel}\cdot T_{\perp} \\
&= A_{\alpha,\tau_2}\cdot(-\tau_1)\,T_{\perp} \\
&= {}^2A_{\alpha,(\tau_2-\tau_1)}\,T_{\perp} \\
&= B_{\alpha,(\tau_2-\tau_1)}
\end{aligned}
\tag{40}
$$

This can be interpreted to mean that if two sets, S_1 and S_2 (as represented by their subsets U_1 and U_2) have parallel symmetry axes, their image set S_1S_2 has a parallel symmetry axis whose angular component is the common angular component α and whose translation component is the difference of the translation components of the symmetries of the second and first sets. If the parallel symmetry elements are symmetry planes, the corresponding relation can be proven, except that τ_2 and τ_1 are then vectors, that is, the translation components of the glide plane.

For self-image sets, $S_2 = S_1$ and $\tau_2 = \tau_1$, so that (40) shows that all translation components vanish. This is the reason for the non-existence of screw axes and glide planes in the symmetries of Patterson functions.

6. Symmetries of Convolutions

If the same treatment is applied to convolutions, the first term in the convolution product of two sets is the inverse of the first set. This causes a change in sign of τ in (40), so the result is

$$
^2A_{\alpha,\tau_2}\cdot T = B_{\alpha,(\tau_2+\tau_1)}
\tag{41}
$$

and a corresponding result holds for glide planes. Thus a convolution also preserves the common angular component of parallel symmetry elements of the sets of the product, but the translation component is the sum of the components of the terms in the product.

In the special case of the self-convolution,

$$
\widehat{S}_3 = \bar{S}_1 S_1
\tag{42}
$$

the translation component of the symmetry element is not annihilated as in the self-image, but is doubled, so that the equivalent of (41) for self-convolution is

$$
A_{\alpha,\tau}\cdot T = B_{\alpha,2\tau}
\tag{43}
$$

7. Self-images and Self-convolutions

The self-image of S_1 is

$$
S_3 = S_1 S_1
\tag{44}
$$

while the self-image of its inverse, $\bar{S}_1$, is

$$S_4 = \bar{S}_1 \bar{S}_1 \tag{45}$$

According to (16) the terms on the right of (45) can be interchanged with change of signs to give

$$S_4 = S_1 S_1 \tag{46}$$

which is identical with (44).

THEOREM: *The self-image of a set and its inverse are the same.*

The same situation does not occur in convolutions, for

$$\widehat{S}_3 = \bar{S}_1 S_1 \tag{47}$$

but the self-convolution of $\bar{S}_1$ is

$$\widehat{S}_4 = S_1 \bar{S}_1$$
$$= -\bar{S}_1 S_1$$
$$= -\widehat{S}_3 \tag{48}$$

THEOREM: *The self-convolution of an inverse set is the inverse of the self-convolution of the set.*

The self-convolution of a set and its inverse are the same only if the set and its inverse are the same, that is, if the set is centrosymmetrical. In this case the distinction between self-image and self-convolution vanishes.

It can be shown that the possibility of homometry in the self-image of non-periodic sets is basically due to the fact that the set and its inverse have the same self-image. But the set and its inverse do not have the same self-convolution.

THEOREM: *There do not exist distinct non-periodic sets with the same self-convolutions unless the set is centrosymmetrical.*

8. Homometric Periodic Self-image Sets

The algebra of images permits throwing some light on periodic homometric sets. Consider a 3-point set S_3. If a fourth point p be added, the new set is $p + S_3$, and its self-image is

$$(p + S_3)(p + S_3) = pp + pS_3 + S_3 p + S_3 S_3 \tag{49}$$

The first term is always a point at the origin; the last term is always the self-image of S_3, but the terms pS_3 and $S_3 p$, which are inverses, depend on the relative location of p and S_3. If this is adjusted, there are two ways of arranging them to produce the same periodic set of points in the self-image provided two points of S_3 are separated by half a cell diagonal. This demonstration focuses attention on the part of the set responsible for the homometric feature.

If the self-convolution is formed of $p + S_3$ the result is

$$
\begin{aligned}
(\bar{p} + \bar{S}_3)(p + S_3) &= \bar{p}p + \bar{p}S_3 + \bar{S}_3 p + \bar{S}_3 S_3 \\
&= \bar{p}p + \bar{p}S_3 + \bar{p}S_3 + \bar{S}_3 S_3 \\
&= \bar{p}p + 2\bar{p}S_3 + \bar{S}_3 S_3
\end{aligned}
\tag{50}
$$

This is the sum of three convolutions. The set $\bar{S}_3 S_3$ is common to all convolutions of 4-point sets based upon the left of (50). The point $\bar{p}p$ is not at the origin, but it has a location characteristic of the location of p. The term $2\bar{p}S_3$ is a double weight convolution of p and S_3 and is, in general, noncentrosymmetrical. These facts suggest the following:

CONJECTURE: *There probably do not exist distinct periodic sets with the same self-convolution unless the set is centrosymmetrical.*

REFERENCES

Buerger, M. J. (1956). *Elementary Crystallography*. Wiley, New York.
Buerger, M. J. (1959). *Vector Space and Its Application in Crystal Structure Investigation*. Wiley, New York.
Buerger, M. J. (1961). *Z. Kristallogr.* **116**, 430.
Buerger, M. J. (1961–62). *Atti Accad. Sci., Torino* **96**, 175.
Buerger, M. J. (1962). *Atti Accad. Naz., Lincei* **6**, 83.
Buerger, M. J. (1963). *Z. Kristallogr.* **118** (In press).
Joel, N. (1963). *Z. Kristallogr.* **118** (In press).

DISCUSSION

G. N. RAMACHANDRAN: Every one of the results you have described here could, I think, be shown from the point of view of Fourier transform theory.

M. J. BUERGER: Yes. In fact, Joel has worked out these results using not merely the point set, but the function itself by the use of the convolution theorem. These results are about to appear in a paper in the *Zeitschrift für Kristallographie*.

The Direct Instrumentation of Phase-determining Techniques

Dan McLachlan, Jr.

*Department of Metallurgy, University of Denver, Denver,
Colorado, U.S.A.*

ABSTRACT

The three phase-determining techniques which are easily handled by analogue computers are the vector convergence method, the McLachlan-Harker method and the squaring method of Sayre. The paper describes how optical arrangements can be devised which will perform these three methods of phase determination.

1. Introduction

Perhaps the most diligently pursued aspect of theoretical crystallography in the last decade has been the determination of the phases (or signs) of the F values. Although several methods of phase determination have showed great promise, the most fruitful one so far has been the heavy atom method much preferred by Robertson of Glasgow. Other methods of note include the Harker-Kasper inequalities and the methods of Karle and Hauptman. This paper deals with the instrumentation of just three methods; (a) the vector convergence method, (b) the McLachlan-Harker method, and (c) the squaring method of Sayre. Because of some similarities among these methods, certain types of instrumentation can be applied to more than one of them. Some of these instruments are more useful as teaching aids than for the more practical applications in the determination of structures. This is a question which the reader or anticipated user can determine. Nevertheless, these procedures are being implemented in the laboratories at the University of Denver. Since much of the understanding of the functioning of these instruments depends upon a knowledge of correlation functions of which Patterson maps are a special class, we shall devote a few paragraphs at the beginning of the paper to reviewing these functions.

2. Some Properties of Patterson Maps

Although the Patterson procedure has recently become more frequently applied to three dimensions because of the increasing complexity of the structures attacked by X-ray crystallographers, most of the

15

principles can be demonstrated in two dimensions, to which the following
equations apply

$$A(u, v) = \frac{1}{ab} \int_0^a \int_0^b \rho(x, y)\, \rho(x + u, y + v)\, \mathrm{d}x\, \mathrm{d}y$$

$$= \frac{2}{A} \sum_h \sum_k |F_{hk0}|^2 \cos 2\pi(hx + ky) \tag{1}$$

where x and y are the fractional co-ordinates. If the atoms are located in
the original structure at $x_j y_j$, the Patterson atoms are at $u_k, v_k = u_{jj'}, v_{jj'}$
determined by

$$u_{jj'} = x_j - x_{j'}$$

$$v_{jj'} = y_j - y_{j'} \tag{2}$$

and if the atomic structure factors of the original atoms are f_j those of
the Patterson "atoms" are $f_j f_{j'}$.

Let us illustrate with the simplest non-trivial two-dimensional structure, i.e. Fig. 1 (a). The Patterson map of this structure is shown in Fig.
1 (b). If the Patterson procedure is applied to a Patterson map, a
"squared" Patterson map is obtained according to

$$B(s, t) = \frac{1}{ab} \int_0^a \int_0^b A(u, v)\, A(u + s, v + t)\, \mathrm{d}u\, \mathrm{d}v \tag{3}$$

and is shown in Fig. 1(c), with "squared Patterson atoms" located at
$s_l = u_k - u_{k'}$ and $t_l = v_k - v_{k'}$. Whereas the original pattern containing
n atoms gives $N = n(n-1)$ Patterson atoms (in this case $n = 3$ and $N = 6$),
besides the peak at the origin, the squared Patterson gives no less than
$N(N-1) = 49$ squared Patterson atoms. Figure 1 (c) shows only 18
"atoms" besides the one at the origin. This is because there are several
coincidences giving strong peaks such as a, b, c, d, e and f in Fig. 1 (c).
These strong peaks have the same configuration as the peaks in the
Patterson map. The manner by which these strong peaks occur is shown
in Fig. 2, wherein the peak at the origin of the original pattern is translated to new positions in the squared Patterson. A second reason for the
fewer-than-expected number of peaks is that there are $(n-1)$ identical
distances of each length in a Patterson map which when applied to a
squared Patterson appear as a single maximum upon it. These factors
are useful in structure determination.

Figure 2 also shows a principle worth noting. Figure 2 (a) is the Patterson in its $s = 0$, $t = 0$ position, while Fig. 2(b) shows superimposed upon
it a second Patterson translated by the distance 7–3. If these maps were
multiplied through and integrated in accordance with Eq. (3) one would

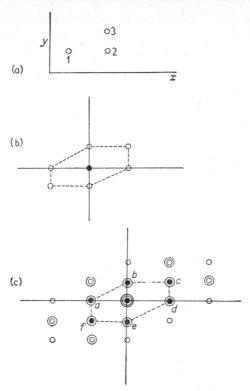

Fig. 1. (a) A structure of three atoms. (b) A Patterson map of (a). (c) A squared Patterson map.

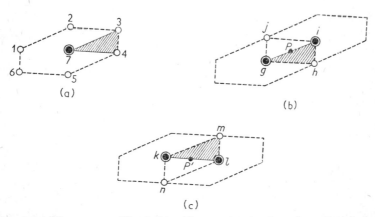

Fig. 2. (a) The same as Fig. 1 (b) with one structural configuration shaded. (b) A shift of distance 7–3 and the same structure shaded. (c) A shift 7–4 and the same structure shaded.

get the peak c in Fig. 1 (c) of the squared Patterson; and Fig. 2 (c) shows how the peak d of Fig. 1 (c) is produced. The reader will recognize that these are the essential steps in producing a squared Patterson map and also the reader will recognize that without the integration these steps are each a "shifted Patterson product" or a "vector convergence", now well-known as a method for the interpretation of Patterson maps. Note in Fig. 2 (b) that the original structure (see Fig. 1 (a)) shows as ghi in Fig. 2 (b); and incidentally its inverse as gij, the two patterns being inverted about the point P. Also in Fig. 2 (c) the original pattern shows as klm and its inverse as knl, the inversion point being P'. It is of interest that the patterns ghi and klm are in identical positions, while the inverted patterns gij and knl are not identically situated. There are in general n shift positions for the Patterson of an n-atom structure which shows the original pattern identically located. If equipment were built for demonstrating this principle, teaching, as well as structure determination could be made easier. Two such devices are described below.

3. THEORETICAL PATTERSON MAPS

Two machines are to be described, (A) the direct translator and (B) the Fourier translator.

A. *The direct translator*

The synthetic Patterson machine of the optical kind as shown in Fig. 3 is well-known from the several publications on the subject. A known structure placed on the plane A and a copy of it placed on the lens L at B results in a synthetic Patterson map on plane P when the light is turned on in the light box LB striking the ground glass GG. Or, if Patterson maps are placed on A and B a "squared" Patterson map appears on P. The advantage of this optical method is that the entire map $A(uv)$ or $B(st)$ for all values of u and v, or s and t are obtained instantaneously. But this advantage is a disadvantage from the pedagogical standpoint, since no steps in the process can be observed by the student and the method of shifted Patterson products or (vector convergence) is difficult to arrange or to change. A mechanical means devised and in use at the University of Denver is more interesting.

As shown schematically in Fig. 4 (a) a pattern placed on A and a second one placed in contact with it at B are illuminated by a light box and a ground glass GG placed at almost contact with A. The pattern A, the ground glass GG and the recording paper P are fixed, but the plane B is arranged to move as governed by the mechanism M. The motion of B is a spiral one without rotation as shown by the curve OZ in Fig. 4 (b). If by the motion of B over A the light shows through because of a coincidence of spots, then the pointer P_0 is pressed manually producing a mark on stationary paper P. The pattern of marks on P is the configuration of Patterson maxima (or squared Patterson maxima) of the patterns

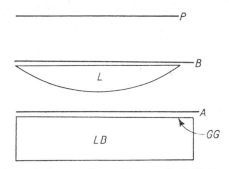

FIG. 3. An optical means for making synthetic Patterson maps.

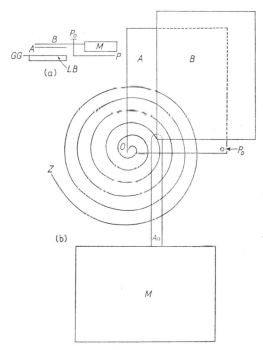

FIG. 4. A mechanical means for making synthetic Patterson maps.

mounted at A and B. Every time an observer sees a repetition of the original structure (from two Pattersons placed on A and B) showing up on this apparatus at the same place n times, he becomes more conscious of the structure.

One difficulty with these methods is that they apply only to projections, that is, two-dimensional patterns. Frequently with minerals and almost always with giant organic molecules, the maxima on a projection are not resolved because the maxima are so numerous that they interfere and overlap. Three-dimensional patterns are desired by almost all crystallographers. However, some of the features of three-dimensional studies without the disadvantage of large numbers of maxima can be gained by the use of Patterson slices, a heretofore neglected aspect of the structure problem. Before discussing Patterson slices, let us describe the Fourier translator.

B. *The Fourier translator*

It was implied in a paper by McLachlan and Harker (1951) that if one wished to produce a shifted Patterson product map directly from the $|F_{hk0}|^2$ values without first making a Patterson projection $A(uv)$ one could use the equation

$$\rho(u', v'; \Delta x, \Delta y) = \frac{1}{A} \sum_h \sum_k (F_{hk0})_s \exp\left\{-2\pi i(hu' + kv')\right\} \qquad (4)$$

where Δx and Δy are the shift distances and the structure factor of the resulting map is

$$(F_{hk0})_s = \left(\frac{2b}{a\pi}\right)^3 \frac{1}{4} \sum_{h'} \sum_{k'} |F_{h'k'}|^2 |F_{h'-h,\,k'-k}|^2 \times$$

$$\times \cos 2\pi[2(h'-h)\,\Delta x + 2(k'-k)\,\Delta y] \qquad (5)$$

The first thing to be noticed about Eq. (5) is that the term

$$\sum_{h'} \sum_{k'} |F_{h'k'}|^2 |F_{h'-h,\,k'-k}|^2 \qquad (5a)$$

is really an auto-correlation or self-convolution of the $|F_{hk0}|^2$ that is, a Patterson map of reciprocal space in two dimensions. Therefore, if the reciprocal lattice of $|F|^2$ is placed on A of Fig. 3 and another on B, the term (5a) will appear all worked out on P†.

The second thing to be noticed about Eq. (5) is that the term

$$\cos 2\pi[2(h-h')\,\Delta x + 2(k-k')\,\Delta y] \qquad (5b)$$

is just of the form for which the Bragg-Huggins masks were devised:

$$\cos 2\pi(hx + ky) \qquad (5c)$$

with the interchange of terms:

---

† The inner products in the Sayre method can be obtained in the same way.

$$h \to 2\Delta x$$

$$k \to 2\Delta y$$

$$x \to h' - h$$

$$y \to k' - k$$

Therefore a Bragg-Huggins mask must be placed over B in Fig. 3 along with the map of $|F|^2$ for each shift Δx, Δy. Since the values of $2\Delta x$ and $2\Delta y$ are not integral as are h and k from which they were derived (see Eq. (5b)), a variable producer of masks needs to be provided. The synthesizer for triangular wave functions (McLachlan, 1957) or the von Eller (1951) machine is satisfactory.

4. A Composite of Dreams

To get a structure from the X-ray data without computation, Fig. 5 shows the schematic arrangement of apparatus. The reciprocal lattice of $|F_{hk0}|^2$ is placed at A and similarly at B. These lattices are arrays of

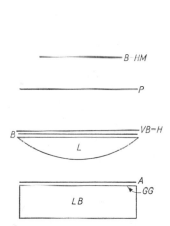

FIG. 5. A schematic drawing of a mechanism for going directly from X-ray data to shifted Patterson products of any extent of shifting.

transparent dots arranged in rows numbered h and columns numbered k, and whose area (or total transmissions) are proportional to $|F_{hk0}|^2$. Then at $VB\text{-}H$ is a variable Bragg-Huggins mask to perform the operation Eq. (5b). On P then, will appear the reciprocal lattice of values $(F_{hk0})_s$ as expressed in Eq. (5). This is an array of dots of light proportional in intensity to the magnitude of $(F_{hk0})_s$. All that is left is to do a Fourier summation according to Eq. (4). Fortunately the "multiple projector" of McLachlan and Woolley (1951) requires this set up. The array of Bragg-Huggins masks (as specified in the paper describing the projector) is placed at B-HM and the shifted Patterson product appears at SPP.

The only thing to be varied to change the shifts Δx, Δy is the mask VB-H, which can be achieved through either the von Eller machine or the triangular synthesizer. The pattern on SPP can be observed while VB-H is varied to detect repetitions of the original structure as depicted in Figs. 2 (b) and 2 (c).

The big thing that makes this scheme a dream instead of a feasible reality is that after the light from the light box LB has gone through so many scattering and absorbing stages, it is too weak to be visible at SPP. We need commercial light intensifiers to boost the intensity at each stage. A discussion of this subject is provided by Goetze and Taylor (1962) of Westinghouse.

5. PATTERSON SLICES

In 1936, Harker noticed that certain point group and space group operators in crystals assured predictable $\Delta x_{jj'}$ (or $\Delta y_{jj'}$, or $\Delta z_{jj'}$) between chosen atoms in the structure. For example a two-fold rotor down the c-axis assured that the atoms would be paired so that $\Delta z_{jj'} = 0$, and consequently a Patterson section through $w = 0$ produced a map containing a number of Patterson "atoms" equal to the number of atoms in the structure. What we need in the absence of these fortunately convenient operations is a means of investigating the cases where pairs of atoms are not necessarily at zero distances from one another along Z, but within certain specified distances. A Patterson slice (James, 1948) does this and reduces the number of Patterson maxima to be studied at any one time.

Starting with the Patterson equation

$$A(uvw) = 1/V \sum_h \sum_k \sum_l |F_{hkl}|^2 \exp\{-2\pi i(hu+kv+lw)\} \qquad (6)$$

which represents the density of termination of Patterson vectors throughout the Patterson space u, v, w, one can pass two planes through the cell perpendicular to the c-axis, one at $w = w_1$ and the other at $w = w_2$ and integrate over w between these limits to get the number of vectors $G_{12}(uv)$ within the slice:

$$G_{12}(uv) = N\left(\frac{ab}{A}\right) \int_{w_1}^{w_2} A(uvw)\,dw$$

$$= \frac{1}{\pi A} \sum_h \sum_k \sum_l \frac{|F_{hkl}|^2}{l} \exp\left\{-2\pi i\left[hu+kv+l\frac{(w_2+w_1)}{2}\right]\right\} \times$$

$$\times \sin \pi l(w_2-w_1) \qquad (7)$$

In this equation $(w_2 + w_1)/2$ is the position along w of the mid-plane of the slice and $w_2 - w_1$ is the thickness of the slice. If the thickness is made small enough so that only a few Patterson "atoms" can possibly be included, then the analysis becomes simple for each slice. By migrating up the w-axis at constant thickness by gradually increasing $(w_2 + w_1)/2$ from zero to c, the observer can carry his successive deductions along as he goes upward.

The reader will readily notice that Eq. (7) is readily summed using standard methods by the equation

$$G_{12} = \frac{1}{V} \sum_h \sum_k (F_{hk})_G \exp\left\{ -2\pi i(hu + kv) \right\} \tag{8}$$

where

$$(F_{hk})_G = \sum_l \frac{|F_{hkl}|^2}{2\pi l} \exp\left\{ 2\pi i l \left(\frac{w_2 + w_1}{2} \right) \right\} \sin \pi l(w_2 - w_1) \tag{9}$$

In the composite of dreams the terms for $(F_{hk})_G$ expressed in Eq. (9) are to be placed on A and B in Fig. 5.

References

Goetze, G. W. and Taylor, A. (1962). *Rev. sci. Instrum.* **33**, 353.
James, R. W. (1948). *The Optical Principles of the Diffraction of X-Rays.* G. Bell and Sons Ltd., London.
McLachlan, D. (1957). *J. sci. Instrum.* **34**, 201.
McLachlan, D. and Harker, D. (1951). *Proc. nat. Acad. sci., Wash,* **37**, 846.
McLachlan, D. and Woolley, R. H. (1951). *Rev. sci. Instrum.* **22**, 423.
von Eller, G. (1951). *C. R. Acad. Sci., Paris* **232**, 1122.

Discussion

D. HARKER: The McLachlan-Harker method would not work if there is overlap in the Patterson function. Also this is only valid for centrosymmetric structures.

D. MCLACHLAN: Two Patterson maps of a crystal can, in principle, be laid over one another in relative shifted positions and their densities multiplied through without actually having the Patterson map at hand. The McLachlan-Harker method shows how to do this directly from intensity data. The most fruitful distance for shifting the Patterson maps before multiplication is usually chosen from the resolved peaks on the Patterson map, but with the method of seeking described in the paper, the meaningful shift can be determined by inspection or from the maximum of the integrated shifted Patterson product.

Fourier Syntheses for Feeding in Isomorphous Replacement and Anomalous Dispersion Data

G. N. Ramachandran and R. Ramachandra Ayyar

Department of Physics, University of Madras, Madras, India

ABSTRACT

The paper deals with Fourier methods which can be used for a pair of isomorphous crystals or with anomalous dispersion data. It is not necessary to determine the phases but by feeding in a suitable combination of the observed intensities and the calculated structure amplitudes of the known atoms into the proper Fourier syntheses (β_{is} or β_{an} syntheses) the remaining part of the structure can be obtained. These new syntheses have actually been tested in the case of a non-centrosymmetric crystal and found to work quite satisfactorily. Both the isomorphous as well as the anomalous syntheses gave stronger peaks at the unknown atomic positions than the simple heavy-atom synthesis.

The relative advantages of the β synthesis proposed by Ramachandran and Raman and the usual heavy-atom synthesis have also been tested both for a centrosymmetric as well as a non-centrosymmetric projection. In both cases, the ratio of the peak heights of the unknown to the known atoms was found to be higher for the beta than for the heavy-atom synthesis, thus proving the superiority of the former.

1. Introduction

Ever since the discovery of the isomorphous replacement method by Robertson (1936), this method has been used, with modifications, for the solution of a variety of structures, including in particular those of crystalline proteins. The difference-Patterson (D.P.) which employs $(|F^{(1)}|^2 - |F^{(2)}|^2)$ as the Fourier coefficients (where $F^{(1)}$, $F^{(2)}$ are the structure factors of the two isomorphous crystals) was first discussed by Buerger (1942). Kartha and Ramachandran (1955) showed that this diagram could be solved for the crystal structure, provided the positions of the replaceable atoms are known, by making use of superposition methods, and that this could be done for all space groups, both centrosymmetric as well as non-centrosymmetric, except for 11 non-centrosymmetric space groups. In these cases alone, viz. $P1$, $P2$, $P2_1$, $C2$, Pm, Pc, Cm, Cc, $P4$, $I4$, $P6$, if there is only one set of replaceable atoms per unit cell, then the constellation of replaceable atoms is centrosymmetric, while the crystal structure is non-centrosymmetric, so that the superposition method leads to the correct structure accompanied by

25

its inverse about the centre of symmetry of the replaceable atoms. On the other hand, if there is more than one replaceable atom in the asymmetric unit, this difficulty does not arise.

This suggests that the intensity data of a pair of isomorphous crystals contain within themselves, in general, all the information necessary for the determination of the structure and it would be interesting to work out *Fourier* methods which would lead to the same result. When more than two isomorphous derivatives are available, and the replacement is at different sites in the different pairs, the approach *via* superposition methods on the difference-Pattersons indicates that the solution of the crystal structure is unique.

The approach via the phase method has been discussed by Bokhoven *et al.* (1949) and Harker (1956). The phase determination is ambiguous when there is only one pair of isomorphous crystals, but becomes unique with multiple isomorphous replacement. This method has been widely used for the analysis of protein structures, particularly for haemoglobin and myoglobin (see Dickerson *et al.*, 1961). In all these cases, the best phase angle was determined by combining the phase determinations from the different isomorphous derivatives. The purpose of this paper is to point out a possibility of combining the different data, without actually determining the phases, but only making use of simple combinations of the observed intensities.

Very similar methods can also be developed for dealing with the anomalous dispersion data. Although the possibility of determining phases from the differences in intensity between inverse reflections has been in the air for a long time (see, for example, Bijvoet, 1951; and Peerdeman and Bijvoet, 1956), the method was first put to a practical test by Ramachandran and Raman (1956) and was shown to lead to reasonably good values for the phases in a crystal whose structure was known. Later it was actually applied to solve an unknown structure of reasonable complexity, that of L-lysine monohydrochloride dihydrate (Raman, 1959a). The essential correctness of this structure has been confirmed recently by a full three-dimensional study (Wright and Marsh, 1962). Simultaneously with the work of Ramachandran and Raman (1956), Pepinsky and co-workers (Okaya *et al.*, 1955; Pepinsky and Okaya, 1956) pointed out a different way of making use of the anomalous dispersion data, namely by calculating a Patterson (P_s function) in which the coefficients are $|F(hkl)|^2 - |F(\bar{h}\bar{k}\bar{l})|^2$. The properties of this function and its various applications have been reviewed in a recent paper by Okaya and Pepinsky (1961). This Patterson, like the difference-Patterson for isomorphous crystals, can in principle be solved for the structure by means of superposition methods, and the structure is then, in fact, obtained in its absolute configuration.

As in the case of single isomorphous replacement, the phase determination is ambiguous with anomalous dispersion data also. Since the anomalous Patterson can, in principle, be solved uniquely for the structure and since this uses the same data, namely the difference in intensities (or structure amplitudes) of the inverse reflections, it appeared that some method should be sought for by which a Fourier series with the property of revealing the structure could be obtained, making use of only the differences in intensities of the inverse reflections (Bijvoet differences) and the anomalous atom positions. In fact, such a series has properties very similar to that for a pair of isomorphous crystals, and hence it seems to be appropriate to discuss the two together.

In what follows, the terminology and notation adopted in the series of papers from this laboratory in *Acta Crystallographica*, entitled "Deconvolution of the Patterson Function", are freely made use of. In particular, the first two parts (Ramachandran and Raman, 1959; Raman, 1959b) may be referred to for details.

2. The Beta-isomorphous Synthesis

Denoting the contributions from the replaceable atoms alone in the two isomorphous crystals (1) and (2) by $F_P^{(1)}$, $F_P^{(2)}$, where

$$F_P^{(1)} = \sum f_{Pj}^{(1)} \exp 2\pi i \mathbf{H} \cdot \mathbf{r}_{Pj} \tag{1a}$$

$$F_P^{(2)} = \sum f_{Pj}^{(2)} \exp 2\pi i \mathbf{H} \cdot \mathbf{r}_{Pj} \tag{1b}$$

and that from the other atoms (Q) by

$$F_Q = \sum f_{Qj} \exp 2\pi i \mathbf{H} \cdot \mathbf{r}_{Qj} \tag{2}$$

we have

$$F^{(1)} = F_P^{(1)} + F_Q, \quad F^{(2)} = F_P^{(2)} + F_Q \tag{3}$$

so that

$$\delta |F|^2 = |F^{(2)}|^2 - |F^{(1)}|^2 = \delta |F_P|^2 + (\delta F_P F_Q^* + \delta F_P^* F_Q) \tag{4}$$

where the δ stands for the difference between the corresponding quantities for the two isomorphous crystals.

Consequently we have

$$\beta_{\text{is}} = \frac{[\delta |F|^2 - \delta |F_P|^2] \exp i\alpha_P}{|\delta F_P|} \tag{5a}$$

$$= F_Q + \frac{\delta F_P}{\delta F_P^*} F_Q^* = F_Q + F_Q^* \exp 2i\alpha_P \tag{5b}$$

Thus, a Fourier synthesis employing β_{is} as coefficients would yield a diagram containing peaks at the unknown atomic positions (F_Q) on a background composed of the modulation (convolution) of the inverse structure with the phase squared structure of the P atoms. The latter will be distributed if the group of P atoms is not centrosymmetric and would not lead to concentrated peaks. Thus, this synthesis, which makes use of only the observed intensities and the calculated structure amplitudes of the known atoms, will reveal the unknown part of the structure, while at the same time completely suppressing the known peaks.

It would be interesting to compare this with the results of the phase determination method. It can be shown that it is possible to determine $F_Q = |F_Q| \exp i\alpha_Q$ from the known quantities, namely $|F_P^{(1)}|$, $|F_P^{(2)}|$ and δF_P, but for an ambiguity in the phase α_Q. In the usual method of phase determination α_Q is not determined; instead $\alpha^{(1)}$ (or $\alpha^{(2)}$) is determined and this is combined with $|F^{(1)}|$ (or $|F^{(2)}|$) and these are used in the Fourier series. However, as is well known, the phase determination is ambiguous, and this leads to an ambiguity in the sign of $\phi^{(1)} = \alpha^{(1)} - \alpha_P$. A slight extension of this argument shows that there will also be an ambiguity in the sign of $\phi_Q = \alpha_Q - \alpha_P$ determined from a single pair of isomorphous crystals. If the correct phase is α_Q, then the two values thus obtained for the phase will be α_Q and $2\alpha_P - \alpha_Q$.

Suppose now we use both the phases in a Fourier synthesis, with the same magnitude for $|F_Q|$. Then, the coefficients are

$$|F_Q| \exp i\alpha_Q + |F_Q| \exp 2i\alpha_P \exp - i\alpha_Q = F_Q + F_Q^* \exp 2i\alpha_P \qquad (6)$$

which is identical with β_{is} in Eq. (5b). Thus, it is seen that the β_{is} synthesis is *identically* equivalent to taking both the possible values of the phase in a Fourier synthesis. On the other hand, in the form given in Eq. (5a), we completely avoid the necessity of actually determining the phases, and it is therefore very convenient for numerical computations.

It should be emphasized that, when only a single pair of isomorphous crystals is available, there is no way of distinguishing between the two ambiguous values obtained for the phase, so that the β_{is} synthesis is the only one that can be calculated. It is interesting that, when the P group of known atoms is not centrosymmetric, this synthesis would theoretically be expected to reveal the unknown atoms in the structure.

This has actually been tested out in a hypothetical case constructed out of an actual crystal structure. The structure chosen was that of phosphorus pentasulphide P_4S_5, solved by Van Houten and Wiebenga (1957). The crystal belongs to the space group $P2_1$ and the atomic coordinates, as reported, are given in Table I. The reason for this choice was that all the atoms are well resolved both in the centrosymmetric b projection as well as the non-centrosymmetric a projection.

The replaceable atoms (P atoms) were taken to be S_1, S_3 and S_5 and their scattering factors in the two isomorphous crystals were taken to be

f_S and $3f_S$. The coefficients β_{is} were calculated from Eq. (5a), and the resulting β_{is} synthesis for the non-centrosymmetric a projection is shown in Fig. 1 (a). It is seen that the remaining six atoms in the structure (Q atoms, marked by crosses) have all come out prominently. The few spurious peaks in the diagram are much weaker than the atomic peaks. It will be noticed that the known P atoms are suppressed (positions marked by black dots).

For comparison, a simple Fourier synthesis (F_Q synthesis) of the Q atoms is shown in Fig. 1 (c) and the heavy-atom synthesis

$$\gamma'_{\mathrm{mod}} \equiv (W|F_N| - |F_P|)\exp i\alpha_P$$

where W is the weighting function suggested by Woolfson (1956) and Sim (1960), and α_P is the phase of the P atoms for the second crystal

TABLE I. Fractional co-ordinates of the atoms in the structure of P_4S_5; Space group $P2_1$. Unit-cell dimensions: $a = 6\cdot41$ Å; $b = 10\cdot94$ Å; $c = 6\cdot69$ Å; $\beta = 111\cdot7°$

Atom	x	y	z
P_1	0·684	0·004	0·401
P_2	0·470	0·132	0·495
P_3	0·758	0·259	0·575
P_4	0·480	0·237	0·052
S_1	0·627	0·065	0·088
S_2	0·251	0·209	0·212
S_3	0·722	0·349	0·288
S_4	0·970	0·106	0·622
S_5	0·856	0·378	0·805

($3f_S$), is shown in Fig. 1 (d). It will be noticed that the peaks in the β_{is} synthesis are in fact even stronger than those in the simple Fourier synthesis (although there is a fluctuating background), while those in the heavy atom (γ') synthesis are much weaker. For comparison, the peak values of the electron density in the different diagrams are listed in Table II.

Thus, although the phase ambiguity is inherent in the β_{is} synthesis, it definitely shows up the unknown atoms, and can be confidently used for a non-centrosymmetric crystal. It may be remarked that Kartha (1961) has calculated the double-phased synthesis using as coefficients $|F_N|(\exp i\alpha_1 + \exp i\alpha_2)$, where α_1 and α_2 are the two possible values of the phase found by the isomorphous replacement method. He also found that all the unknown atoms were revealed by the synthesis.

When more than one set of atoms can be replaced, it should naturally

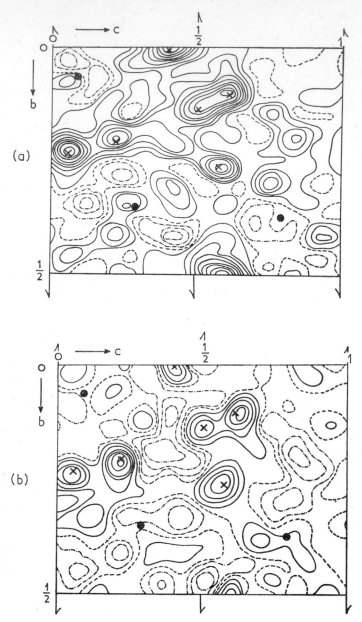

FIG. 1. (a) The beta-isomorphous (β_{is}) synthesis for the P_4S_5 structure with three replaceable atoms, marked by dots in the figure. (b) The beta-anomalous (β_{an}) synthesis, with the same three atoms as in (a) scattering anomalously. (c) Simple Fourier synthesis using F_Q, the structure amplitude of the unknown atoms as the coefficients. (d) Heavy-atom phased synthesis, with the same three atoms as in (a) and (b) as the heavy atoms. The contributions of the

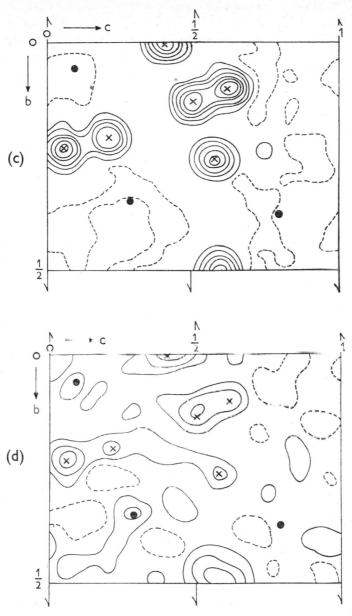

heavy atoms have been subtracted and a weighting function has been used. In all the diagrams, unknown atomic positions are indicated by crosses. Contours have been drawn at intervals of 4 $e/Å^2$. Positive contours are continuous lines, the zero contour is dashed and negative contours have dots and dashes.

be possible to combine two or more coefficients of the type (Eq. (5a)). Thus, if three crystals (1), (2) and (3) are available, in which one group of atoms (P) of (1) are replaced in (2) and another group (P') is replaced in (3), then we obtain

$$\beta_{is}^{(1,2)} = \frac{(|F^{(2)}|^2 - |F^{(1)}|^2) - (|F_P^{(2)}|^2 - |F_P^{(1)}|^2)}{|F_P^{(2)} - F_P^{(1)}|} \tag{7a}$$

$$\beta_{is}^{(1,3)} = \frac{(|F^{(3)}|^2 - |F^{(1)}|^2) - (|F_{P'}^{(3)}|^2 - |F_{P'}^{(1)}|^2)}{|F_{P'}^{(3)} - F_{P'}^{(1)}|} \tag{7b}$$

TABLE II. Peak strengths, in $e/\text{Å}^2$, of the peaks observed in the various syntheses

Atom	Type of synthesis			
	β_{is} (Fig. 1 (a))	β_{an} (Fig. 1 (b))	F_Q (Fig. 1 (c))	γ'_{mod} (Fig. 1 (d))
P_1	38	14	22	14
P_2	33	16	24	12
P_3	29	19	21	9
P_4	38	20	24	14
S_2	29	24	24	9
S_4	38	19	27	12
Average	34	19	24	12

and take as Fourier coefficients for the synthesis the quantity

$$\tfrac{1}{2}[\beta_{is}^{(1,2)} + \beta_{is}^{(1,3)}].$$

This should reveal the unknown atoms very strongly. The extension of this to a series of derivatives, in which replacement occurs at different sites is obvious. It is easy also to incorporate any type of weighting that may be necessary for the different measurements. Tests of these results are being planned.

Incidentally, when there is no *replacement* of an atom or group, but only an *addition*, as happens for instance with the various protein derivatives, the coefficient in the β_{is} synthesis takes a particularly simple form. Since $|F_P^{(1)}| = 0$ in this case, we may write $F_P^{(2)} = F_P$, so that

$$\beta_{is} = \frac{\delta |F|^2}{|F_P|} - |F_p| \tag{8}$$

Finally, in the case when the P group is centrosymmetric, if the origin is taken at the centre of symmetry of the P atoms, then $\alpha_P = 0$ or π and $\exp 2i\alpha_P = +1$ and Eq. (5) becomes

$$\beta_{is} = F_Q + F_Q^* \qquad (9)$$

Thus, the structure is duplicated by its inverse in the β_{is} synthesis, which is to be expected (Kartha and Ramachandran, 1955).

3. The Beta-anomalous Synthesis

So far we have been discussing the case of isomorphous crystals. In the case when a group of P atoms exhibits anomalous dispersion, the use of the resultant *differences* between $|F(hkl)|$ and $|F(h\bar{k}\bar{l})|$ is closely similar to the case of two isomorphous crystals. To simplify the discussion, we shall assume that all the atoms in the P group are alike, so that the ratios of the imaginary part of their scattering factor to the real part (f''/f') are all the same.

Denote the Bijvoet difference for a reflection $\mathbf{H} = hkl$ by $\Delta|F(\mathbf{H})|^2$. Thus

$$\Delta|F(\mathbf{H})|^2 = |F(\mathbf{H})|^2 - |F(-\mathbf{H})|^2 \qquad (10)$$

Similarly, the symbol Δ will indicate the difference between the corresponding quantities for two inverse reflections. We may then define the beta-anomalous synthesis (β_{an}) as one in which the Fourier coefficients are

$$\beta_{an} = \frac{\Delta|F|^2}{|\Delta F|} \exp i\alpha_P'' \qquad (11a)$$

$$= \frac{[|F(\mathbf{H})|^2 - |F(-\mathbf{H})|^2]}{|F_P''(\mathbf{H})|} \exp i\alpha_P'' \qquad (11b)$$

where $F_P'' = |F_P''| \exp i\alpha_P''$ is the contribution from the imaginary (absorption) component of the scattering factor $(f_{Pj} = f_{Pj}' + if_{Pj}'')$ from the P atoms. This is readily calculated from the known positions of the P atoms; thus

$$F_P'' = \sum f_{Pj}'' \exp 2\pi i\left(\mathbf{r}_{Pj} \cdot \mathbf{H} + \frac{\pi}{2}\right) \qquad (12)$$

By a simple algebraic manipulation, Eq. (11b) can be put in the form

$$\beta_{an} = F_Q + F_Q^* \exp(2i\alpha_P'') \qquad (13a)$$

$$= F_Q - F_Q^* \exp(2i\alpha_P) \qquad (13b)$$

which is very similar to Eq. (5b) of the isomorphous case. [The result shown in Eq. (13a) is true also when the atoms in the P group are different. However, the definition of β_{an} is slightly different from that in Eq. (11)—see Eq. (38) of Raman (1959b).]

It will be seen from Eq. (13) that the β_{an} synthesis also will reveal the structure (F_Q) with a background arising from the term $F_Q^* \exp(2i\alpha_P'')$, which will, however, be spread out. Thus, provided the locations of the anomalously scattering atoms are known, and the Bijvoet differences are accurately measured, it should be possible to obtain the positions of the unknown atoms by performing a synthesis, whose coefficients are given by the very simple expressions in Eq. (11).

This synthesis has also been tested in a practical case. The structure chosen was the same as for the β_{is} synthesis, but now the three P atoms (S_1, S_3, S_5) were assumed to scatter anomalously with a scattering factor given by $(3f_S + if_S)$, where f_S is the scattering factor for sulphur. A large imaginary component was used for convenience in calculating the coefficients β_{an}; however, it can be shown that the coefficient obtained is independent of the magnitude of F_P''.

The β_{an} synthesis thus obtained for the a projection is shown in Fig. 1 (b). The remaining six atoms have once again come out prominently, the known P atoms being suppressed. The absolute values of their peaks (Table II) are, however, slightly smaller than in the simple Fourier, but still larger than in the heavy atom synthesis.

It follows from Eqs. (5b) and (13b) that $\frac{1}{2}(\beta_{is} + \beta_{an}) = F_Q$. This was also verified in our tests, the small discrepancy observed being due to rounding off errors in the calculations. It will also be seen that the mean of the average peak strengths in the β_{is} and β_{an} syntheses is nearly the same as for the Fourier synthesis.

4. OTHER SYNTHESES OF THE BETA CLASS

It will be noticed that the function obtained from the Fourier synthesis, using β_{is} or β_{an} for the coefficients, has essentially the nature of an electron density function. It is composed of the true electron density of the unknown atoms, superposed on a fluctuating background. Further in both β_{is} and β_{an}, a function of the observed and calculated *intensities* occurs in the numerator, and this is divided by a function of the *amplitude* of the known atoms, e.g. $\delta|F_P|$ in β_{is} and $|F_P''|$ in β_{an}, and the *phase* is that of the *known* atoms. The same general principle can be used to construct other syntheses of the beta class, in which only the structure amplitudes of the P group of known atoms is used, as has been shown by Ramachandran and Raman (1959). The two syntheses, that have been suggested, namely β_{mod} (Eq. (14)) and β_{gen} (Eq. (15)) have also the properties of an electron density function:

$$\beta_{\mathrm{mod}} = \frac{\{|F_N|^2 - |F_P|^2 - \Sigma f_{Qj}^2\}}{|F_P|}\exp[i\alpha_P] \tag{14a}$$

$$= F_Q + F_Q^* \exp[2i\alpha_P] + \frac{\{|F_Q|^2 - \Sigma f_{Qj}^2\}}{F_P^*} \tag{14b}$$

$$\beta_{\mathrm{gen}} = \frac{|F_N|^2}{|F_P|}\exp[i\alpha_P] \tag{15a}$$

$$= F_Q + F_Q^* \exp[2i\alpha_P] + F_P + \frac{|F_Q|^2}{F_P^*} \tag{15b}$$

A comparison of the right-hand sides of Eqs. (14b) and (15b) with Eq. (5b) shows that they also should reveal the unknown atoms, have the same background as β_{is}, but that they would have an additional background, in which the known atoms are also present in β_{gen}, but absent in β_{mod}. This shows quite generally that feeding in the data of a pair of isomorphous crystals is definitely superior to that of using only the phases of a heavy-atom derivative (as is obvious also from first principles).

It would appear from the above that the beta syntheses are the natural ones to use when a part of the structure is known, as in the heavy-atom method. However, the last term in Eqs. (14b) and (15b) can sometimes lead to a large fluctuating background, which is undesirable. This happens because the corresponding coefficient is large when $|F_P|$ is small. One method of eliminating this was suggested earlier (Ramachandran and Raman, 1959), namely that of omitting from the Fourier syntheses those coefficients for which $|F_P|$ is less than a small fraction of its root-mean-square value. A more satisfactory method seems to be to use a suitable weighting factor.

The idea of a weighted Fourier synthesis has already been developed in connection with the heavy-atom synthesis by Woolfson (1956) and Sim (1960). The weighting function may be calculated by averaging over all possible values of the phase of F_N, assuming that the phase of F_Q is completely random. The weighting function W is

$$W = \tanh X \quad \text{for a centrosymmetric crystal} \tag{16a}$$

and

$$W = \frac{I_1(2X)}{I_0(2X)} \quad \text{for a non-centrosymmetric crystal} \tag{16b}$$

where

$$X = |F_N|\,|F_P|/\Sigma f_{Qj}^2 \tag{17}$$

Thus, $W|F_N|$ is to be used instead of $|F_N|$ in the Fourier synthesis. It is natural to suppose that we may also apply the same weighting function to $|F_N|$ in the β synthesis. Then, the coefficient to be used is $W^2\beta_{\text{gen}}$ instead of β_{gen}. Since, for small $|F_P|$,

$$W^2 \to X^2 \propto |F_P|^2$$

for both a centrosymmetric and a non-centrosymmetric crystal, no terms will become abnormally large in the $W^2\beta_{\text{gen}}$ synthesis. This has actually been tested, and the $W^2\beta_{\text{gen}}$ synthesis has been found to give satisfactory results (see below).

The relative merits of the β_{gen} synthesis and the heavy-atom synthesis, which in our notation is $\gamma' = |F_N|\exp i\alpha_P$, have been considered by Srinivasan (1961), who has shown that the peaks at the unknown atoms will be relatively stronger in the β than in the γ' synthesis. This has actually been tested out, both for the centrosymmetric as well as the non-centrosymmetric projection and the results are discussed below. The crystal structure used was that of P_4S_5, the same as that used in Section 3. However, six atoms, namely P_1, P_3, P_4, S_1, S_2, S_5 were assumed to be known. The Fourier syntheses, using the coefficients $W^2\beta_{\text{gen}}$, $W\gamma'$ and F_N (simple Fourier) were calculated for both projections and are shown in Figs. 2 (a), (b), (c) and 3 (a), (b), (c).

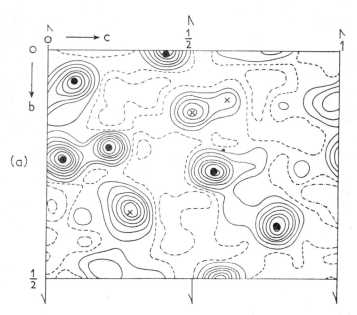

FIG. 2. (a) The weighted beta-general synthesis ($W^2\beta_{\text{gen}}$).

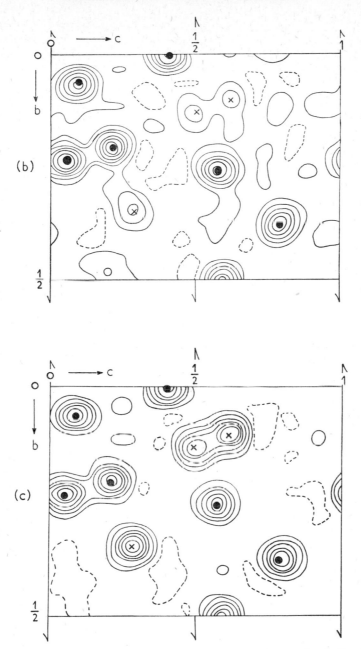

FIG. 2. (b) the weighted heavy-atom synthesis ($W\gamma'$); (c) simple Fourier synthesis (F_N) for the non-centrosymmetric bc projection of P_4S_5. The known atoms are indicated by dots and the unknown by crosses. Contours as in Fig. 1.

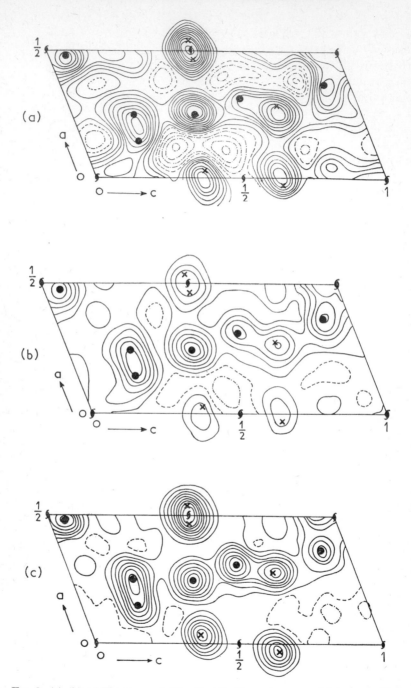

FIG. 3.   (a), (b), (c) The same as in Fig. 2 but for the centrosymmetric *ac* projection,

Figure 2 refers to the non-centrosymmetric projection on the bc plane. The peak values of the electron density at both the known as well as the unknown atoms are listed in Table III. It will be noted that, although both the weighted β_{gen} and the weighted γ' syntheses show up the unknown atoms, the ratio of the peak values of the unknown to the known atoms is higher in the beta synthesis. Further, although the β synthesis has an appreciable negative background at some places, it does not have a large positive peak at any places other than those exhibited by the γ' synthesis also (note two such at 0·12, 0·97 and 0·48, 0·20). Thus, the weighted beta synthesis is a perfectly useful synthesis and it has the advantage that it gives a larger peak height than the heavy atom synthesis at the unknown atomic positions.

Figure 3 contains the various syntheses for the centrosymmetric projection on the ac plane. It will be noticed that in this case also, the peaks at the unknown atomic positions are stronger in the β synthesis than in the γ' synthesis. The numerical data relating to peak heights are

TABLE III. Comparison of the peak heights at the known and unknown positions for the different syntheses†

(a) *Non-centrosymmetric case*

	Atom	Peak heights ($e/\text{Å}^2$)			Ratio of peak heights	
		$W^2 \beta_{gen}$ (Beta)	$W\gamma'$ (Heavy atom)	F_N (Fourier)	$W^2 \beta_{gen}/F_N$	$W\gamma'/F_N$
Known	P_1	25	25	25	1·00	1·00
(P atoms)	P_3	29	25	21	1·38	1·19
	P_4	34	29	24	1·42	1·21
	S_1	27	25	24	1·13	1·04
	S_2	25	26	24	1·04	1·08
	S_5	29	24	24	1·21	1·00
				Average (P)	1·20	1·09
Unknown	P_2	24	9	24	1·00	0·38
(Q atoms)	S_3	26	13	27	0·96	0·48
	S_4	16	10	28	0·57	0·36
				Average (Q)	0·84	0·41
		Ratio of Av. (Q)/Av. (P)	Observed		0·70	0·38
			Theory‡		0·66	0·22

† $\sigma_P^2 = \sum f_{Pj}^2 / \sum f_{Nj}^2 = 0.66$,
‡ Srinivasan (1961),

TABLE III—*continued*

(b) *Centrosymmetric case*

		Peak heights ($e/\text{Å}^2$)			Ratio of peak heights	
	Atom	$W^2\,\beta_{\text{gen}}$ (Beta)	$W\gamma'$ (Heavy atom)	F_N (Fourier)	$W^2\,\beta_{\text{gen}}/F_N$	$W\gamma'/F_N$
Known (P atoms)	P_1	20	18	31	0·65	0·58
	P_3	45	27	31	1·45	0·87
	P_4	41	26	29	1·41	0·89
	S_1	30	25	24	1·25	1·04
	S_2	33	23	30	1·10	0·77
	S_5	35	23	25	1·40	0·92
				Average (P)	1·21	0·85
Unknown (Q atoms)	P_2	48	18	37	1·29	0·48
	S_3	37	20	29	1·28	0·69
	S	25	9	25	1·00	0·36
				Average (Q)	1·19	0·51

Ratio of Av. (Q)/Av. (P)	Observed	0·98	0·60
	Theory‡	0·66	0·21

‡ Srinivasan (1961).

contained in Table III (b), from which it will be seen that the ratio of the peak heights of the unknown to the known atoms is also higher in the β synthesis. The negative regions are slightly more pronounced in the β synthesis than in the γ' synthesis but the β synthesis does not have any false peak having a height as large as the real peaks. Although the present studies thus show that the β synthesis gives stronger peaks in the unknown atomic positions than in the usual heavy-atom method, as was also shown theoretically by Srinivasan (1961), the numerical agreement with the theory is reasonably good only in the non-centrosymmetric case. It is therefore likely that the theory requires some modification for a centrosymmetric crystal.

However, the general conclusion remains, namely that the beta synthesis is *superior* to the heavy-atom phased synthesis in revealing the unknown atoms. By introducing the weighting function proposed in this paper, it has been possible to avoid unduly large fluctuations in the background, which was one of the defects in the original form of this synthesis. It is suggested that the weighted beta synthesis should be given a fair trial in future structure determinations.

Acknowledgment

We wish to acknowledge that the work in connection with the isomorphous and anomalous syntheses (Sections 2 and 3) was carried out jointly with Mr. V. R. Sarma.

REFERENCES

Bijvoet, J. M. (1951). In *Computing Methods and the Phase Problem in X-ray Crystal Analysis*, p. 84 (R. Pepinsky, ed.). The Pennsylvania State College, Pa.

Bokhoven, C., Schoone, J. C. and Bijvoet, J. M. (1949). *Proc. Acad. Sci. Amst.* **52**, 120.

Buerger, M. J. (1942). *Proc. nat. Acad. Sci., Wash.* **28**, 281.

Dickerson, R. E., Kendrew, J. C. and Strandberg, B. E. (1961). In *Computing Methods and the Phase Problem in X-ray Crystal Analysis*, p. 236 (R. Pepinsky, J. M. Robertson and J. C. Speakman, eds.). Pergamon Press, London.

Harker, D. (1956). *Acta cryst.* **9**, 1.

Kartha, G. (1961). *Acta cryst.* **14**, 680.

Kartha, G. and Ramachandran, G. N. (1955). *Acta cryot.* **8**, 195.

Okaya, Y. and Pepinsky, R. (1961). In *Computing Methods and the Phase Problem in X-ray Crystal Analysis*, p. 273 (R. Pepinsky, J. M. Robertson and J. C. Speakman, eds.). Pergamon Press, London.

Okaya, Y., Saito, Y. and Pepinsky, R. (1955). *Phys. Rev.* **98**, 1857.

Peerdeman, A. F. and Bijvoet, J. M. (1956). *Acta cryst.* **9**, 1012.

Pepinsky, R. and Okaya, Y. (1956). *Proc. nat. Acad. Sci., Wash.* **42**, 286.

Ramachandran, G. N. and Raman, S. (1956). *Current Sci. (India)* **25**, 348.

Ramachandran, G. N. and Raman, S. (1959). *Acta cryst.* **12**, 1957.

Raman, S. (1959a). *Z. Kristallogr.* **111**, 301.

Raman, S. (1959b). *Acta cryst.* **12**, 964.

Robertson, J. M. (1936). *J. chem. Soc.* 1195.

Sim, G. A. (1960). *Acta cryst.* **13**, 511.

Srinivasan, R. (1961). *Acta cryst.* **14**, 607.

Van Houten, S. and Wiebenga, E. H. (1957). *Acta cryst.* **10**, 156.

Woolfson, M. M. (1956). *Acta cryst.* **9**, 804.

Wright, D. A. and Marsh, R. E. (1962). *Acta cryst.* **15**, 54.

DISCUSSION

R. PARTHASARATHY: When I attempted to see if the inequality methods would become more powerful if the information about the known atoms is fed in, I found that the resultant inequalities are actually inferior to the known ones.

G. N. RAMACHANDRAN: I am not quite clear why the inequalities should be less effective when (say) the heavy atom information is taken into account.

K. VENKATESAN: While using the anomalous dispersion method, experience has shown that it is sufficient to use the phase close to the heavy atom phase to obtain the Fourier. I am wondering what is the need to do the synthesis using both the phases.

G. N. RAMACHANDRAN: The advantage is that it is not even necessary to calculate the phase angles to see which one is close to the phase of the heavy atom. The data are fed into the calculation directly in the form of intensities and this simplifies the procedure in practice.

K. VENKATESAN: In the anomalous Fourier you have negative peaks also. I am wondering whether they may overlap with the real peaks to produce partial cancellation.

G. N. RAMACHANDRAN: Yes, it is possible.

On the Statistical Method of Sign Determination

S. Naya, I. Nitta

Kwansei Gakuin University, Nishinomiya, Japan

AND T. Oda

*Osaka University of Liberal Arts and Education,
Tennoji, Osaka, Japan*

ABSTRACT

To consolidate the statistical theory of sign determination of structure factors, a notion of joint probability for a set of signs is put forward. It is then shown how this joint probability for signs is related to that for structure factors. The results of our generalized treatment will be discussed with reference to the theories given by Karle and Hauptman, Bertaut, Klug and others.

1. Introduction

For the direct determination of crystal structure various methods have been put forward by many authors. Among these the statistical methods have been developed by Karle and Hauptman, Bertaut, Klug and others. To consolidate, in a sense, these statistical methods, we propose first a concept of joint probability distribution for a set of m signs, s_1 to s_m, corresponding to a set of m structure factors of a centrosymmetric crystal. Secondly, we have studied a statistical theory for the joint probability distribution of structure factors from the point of view mainly of Bertaut (1955a, b) and Klug (1958), trying to generalize their methods in some respects. Utilization of the results of these two theories will be shown to clarify the situation of the important relations already obtained in the theories of Karle and Hauptman, Bertaut, Klug and others.

2. Joint Probability Distribution of Signs

The joint probability distribution for a set of m signs can be given as a power series of signs as shown in Eq. (1).

$$P(s_1, \ldots, s_m) = \frac{1}{2^m}\left\{1 + \sum_{i=1}^{m} \langle s_i \rangle s_i + \sum_{i>j=1}^{m} \langle s_i s_j \rangle s_i s_j + \right.$$
$$\left. + \sum_{i>j>l=1}^{m} \langle s_i s_j s_l \rangle s_i s_j s_l + \ldots + \langle s_1 \ldots s_m \rangle s_1 \ldots s_m\right\}, \quad (1)$$

43

where

$$\langle s_i \rangle = \sum_{s_1 = \pm 1} \cdots \sum_{s_m = \pm 1} s_i \, P(s_1, \ldots, s_m), \tag{2}$$

$$\langle s \, s_j \rangle = \sum_{s_1 = \pm 1} \cdots \sum_{s_m = \pm 1} s_i \, s_j \, P(s_1, \ldots, s_m), \text{ etc.} \tag{3}$$

are the so-called expected (or expectation) values of signs or sign products. Further, on the basis of Eq. (1), we can give the reduced probabilities as in Eqs. (4), (5) and (6).

$$P(s_1) = \sum_{s_2 = \pm 1} \cdots \sum_{s_m = \pm 1} P(s_1, \ldots, s_m) = \tfrac{1}{2}\{1 + \langle s_1 \rangle s_1\}, \tag{4}$$

$$P(s_1, s_2) = \sum_{s_3 = \pm 1} \cdots \sum_{s_m = \pm 1} P(s_1, \ldots, s_m)$$

$$= \frac{1}{2^2}\{1 + \langle s_1 \rangle s_1 + \langle s_2 \rangle s_2 + \langle s_1 s_2 \rangle s_1 s_2\}, \tag{5}$$

$$P(s_1, s_2, s_3) = \sum_{s_4 = \pm 1} \cdots \sum_{s_m = \pm 1} P(s_1, \ldots, s_m)$$

$$= \frac{1}{2^3}\{1 + \langle s_1 \rangle s_1 + \langle s_2 \rangle s_2 + \langle s_3 \rangle s_3 + \langle s_1 s_2 \rangle s_1 s_2 +$$

$$+ \langle s_2 s_3 \rangle s_2 s_3 + \langle s_3 s_1 \rangle s_3 s_1 + \langle s_1 s_2 s_3 \rangle s_1 s_2 s_3\}, \text{ etc.} \tag{6}$$

Using these results, the probability $P^+(s_1)$ that s_1 is plus 1, and some other probabilities are given as in Eqs. (7) and (8).

$$P^+(s_1) = \tfrac{1}{2}\{1 + \langle s_1 \rangle\}, \qquad\qquad P^-(s_1) = \tfrac{1}{2}\{1 - \langle s_1 \rangle\}, \tag{7}$$

$$P^+(s_1 s_2 s_3) = \tfrac{1}{2}\{1 + \langle s_1 s_2 s_3 \rangle\}, \qquad P^-(s_1 s_2 s_3) = \tfrac{1}{2}\{1 - \langle s_1 s_2 s_3 \rangle\}, \text{ etc.} \tag{8}$$

Further, there is given also the conditional probability $P(s_1 | s_2)$ of s_1 for a given s_2 as follows.

$$P(s_1, s_2) = P(s_2) \, P(s_1 | s_2), \tag{9}$$

or

$$P(s_1 | s_2) = \frac{P(s_1, s_2)}{P(s_2)} \equiv \tfrac{1}{2}\{1 + \langle s_1 \rangle_{s_2} \cdot s_1\}, \tag{10}$$

where

$$\langle s_1 \rangle_{s_2} = \frac{\langle s_1 \rangle + \langle s_1 s_2 \rangle s_2}{1 + \langle s_2 \rangle s_2} \tag{11}$$

is a conditional expected value. Some other examples are easily derived by the method similar to that which led to Eqs. (9), (10) and (11).

$$\langle s_1 \rangle_{s_2, s_3} = \frac{\langle s_1 \rangle + \langle s_1 s_2 \rangle s_2 + \langle s_1 s_3 \rangle s_3 + \langle s_1 s_2 s_3 \rangle s_2 s_3}{1 + \langle s_2 \rangle s_2 + \langle s_3 \rangle s_3 + \langle s_2 s_3 \rangle s_2 s_3}, \qquad (12)$$

$$\langle s_1 \rangle_{s_2 s_3} = \frac{\langle s_1 \rangle + \langle s_1 s_2 s_3 \rangle s_2 s_3}{1 + \langle s_2 s_3 \rangle s_2 s_3}, \qquad (13)$$

$$\langle s_1 \rangle_{s_1 s_2 s_3} = \frac{\langle s_1 \rangle + \langle s_2 s_3 \rangle s_1 s_2 s_3}{1 + \langle s_1 s_2 s_3 \rangle s_1 s_2 s_3}, \text{ etc.} \qquad (14)$$

Now, to calculate the expected values of signs or sign products, we are led to the joint probability distribution of structure factors $P(E_1, \dots, E_m)$ used by Karle, Hauptman, Bertaut, Klug and others. The relation between this and our joint probability distribution of signs is obvious from the following equations.

$$P(\mathbf{E}_1, \dots, \mathbf{E}_m) = P(E_1, \dots, E_m) P(s_1, \dots, s_m | E_1, \dots, E_m), \qquad (15)$$

$$P(s_1, \dots, s_m) \equiv P(s_1, \dots, s_m | E_1, \dots, E_m) = \frac{P(E_1 s_1, \dots, E_m s_m)}{P(E_1, \dots, E_m)}, \qquad (16)$$

where

$$\mathbf{E}_i \equiv E_i s_i, \quad E_i = |\mathbf{E}_i|,$$

$$P(E_1, \dots, E_m) = \sum_{s_1 = \pm 1} \cdots \sum_{s_m = \pm 1} P(E_1 s_1, \dots, E_m s_m). \qquad (17)$$

It is seen that the joint probability distribution of signs is nothing other than the conditional probability of signs for a set of m given absolute values of structure factors.

3. JOINT PROBABILITY DISTRIBUTION OF STRUCTURE FACTORS

Our calculation of the joint probability distribution of structure factors follows closely the method of Klug (1958); that is, starting from moments (see Appendix I) of geometrical structure factor products, via corresponding cumulants, the moment generating function, and finally to the joint probability distribution of structure factors. Such a procedure is carried out, not for some special space groups case by case, as was done by Klug, but in a more general manner by making use of a general space-group symmetry operator applicable to any space group. As the result of laborious calculations, we finally obtain the general expression of joint probability distribution applicable to any centrosymmetric space group as given by Eqs. (18) and (19).

$$P(\boldsymbol{E}_1, \ldots, \boldsymbol{E}_m) = \frac{1}{(2\pi)^{m/2}}[\exp - \tfrac{1}{2}(\boldsymbol{E}_1^2 + \ldots + \boldsymbol{E}_m^2)] \times$$

$$\times \left[1 + \frac{z_3}{S}\Sigma_3 + \frac{z_4}{S}\{\Sigma_4 - \tfrac{1}{2}\Sigma_{22}\} + \frac{z_3^2}{2S^2}\Sigma_{33} + \frac{z_5}{S}\{\Sigma_5 - \Sigma_{32}\} + \right.$$

$$+ \frac{z_3 z_4}{S^2}\{\Sigma_{43} - \tfrac{1}{2}\Sigma_{322}\} + \frac{z_3^3}{6S^3}\Sigma_{333} + \frac{z_6}{S}\{\Sigma_6 - \Sigma_{42} - \tfrac{1}{2}\Sigma_{33} + \tfrac{1}{3}\Sigma_{222}\} +$$

$$+ \frac{z_3 z_5}{S^2}\{\Sigma_{53} - \Sigma_{332}\} + \frac{z_4^2}{2S^2}\{\Sigma_{44} - \Sigma_{422} + \tfrac{1}{4}\Sigma_{2222}\} + \frac{z_3^2 z_4}{2S^3}\{\Sigma_{433} -$$

$$- \tfrac{1}{2}\Sigma_{3322}\} + \frac{z_3^4}{24S^4}\Sigma_{3333} + \frac{z_7}{S}\{\Sigma_7 - \Sigma_{52} - \Sigma_{43} + \Sigma_{322}\} +$$

$$+ \frac{z_3 z_6}{S^2}\{\Sigma_{63} - \tfrac{1}{2}\Sigma_{333} - \Sigma_{432} + \tfrac{1}{3}\Sigma_{3222}\} + \frac{z_4 z_5}{S^2}\{\Sigma_{54} - \tfrac{1}{2}\Sigma_{522} -$$

$$- \Sigma_{432} + \tfrac{1}{2}\Sigma_{3222}\} + \frac{z_3^2 z_5}{2S^3}\{\Sigma_{533} - \Sigma_{3332}\} + \frac{z_3 z_4^2}{2S^3}\{\Sigma_{443} - \Sigma_{4322} +$$

$$+ \tfrac{1}{4}\Sigma_{32222}\} + \frac{z_3^3 z_4}{6S^4}\{\Sigma_{4333} - \tfrac{1}{2}\Sigma_{33322}\} + \frac{z_3^5}{120S^5}\Sigma_{33333} +$$

$$+ \ldots \Bigg], \tag{18}$$

where

$$\Sigma_{a \ldots f} \equiv \sum_{\Sigma(\alpha'_p + \ldots + \omega'_p) = a} \cdots \sum_{\Sigma(\alpha'''_p + \ldots + \omega'''_p) = f} \times$$

$$\times \frac{\left(\dfrac{\sqrt{\tau}}{\sqrt{\epsilon_1}}\right)^{\Sigma(\alpha'_p + \ldots + \alpha'''_p)} \cdots \left(\dfrac{\sqrt{\tau}}{\sqrt{\epsilon_m}}\right)^{\Sigma(\omega'_p + \ldots + \omega'''_p)}}{\displaystyle\prod_{p=0}^{s-1}(\alpha'_p! \ldots \omega'_p!) \ldots (\alpha'''_p! \ldots \omega'''_p!)} \times$$

$$\times \exp\left[2\pi i \left(\sum_{p=0}^{s-1}\{(\alpha'_p + \ldots + \alpha'''_p)\,\boldsymbol{h}_1 + \ldots + (\omega'_p + \ldots + \omega'''_p)\,\boldsymbol{h}_m\}\,\boldsymbol{t}_p\right)\right]$$

$$\times H_{\Sigma(\alpha'_p + \ldots + \alpha'''_p)}(\boldsymbol{E}_1) \ldots H_{\Sigma(\omega'_p + \ldots + \omega'''_p)}(\boldsymbol{E}_m) \times$$

$$\times \delta\left\{\sum_{p=0}^{s-1}\boldsymbol{R}_p(\alpha'_p \boldsymbol{h}_1 + \ldots + \omega'_p \boldsymbol{h}_m)\right\} \ldots \delta\left\{\sum_{p=0}^{s-1}\boldsymbol{R}_p(\alpha'''_p \boldsymbol{h}_1 + \ldots + \omega'''_p \boldsymbol{h}_m)\right\},$$

$$\tag{19}$$

$$z_n = \sum_{j=1}^{N} \phi_j^n, \qquad \phi_j = \frac{f_j}{\left(\sum_{j=1}^{N} f_j^2\right)^{1/2}}. \tag{20}$$

This expression (18) is correct to the order of $N^{-5/2}$. N is the number of atoms in a unit cell. f_j is atomic structure factor, $S = s\tau$ the symmetry number (s is the order of factor group, τ the order of translation group), $\epsilon_1, \ldots, \epsilon_m$ the statistical weights to be accounted for as reflections of special type (Bertaut, 1956, 1960a), H_n is the Hermite polynomial of the nth order, R_p and t_p are the rotational and translational parts of the pth operation of the group, and δ the Kronecker delta. The summations in (19) are carried out over all the possible combinations of the non-negative integers $\alpha_p', \ldots, \omega_p''{}^{,'}, (p - 0, \ldots, s-1)$ under the relationships

$$\sum_{p=0}^{s-1} (\alpha_p' + \ldots + \omega_p') = a, \text{ etc.}$$

So far our treatment is general.

4. Some Examples of Applications

The next expression shows a special example of the joint probability $P(E_1, E_2, E_3)$, where $E_1 \equiv E_{h_1}$, $E_2 \equiv E_{h_2}$, $E_3 \equiv E_{h_3}$ and $h_1 + h_2 + h_3 = 0$, for the case of $P\bar{1}$.

$P(E_1, E_2, E_3)$

$$= \frac{1}{(2\pi)^{3/2}} \exp\left[-\tfrac{1}{2}(E_1^2 + E_2^2 + E_3^2)\right]\left[1 + z_3 H_1(E_1) H_1(E_2) H_1(E_3) - \right.$$

$$-\frac{z_4}{8}\{H_4(E_1) + \text{cyc.}\} + \frac{z_3^2}{2} H_2(E_1) H_2(E_2) H_2(E_3) -$$

$$-\frac{z_5}{2}\{H_3(E_1) H_1(E_2) H_1(E_3) + \text{cyc.}\} -$$

$$-\frac{z_3 z_4}{8}\{H_5(E_1) H_1(E_2) H_1(E_3) + \text{cyc.}\} + \frac{z_3^3}{6} H_3(E_1) H_3(E_2) H_3(E_3) +$$

$$+ z_6\{\tfrac{1}{18}[H_6(E_1) + \text{cyc.}] - \tfrac{7}{8} H_2(E_1) H_2(E_2) H_2(E_3)\} -$$

$$-\frac{z_3 z_5}{2}\{H_4(E_1) H_2(E_2) H_2(E_3) + \text{cyc.}\} + z_4^2\{\tfrac{1}{128}[H_8(E_1) + \text{cyc.}] +$$

$$+ \tfrac{1}{64}[H_4(E_1) H_4(E_2) + \text{cyc.}]\} - \frac{z_3^2 z_4}{16}\{H_6(E_1) H_2(E_2) H_2(E_3) + \text{cyc.}\} +$$

$$+ \frac{z_3^4}{24} H_4(\mathbf{E}_1) H_4(\mathbf{E}_2) H_4(\mathbf{E}_3) + z_7 \{ \tfrac{1}{3}[H_5(\mathbf{E}_1) H_1(\mathbf{E}_2) H_1(\mathbf{E}_3) + \text{cyc.}] +$$

$$+ \tfrac{1}{4}[H_3(\mathbf{E}_1) H_3(\mathbf{E}_2) H_1(\mathbf{E}_3) + \text{cyc.}] \} + z_3 z_6 \{ \tfrac{1}{18}[H_7(\mathbf{E}_1) H_1(\mathbf{E}_2) H_1(\mathbf{E}_3) +$$

$$+ \text{cyc.}] - \tfrac{7}{8} H_3(\mathbf{E}_1) H_3(\mathbf{E}_2) H_3(\mathbf{E}_3) \} + \frac{z_4 z_5}{16} \{ [H_7(\mathbf{E}_1) H_1(\mathbf{E}_2) H_1(\mathbf{E}_3) +$$

$$+ \text{cyc.}] + [(H_5(\mathbf{E}_1) H_3(\mathbf{E}_2) + H_3(\mathbf{E}_1) H_5(\mathbf{E}_2)) H_1(\mathbf{E}_3) + \text{cyc.}] \} -$$

$$- \frac{z_3^2 z_5}{4} \{ H_5(\mathbf{E}_1) H_3(\mathbf{E}_2) H_3(\mathbf{E}_3) + \text{cyc.} \} +$$

$$+ z_3 z_4^2 \{ \tfrac{1}{128}[H_9(\mathbf{E}_1) H_1(\mathbf{E}_2) H_1(\mathbf{E}_3) + \text{cyc.}] +$$

$$+ \tfrac{1}{64}[H_5(\mathbf{E}_1) H_5(\mathbf{E}_2) H_1(\mathbf{E}_3) + \text{cyc}.] \} - \frac{z_3^3 z_4}{48} \{ H_7(\mathbf{E}_1) H_3(\mathbf{E}_2) H_3(\mathbf{E}_3) +$$

$$+ \text{cyc.} \} + \frac{z_3^5}{120} H_5(\mathbf{E}_1) H_5(\mathbf{E}_2) H_5(\mathbf{E}_3) + \ldots]. \tag{21}$$

This is calculated up to the order of $N^{-5/2}$, while other authors give a simpler expression up to $N^{-3/2}$.

Another example is given for the case of the joint probability distribution $P(\mathbf{E}_1, \mathbf{E}_2)$, where $\mathbf{E}_1 \equiv \mathbf{E}_{\mathbf{h}_1}$, $\mathbf{E}_2 \equiv \mathbf{E}_{\mathbf{h}_2}$, and $\mathbf{h}_1 = (2h, 0, 2l)$, $\mathbf{h}_2 = (h, k, l)$ in $P2_1/c$.

$$P(\mathbf{E}_1, \mathbf{E}_2) = \frac{1}{2\pi} \exp \left[- \tfrac{1}{2}(\mathbf{E}_1^2 + \mathbf{E}_2^2) \right] [1 + \frac{z_3}{\sqrt{2}} H_1(\mathbf{E}_1) H_2(\mathbf{E}_2)(-1)^{k+l} -$$

$$- z_4 \{ \tfrac{1}{4} H_4(\mathbf{E}_1) + \tfrac{1}{8} H_4(\mathbf{E}_2) \} + \frac{z_3^2}{4} H_2(\mathbf{E}_1) H_4(\mathbf{E}_2) -$$

$$- z_5 \left\{ \frac{1}{\sqrt{2}} H_1(\mathbf{E}_1) H_4(\mathbf{E}_2) + \frac{1}{\sqrt{2}} H_3(\mathbf{E}_1) H_2(\mathbf{E}_2) \right\} (-1)^{k+l} -$$

$$- z_3 z_4 \left\{ \frac{1}{8\sqrt{2}} H_1(\mathbf{E}_1) H_6(\mathbf{E}_2) +$$

$$+ \frac{1}{4\sqrt{2}} H_5(\mathbf{E}_1) H_2(\mathbf{E}_2) \right\} (-1)^{k+l} +$$

$$+ \frac{z_3^3}{12\sqrt{2}} H_3(\mathbf{E}_1) H_6(\mathbf{E}_2)(-1)^{k+l} + \ldots]. \tag{22}$$

This is calculated up to the order of $N^{-3/2}$. Karle and Hauptman give the first two terms.

The expression for the expected values of $s_{2\mathbf{h}}$, $\langle s_{2\mathbf{h}} \rangle$, obtained from our general calculation in $P\bar{1}$ includes the following four cases corresponding to those of Klug, Bertaut, Karle, Hauptman, Cochran and Vaughan, respectively.

Case 1. When only two structure factors E_h and E_{2h} are used,

$$\langle s_{2h}\rangle = z_3\{\tfrac{1}{2}H_1(E_{2h})\,H_2(E_h)\} - z_5\{\tfrac{1}{3}H_1(E_{2h})\,H_4(E_h) + \tfrac{1}{4}H_3(E_{2h})\,H_2(E_h)\} -$$
$$- z_3 z_4\{\tfrac{1}{16}H_1(E_{2h})\,H_6(E_h) + \tfrac{1}{16}H_5(E_{2h})\,H_2(E_h)\} + z_3^3\{\tfrac{1}{48}H_3(E_{2h})\,H_6(E_h)\}$$
$$+ z_3 z_4\{\tfrac{1}{16}H_1(E_{2h})\,H_2(E_h)\,H_4(E_h) + \tfrac{1}{16}H_1(E_{2h})\,H_4(E_{2h})\,H_2(E_h)\} -$$
$$- z_3^3\{\tfrac{1}{16}H_1(E_{2h})\,H_2(E_{2h})\,H_2(E_h)\,H_4(E_h)\} + \ldots, \tag{23}$$

which agrees with Klug's result.

Case 2. When all such terms as $z_3^2 z_3^3$, $z_3 z_4$ are omitted,

$$\langle s_{2h}\rangle = z_3\{\tfrac{1}{2}H_1(E_{2h})\,H_2(E_h)\} - z_5\{\tfrac{1}{3}H_1(E_{2h})\,H_4(E_h) + \tfrac{1}{4}H_3(E_{2h})\,H_2(E_h)\} +$$
$$+ z_5\{\tfrac{1}{12}H_3(E_{2h})\,H_2(E_{3h}) + \tfrac{1}{24}H_4(E_{h/2})\,H_1(E_{2h})\} $$
$$+ z_5\{\tfrac{1}{4}H_1(E_{2h}) \sum_k H_2(E_{h+k})\,H_2(E_k)\} + \ldots \tag{24}$$

This result is equivalent to that of Bertaut (1955a, b) and the first and fourth terms are found in the monograph by Hauptman and Karle (1953).

Case 3. When a large number of structure factors are used, in an approximate calculation,

$$\langle s_{2h}\rangle = z_3\{\tfrac{1}{2}H_1(E_{2h})\,H_2(E_h)\} -$$
$$- \tfrac{1}{4}\{(2z_3^3 - z_5) + 4z_3(z_3^2 - z_4)\,H_2(E_h)\}\,H_1(E_{2h}) \sum_k H_2(E_{h+k})\,H_2(E_k) -$$
$$- \tfrac{1}{2}z_3(z_3^2 - z_4)\,H_1(E_{2h})\,H_2(E_h) \sum_k H_2(E_{2h+k})\,H_2(E_k) + \ldots \tag{25}$$

For the case of equal atoms, this relation gives the probability formula corresponding to Cochran's equality:

$$E_{2h} = N^{1/2}\{2(E_h^2 - 1) - N\overline{(E_{h+k}^2 - 1)(E_k^2 - 1)}^k\}. \tag{26}$$

Case 4. A more precise calculation than in case 3 gives us the following expression

$$\langle s_{2h}\rangle = \text{the same terms as in case 3} +$$
$$+ z_3 z_4\{\tfrac{1}{4}H_1(E_{2h}) \sum_k H_2(E_{h+k})\,H_2(E_k)\,H_2(E_{2k})\} +$$
$$+ z_3^3\{H_1(E_{2h})\,H_2(E_h) \sum_k H_2(E_{2h+k})\,H_2(E_{h+k})\,H_2(E_k)\} + \ldots \tag{27}$$

This is a formula similar to the regression formula given by Vaughan (1959).

APPENDIX I

The general expression for mixed moments $m_{\alpha\beta\ldots\omega}$ applicable to any space group is derived from trigonometric structure factor

$$\xi(\mathbf{h}) = \tau \sum_{p=0}^{s-1} e^{2\pi i \mathbf{h} \mathbf{r} S_p} = \tau \sum_{p=0}^{s-1} e^{2\pi i R_p \mathbf{h} \mathbf{r}} e^{2\pi i \mathbf{h} \mathbf{t}_p}, \tag{28}$$

with space group operation

$$S_p = (R_p | \mathbf{t}_p), \qquad p = 0, \ldots, s-1, \tag{29}$$

as the following expression

$$m_{\alpha\ldots\omega}(\mathbf{h}_1, \ldots, \mathbf{h}_m) = \overline{\xi^{\alpha}(\mathbf{h}_1) \ldots \xi^{\omega}(\mathbf{h}_m)}$$

$$= \tau^{\alpha + \ldots + \omega} \sum_{\Sigma \alpha_p = \alpha} \cdots \sum_{\Sigma \omega_p = \omega} \frac{\alpha! \ldots \omega!}{\prod_p (\alpha_p! \ldots \omega_p!)} \times$$

$$\times \exp\left[2\pi i \left\{ \sum_{p=0}^{s-1} (\alpha_p \mathbf{h}_1 + \ldots + \omega_p \mathbf{h}_m) \mathbf{t}_p \right\}\right] \delta \left\{ \sum_{p=0}^{s-1} R_p (\alpha_p \mathbf{h}_1 + \ldots + \omega_p \mathbf{h}_m) \right\}. \tag{30}$$

REFERENCES

Bertaut, E. F. (1955a). *Acta cryst.* **8**, 537.
Bertaut, E. F. (1955b). *Acta cryst.* **8**, 544.
Bertaut, E. F. (1956). *Acta cryst.* **9**, 322.
Bertaut, E. F. (1960a). *Acta cryst.* **13**, 546.
Bertaut, E. F. (1960b). *Acta cryst.* **13**, 643.
Cochran, W. (1954). *Acta cryst.* **7**, 581.
Hauptman, H. and Karle, J. (1953). *Solution of the Phase Problem. 1. The Centro-symmetric Crystal.* A.C.A. Monograph No. 3, New York. Polycrystal Book Service.
Klug, A. (1958). *Acta cryst.* **11**, 515.
Vaughan, P. A. (1959). *Acta cryst.* **12**, 981.

Experience with Two New Methods for Structure Determination

W. Hoppe, K. Anzenhofer and R. Huber

*Abteilung für Rontgenstrukturforschung am Max-Planck-Institut
für Eiweiss und Lederforschung, Munich, Germany*

ABSTRACT

The paper deals with two new methods for structure determination which have been developed in the authors' laboratory. The first method is known as the shift product method, while the second method employs the Sayre relation for obtaining the signs of additional structure factors from those of a smaller set. The preliminary results of some practical tests of the two methods are also reported.

Two new methods for structure determination have been worked out in our laboratory. The first method—called the "shift product method" —may facilitate the phase determination (Hoppe, 1962a; Anzenhofer and Hoppe, 1962). The second method improves the heavy-atom method and the isomorphous replacement method (Hoppe, 1962b; Huber and Hoppe, 1962). So far we have not had very much experience with either method and it is difficult to assess their practical value. Our preliminary results however have shown that it is worth while to proceed along these lines. As they should, therefore be of interest, we present our—naturally quite restricted—results.

PART I: The Shift Product Method†

(*In collaboration with K. Anzenhofer*)

The well-known equation for the squared electron density is as follows:

$$\rho^2(\mathbf{r}) = \frac{1}{V^2} \sum_{\mathbf{h}} \sum_{\mathbf{h'}} F_{\mathbf{h'}} F_{\mathbf{h-h'}} \exp[-2\pi i(\mathbf{h \cdot r})] \tag{1}$$

A similar relation can also be formulated for a product of two electron densities, which are shifted against each other by a vector $\mathbf{u}_0$; this leads to the following formula:

$$\rho(\mathbf{r})\rho(\mathbf{r}+\mathbf{u}_0) = \frac{1}{V^2} \sum_{\mathbf{h}} \sum_{\mathbf{h'}} F_{\mathbf{h'}} F_{\mathbf{h-h'}} \exp[-2\pi i(\mathbf{h \cdot r})] \exp[-2\pi i(\mathbf{h' \cdot u_0})] \tag{2}$$

† Extract from a doctoral thesis accepted by the Technische Hochschule, Munich.

The Fourier coefficients of this series have the form

$$F_{\mathbf{h}} \sim \sum_{\mathbf{h}'} F_{\mathbf{h}'} F_{\mathbf{h}-\mathbf{h}'} \exp\left[-2\pi i(\mathbf{h}' \cdot \mathbf{u}_0)\right] \tag{3}$$

If the vector $\mathbf{u}_0$ is chosen the specific way to connect the origin with a point of density "zero" in the Patterson function, the result is

$$\rho(\mathbf{r})\,\rho(\mathbf{r}+\mathbf{u}_0) = 0 \tag{4}$$

Consequently, all structure factors of Eq. (4) are equal to zero. Combining $\rho(\mathbf{r})\rho(\mathbf{r}+\mathbf{u}_0)$ and $\rho(\mathbf{r})\rho(\mathbf{r}-\mathbf{u}_0)$ we obtain

$$\pm \sum_{\mathbf{h}'} F_{\mathbf{h}'} F_{\mathbf{h}-\mathbf{h}'} \cos 2\pi(\mathbf{h}' \cdot \mathbf{u}_0) = 0 \tag{5a}$$

$$\pm \sum_{\mathbf{h}'} F_{\mathbf{h}'} F_{\mathbf{h}-\mathbf{h}'} \sin 2\pi(\mathbf{h}' \cdot \mathbf{u}_0) = 0 \tag{5b}$$

If $\mathbf{h}'$ runs over all possible values, the two contributions for $\mathbf{h}' = \mathbf{h}'$ and for $\mathbf{h}' = \mathbf{h}-\mathbf{h}'$ may be combined as follows:

$$F_{\mathbf{h}-\mathbf{h}'} F_{\mathbf{h}'} \cos 2\pi(\mathbf{h}' \cdot \mathbf{u}_0) + F_{\mathbf{h}'} F_{\mathbf{h}-\mathbf{h}'} \cos 2\pi(\mathbf{h}-\mathbf{h}' \cdot \mathbf{u}_0)$$
$$= 2 F_{\mathbf{h}'} F_{\mathbf{h}-\mathbf{h}'} \cos \pi(\mathbf{h}-2\mathbf{h}' \cdot \mathbf{u}_0) \cos \pi(\mathbf{h} \cdot \mathbf{u}_0)$$

Now we sum the equations for $+\mathbf{h}$ and $-\mathbf{h}$. Again two contributions can be combined:

$$2F_{\mathbf{h}'} F_{\mathbf{h}-\mathbf{h}'} \cos \pi(\mathbf{h}-2\mathbf{h}' \cdot \mathbf{u}_0) \cos \pi(\mathbf{h} \cdot \mathbf{u}_0) +$$
$$+ 2F_{-\mathbf{h}'} F_{-\mathbf{h}+\mathbf{h}'} \cos \pi(-\mathbf{h}+2\mathbf{h}' \cdot \mathbf{u}_0) \cos \pi(-\mathbf{h} \cdot \mathbf{u}_0)$$
$$= 4|F_{\mathbf{h}'}|\,|F_{\mathbf{h}-\mathbf{h}'}| \cos(\phi_{\mathbf{h}'}+\phi_{\mathbf{h}-\mathbf{h}'}) \cos \pi(\mathbf{h}-2\mathbf{h}' \cdot \mathbf{u}_0) \cos \pi(\mathbf{h} \cdot \mathbf{u}_0)$$

In this way we finally obtain Eq. (6):

$$\sum_{\mathbf{h}'=\mathbf{h}/2}^{\mathbf{h}\,\mathrm{max}} |F_{\mathbf{h}'}|\,|F_{\mathbf{h}-\mathbf{h}'}| \cos(\phi_{\mathbf{h}'}+\phi_{\mathbf{h}-\mathbf{h}'}) \cos \pi(\mathbf{h}-2\mathbf{h}' \cdot \mathbf{u}_0) = 0 \tag{6}$$

Constant factors have been omitted. In the case of centrosymmetric structures, the phase-dependent term in Eq. (6) degenerates into the sign of the double-product. The summation starts at $h/2, k/2, l/2$, if h, k, l are even. If at least one of these indices is odd, the start will be at the integers next to $h/2, k/2, l/2$. In the first case the first term of the sum has to be halved.

It is naturally true that these relations are only approximately valid. A structure does not consist of point-atoms and, therefore, the actual resolution of the Fourier map is important. Figure 1 shows electron density maps of fluorene shifted against each other. In both examples the shift vector corresponds to points of "zero" density in the Patterson map. It can easily be seen that no atom of the unshifted structure (full lines) coincides with an atom of the shifted structure (dotted lines). But in the example in Fig. 1 (a), some atoms are closer together than in the other example. Therefore, the atoms overlap partially. Figure 2 shows the influence of the overlap of two Gaussian atoms (Cu radiation), a distance

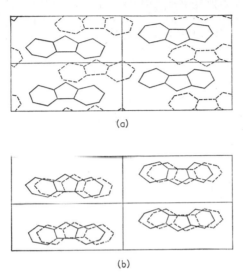

(a)

(b)

FIG. 1. Two flourene structures, shifted against each other (a) by the vector u_6 and (b) by u_2, respectively.

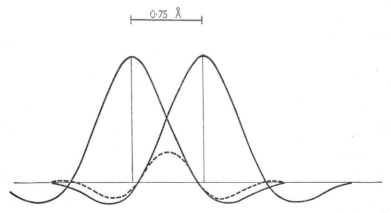

0.75 Å

FIG. 2. Overlap of two "unitary" atoms, the distance of which being 0.75 Å (Cu radiation). The broken curve indicates the product.

of 0.75 Å apart. Similar difficulties also appear in the Sayre relations. Here, however, they are not so serious (at least in three-dimensional work). The minimum distance of two atoms is of the order of 1.5 Å. In the shifted structures of the type in Fig. 1, the atoms are closer together. On the other hand, however, overlaps inherent to the structures are not important for the shift product methods. Moreover, the relations are also valid for structures containing atoms with different weights. In more complicated structures not only may partial overlap of shifted atoms occur, but also single Patterson peaks in the "minimum". But in any of these cases it can be shown by probability principles that the right-hand side of Eq. (6) will be small. In order to study the relations Eq. (2)–Eq. (6) we checked their applicability first on a one-dimensional test-example (Sayre, 1952) (see Fig. 3) and then on flourene. Figure 4

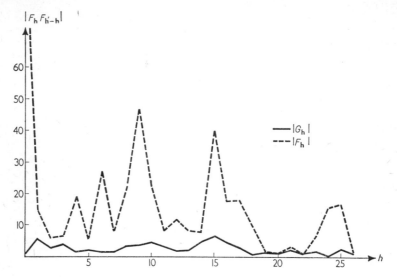

FIG. 3. One-dimensional test structure by D. Sayre. $|F_{\mathbf{h}}|$ are structure factors and $|G_{\mathbf{h}}|$ are right-hand "zeros" of Eq. (6).

contains the Patterson map of flourene. The positions indicated on the map are those of the selected points of density "zero". Formula (6) describes as many relations as there are points of density "zero" in the Patterson function. The known Sayre formula establishes only one single relation ($\mathbf{u}_0 = 0$). This feature provides new facilities in the determination of the phases.

First we tried the following procedure (centrosymmetrical case). Summing all equations (6) corresponding to a constant value of h one gets the following equation:

$$\pm \sum_{\mathbf{h'}} F_{\mathbf{h'}} F_{\mathbf{h}-\mathbf{h'}} \sum_{\nu} S_{\nu} \frac{\cos}{\sin} \pi(\mathbf{h} - 2\mathbf{h'} \cdot \mathbf{u}_{0\nu}) = 0 \qquad (7)$$

in which ν runs over all points of density zero and S_{ν} are arbitrary signs. For example, it is possible to adjust the signs S_{ν} in such a way that the

Fig. 4. Patterson map of fluorene, (001)-projection, with points of density "zero" (negative levels only).

contribution of all terms in the ν-series is positive for a special double-product $F_{h'}F_{h-h'}$. This means that the corresponding term in the sum-series, which contains this double-product, becomes very big compared with the other products. Experience has shown that only a few other products will be comparable in size. Following this scheme, after the summation over ν, we get a reduced h'-series with a small number of significant terms. It is then possible to find the relative signs of these terms. They must be chosen in such a way that the left-hand side of Eq. (7) will be approximately zero. From these relative signs, the signs of the structure factors can be found in a similar way as in the triple-product method. The sign of F_{000} is known, two further signs are available after fixing the origin. Starting from these three signs one may evaluate, step by step, all other signs. Due to eventually contradictory results, which can never be avoided, the best possible set of signs may be obtained after some trial.

The sign of medium or small structure factors is either obtainable with a fair degree of reliability or not at all. An attempt was started to get a set of signs for the (001)-projection of biflorine ($C_{20}H_{20}O_3$), a substance that crystallizes in the space group $C_{2v}^9 - Pna2_1$ with the cell constants $a = 24 \cdot 07$ Å, $b = 9 \cdot 62$ Å and $c = 7 \cdot 9$ Å. The unit cell contains four molecules. At the same time this structure is being investigated by other methods (convolution-molecule and diffuse scattering) in our laboratory.

By absolute scaling according to Wilson, F_{00} was obtained. The origin was fixed by choosing the sign of the two structure factors

$$S(16 \cdot 5) = +$$

$$S(3 \cdot 8) = +$$

Beginning with these data, ninety-four signs were obtained by the application of a simplified method, where from each relation (Eq. (7)) only the two highest terms were taken into account. Of course, they must have opposite signs. Often it is possible to combine several relations and to extract signs of structure factors directly. After the examination of several branches of solutions, fifteen indications out of 179 disagreed with the set of signs which proved to be the best possible one. In principle, it is not difficult to find a group of solutions similar to that in the triple-product multiple solution methods. Figure 5 represents a Fourier map of biflorine, using the ninety-four signs of the best set. Figure 6 shows a Fourier map of this structure, obtained with the structure determination methods mentioned above. The similarity is striking. At the moment, however, it is not certain whether these two maps correspond to the correct structure or if both of them belong to the same nearly homometric structure. Refinement is in progress.

FIG. 5. Fourier map of biflorine, (001)-projection, based on results obtained by the shift product method. Assumed atomic positions for the refinement are indicated by black dots.

FIG. 6. Preliminary Fourier map of biflorine (diffuse scattering, convolution molecule method).

In order to facilitate the calculation, a Fortran-programme for the IBM 704 has been prepared for the most time-consuming steps of the scheme. This programme calculates for each constant **h** all double-products with values exceeding a certain limit. This limit will be set by the machine depending on the value of the greatest double-product. The programme then adjusts the signs S_ν in Eq. (7) in such a way that the terms in Eq. (6), containing this greatest double-product, will be positive and calculates the sum of all equations (Eq. (6)) over ν. The machine then prints all terms of the sum series with their (relative) signs. As described above, one of these terms—i.e. the term corresponding to the highest double-product—will be predominant. These values have been used as the basis for hand calculations in order to determine the signs.

Later on we abandoned this method in favour of a mathematically more elegant method. It is easy to recognize that the equations (Eq. (6)) constitute a system of linear and homogeneous equations. The number of these equations is equal to the number of "zero" points in the Patterson structure. The unknown variables are the signs of the double-products or—in the acentric case—the phases $\cos(\phi_{h'} + \phi_{h-h'})$ (see Eq. (6)). It is possible to solve this system of equations, if the number of unknowns is equal to or less than the number of equations. Because of the homogeneity of the equations, only the relation of the variables to a certain variable (which may be arbitrarily fixed) can be calculated. A Gaussian transformation to normal equations is necessary, if the number of equations is greater than the number of unknowns. The latter number can be adjusted to a certain degree by neglecting the smallest double-products. On the other hand, it is advisable to have more equations than unknowns in order to minimize the errors inherent in the determination of the "zero" points. The same reason suggests a variation for the solution of the homogeneous equations, which was also proposed some time ago for another problem (Rollet and Sparks, 1960).

This straightforward scheme for the determination of the phases of the double-products has been programmed on the IBM 704 and on the IBM 7090. The programme establishes the set of linear equations (Eq. (6)) and solves it, using routine procedures for the solution of linear equations. Until now, the programme has not been used as extensively as the first scheme, but preliminary calculations on the projection of fluorene (see Fig. 1) have shown that it works satisfactorily.

Table I demonstrates the validity of Eq. (6) (fluorene). The "zeros" on the right-hand side of Eq. (6) $(= \Sigma)$ will be compared with the sum of the absolute values of the corresponding double-products $(= \Sigma||)$. It can easily be seen that the Σ-sum is very much smaller than the $\Sigma||$-sum.

Table II demonstrates an interesting feature of the equations (Eq. (6)). If $\mathbf{u}_0 = 0$ (Sayre case), the cosine terms in Eq. (6) have to be omitted and

TABLE I. Test of Eq. (6) on fluorene

h	k	Σ	$\Sigma\|$
1	9	− 261	5864
3	15	− 166	4886
4	5	755	3741
3	10	188	3823
0	2	321	6664
2	13	402	6584
0	1	87	3386
2	9	782	5604
4	13	169	2524
1	6	76	5683
2	14	40	3499

TABLE II. Another test of Eq. (6)

$$h = 0,\, k = 2,\, S(0, 2) = -$$

h'	k'	$h-h'$	$k-k'$	$S(U_{h',k'}U_{h-h',k-k'})$
0	$\bar{2}$	0	4	−
0	$\bar{4}$	0	6	−
0	$\bar{6}$	0	8	−
0	$\bar{8}$	0	10	−
1	1	$\bar{1}$	1	−
1	$\bar{1}$	$\bar{1}$	3	−
$\bar{1}$	$\bar{7}$	1	9	−
$\bar{1}$	$\overline{10}$	1	12	−
$\bar{2}$	$\overline{14}$	2	16	−
$\bar{4}$	$\bar{3}$	4	5	−
$\bar{4}$	$\overline{10}$	4	12	−
$\bar{5}$	0	5	2	−

$$h = 0,\, k = 1,\, U_{h,k} = 0$$

$\bar{1}$	1	1	0	−
$\bar{1}$	$\bar{6}$	1	7	−
$\bar{1}$	$\bar{9}$	1	10	+
$\bar{1}$	$\overline{15}$	1	16	+
$\bar{2}$	$\overline{13}$	2	14	+
$\bar{2}$	$\overline{16}$	2	17	+
$\bar{4}$	$\overline{12}$	4	13	−

the right-hand side has to be replaced by a term proportional to F_h. As all F's will be high, the double-products in the sum have—corresponding to the triple-product rule—probably the same sign. The same rule is naturally also valid in Eq. (6). The first part of Table II shows one example (fluorene, $F_{0,2} \gg 0$). The double-products have the same sign. If F_h is small or zero, the triple-product rule is no longer valid and the double-products have different signs. (See Part 2 of Table II; $F_{0,1} = 0$.)

This rule can be used to determine the signs of triple-products, which contradict the triple-product rule. The example shows on the other hand that our "double-product" method can use structure factor combinations, which have no sense in the triple-product methods.

In a test-run, fifteen sets of equations with 203 double-products have been solved and the relative signs of double-products determined, and 155 signs were in agreement.

Both schemes are somewhat related. In both of them the signs (in the second scheme, on principle, even the phases) of double-products will be determined. In the first scheme only a few of the relative signs of the greatest double-products in Eq. (6) can be calculated. The second scheme is, at least in principle, more powerful, because the number of the determinable signs is only limited by the number of "zero" points. The first scheme can be understood as a very crude "elimination" method for solving linear equations.

It is of principal interest, that the "shift product" method determines double-product phases and not triple-product phases. Double products are not structure invariants and therefore relative and not absolute signs will be found.

One of the problems to be solved in future is the automatic calculation of the phases of the structure factors from the phases of the double-products. If all phases of the double-products were correct, this procedure would be unambiguous. The inherent errors in the double-product phases will make necessary an iterative process. It is certain that these errors will limit the practical value of this access to the phase problem.

PART II: ADDITIONAL STRUCTURE FACTOR SIGNS IN THE HEAVY-ATOM TECHNIQUE BY USE OF THE SAYRE RELATIONS

(In collaboration with R. Huber)

In the heavy-atom technique, the signs of the structure factors with low heavy-atom contribution are unknown. We have shown (Hoppe, 1962b; Huber and Hoppe, 1962) that the structure factors with large heavy-atom contribution can be used to determine the structure factors with low heavy-atom contribution. In order to demonstrate the principle, we first assume all structure factors to be known and the sign of only one structure factor F_{h1} missing. It is now possible to calculate the squared electron density map of the incomplete structure (F_{h1} not included). Their structure factors $F'squ_h$ are given by the (incomplete) Sayre series

$$F'squ_h = \frac{1}{V} \sum_{h'} F_{h'} F_{h-h'} \tag{8}$$

$$\text{for:} \quad \begin{pmatrix} h' \neq \pm h1 \\ h-h' \neq \pm h1 \end{pmatrix}$$

On the other hand it is well known that the structure factors $Fsqu_h$ of the correct squared electron density map are proportional to a shape function S_h and to the structure factors of the structure itself.

$$Fsqu_h = S_h F_h \tag{9}$$

$F'squ_h$ and $Fsqu_h$ can be computed for all structure factors (with the exception of F_{h1}). It can be shown that the following equation is valid:

$$Fsqu_h = F'squ_h + 2\frac{1}{V} F_{h1} F_{h-h1} + 2\frac{1}{V} F_{-h1} F_{h+h1} \tag{10}$$

From Eq. (10) F_{h1} may easily be computed. The problem is overdetermined: Many relations of type (Eq. (10)) can be established to find F_{h1}. It is now possible to generalize Eq. (10) for the determination of m unknown structure factors:

$$Fsqu_h = F'squ_h + \frac{2}{V} \sum_m F_{hm} F_{h-hm} +$$

$$+ \frac{2}{V} \sum_m F_{-hm} F_{h+hm} \tag{11}$$

$$Fsqu_h - F'squ_h = U_h \tag{12}$$

$$\frac{2}{V} (F_{h-hm} + F_{h+hm}) = C_{h,m} \tag{13}$$

$$U_h = \sum_m F_{hm} \cdot C_{h,m} \tag{14}$$

Equation (10) is now changed into a system of linear equations, which can be solved, if all U_h (Eq. (12)) and $C_{h,m}$ are known.

We have checked this procedure on a test structure. The structure factors of a projection $p2$ with 5 Gaussian atoms in the asymmetric unit (Fig. 14) (four atoms with the same weight, one atom with triple weight) were computed.

The signs of the structure factors of the heavy atom were added to the structure factors of the whole structure and the heavy atom contribution was subtracted.

Five structure factors with especially low heavy-atom contribution were chosen as unknown variables F_{hm} in Eq. (14). These structure factors were F_{32}, F_{43}, $F_{\bar{3}1}$, $F_{\bar{6}1}$, $F_{\bar{5}2}$ (Fig. 8). A system of fifteen equations has been established in such a way that the chosen $F\text{squ}_h$ and F_{h-hm} and F_{h+hm} had a large heavy-atom contribution. (This indicates that their signs will be probably correct.)

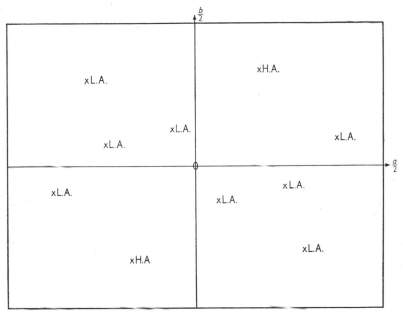

FIG. 7. Diagram of the test structure; H.A. are the heavy atoms, L.A. are the lights atoms; $a = 8$ Å, $b = 6$ Å.

As an example, one of these fifteen equations is written down:

$$F\text{squ}_{40} - F'\text{squ}_{40} = \frac{2}{V}[(F_{\bar{1}2} + F_{72})\,F_{32} + (F_{03} + F_{83})\,F_{43} +$$
$$+ (F_{\bar{7}1} + F_{11})\,F_{\bar{3}1} + (F_{\overline{10}1} + F_{\bar{2}1})\,F_{\bar{6}1} +$$
$$+ (F_{\bar{9}2} + F_{\bar{1}2})\,F_{\bar{5}2}]$$

These fifteen equations have to be transformed to normal equations. Their solutions are shown in Table III.

It is obvious that four structure factors in Table III have the correct sign. Not only the signs but also the absolute values can be computed. The latter could perhaps be used as an indication of the probability of a correct sign.

It is of principal interest that the method supplies additional information in the heavy-atom technique. The reason for this is that the squaring

3*

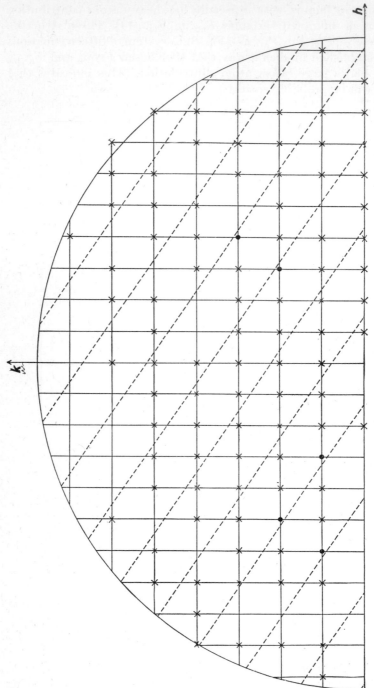

FIG. 8. Reciprocal lattice of the test structure:
● are the wanted structure factors;
× structure factors used as Fsqu$_\mathbf{h}$, $F_{\mathbf{h}-\mathbf{h}_m}$, $F_{\mathbf{h}+\mathbf{h}_m}$;
--- lines of "zero" heavy-atom contribution.

formula sets shape conditions to the electron density. The heavy-atom technique does not restrict the shape of the atomic peaks. It is well known that an atomic "peak" in the first heavy-atom-phased Fourier map can be quite an irregular positive or even negative region.

The method can be used in the isomorphous replacement technique as well and may easily be generalized for phase determination in acentric structures. On the other hand, it must be remarked that the method in the present form is not very useful in practical work. If too many signs are to be determined in one run, it is quite difficult to find enough relations (Eq. (14)) (that means enough U_h and $C_{h, m}$ in Eqs. (12) and (13)). One way out would be an iterative process. In the first cycle, only a few structure factors will be computed; their signs will be added to the set

TABLE III

	F_{32}	F_{43}	$F_{\bar{3}1}$	$F_{\bar{5}1}$	$F_{\bar{6}2}$
Computed	−4·34	+24·15	+27·50	−7·34	+6·91
Correct value	−5·35	+4·87	+15·24	−2·63	−5·61

of the "correct" structure factors. In the next cycle, another small set of unknown structure factors will be calculated, and so on. The difficulty in this scheme is that the "correct" structure factors are never correct, but only probably correct. The final set will, therefore, be better than the heavy-atom set, but it will not be the correct set. It would, therefore, be better to abandon the division into "known" and "unknown" signs, and to substitute this division by probability weights for the phases and to redetermine all structure factor phases in each cycle. Work along these lines is in progress.

REFERENCES

Anzenhofer, K. and Hoppe, W. (1962). Sign Determination by Means of Zero Points in the Patterson Function. Paper read during the Symposium, "Recent Advances in the Experimental and Theoretical Methods of Crystal Structure Research", Munich, 28–31 July, 1962.

Hoppe, W. (1962a). *Naturwissenschaften* (in press).

Hoppe, W. (1962b). *Naturwissenschaften* (in press).

Huber, R. and Hoppe W. (1962). Linear Equations between Structure Factor Products for the Determination of Additional Signs in the Heavy-Atom Technique. Paper read during the Symposium, "Recent Advances in the Experimental and Theoretical Methods of Crystal Structure Research", Munich, 28–31 July, 1962.

Rollet, J. S. and Sparks, R. A. (1960). *Acta cryst.* **13**, 273.

Sayre, D. (1952). *Acta cryst.* **5**, 60.

The Use of an EDSAC Programme for Structure Analysis

W. Cochran, R. Srinivasan† and P. Tollin‡

Crystallographic Laboratory, Cavendish Laboratory, Cambridge, England

ABSTRACT

It is well known that the triple product $s(\mathbf{h})s(\mathbf{h}')s(\mathbf{h}+\mathbf{h}')$ of signs is probably positive when comparatively large unitary structure factors are involved, and the probability can be expressed approximately as a function of $|U(\mathbf{h})U(\mathbf{h}')U(\mathbf{h}+\mathbf{h}')|$. Machine programmes based on this result have been written for EDSAC II and have been used in attempts to determine crystal structures directly, in projection. The method is illustrated with reference to the structure determination of alloxantin and alloxan and its application to solve another structure, a derivative of purine, is also described. A discussion of the limitations of the method is also given.

INTRODUCTION

§ 1. The principle of a computer method for the determination of crystal structures, by using sign relations, has been given in earlier papers (see, for example, Cochran, 1961). One advantage of the method is common to all "direct" methods, namely that assumptions about the stereochemistry of the molecule involved do not have to be made at an early stage. In section 2 we give a qualitative account of the principle of the method and illustrate its use, for centrosymmetric projections, by reference to the structure determinations of alloxantin and alloxan (Chatar Singh, 1961), and we also describe an application of the method to the determination of the structure of a purine derivative. In these three instances there was some doubt about the molecular structures. More mathematical details and some discussion of the limitations of the method are given in section 3.

§ 2. It is well known that the product $s(\mathbf{h})\, s(\mathbf{h}')\, s(\mathbf{h}+\mathbf{h}')$ of the signs of three-structure factors is probably positive, and the probability can be expressed, at least approximately, as a function of $|U(\mathbf{h})\, U(\mathbf{h}')\, U(\mathbf{h}+\mathbf{h}')|$, where $U(\mathbf{h})$ is a unitary structure factor (see, for example, Woolfson, 1961). Thus, while any sign $s(\mathbf{h})$ is ordinarily as likely to be negative as positive, each quantity $Y(\mathbf{hh}')$ defined as

$$Y(\mathbf{hh}') \equiv s(\mathbf{h})\, s(\mathbf{h}')\, s(\mathbf{h}+\mathbf{h}') \tag{1}$$

---

† Visitor from University of Madras.
‡ Now at Physics Department, Queen's College, Dundee.

is more likely to be positive than negative. Programmes have been written for EDSAC II which function as follows.

(i) The machine is supplied with a table of the larger unitary structure factors (not exceeding thirty-eight in number) and their indices. Alternatively the machine will evaluate the unitary structure factors from a table of all the structure factors corresponding to a centrosymmetric projection.

(ii) All the relations of type (1) are found which involve the larger unitary structure factors.

(iii) The machine now generates all those sets of signs for the larger unitary structure factors for which more than some specified proportion of the $Y(\mathbf{hh'})$'s are positive. Thus the first set of signs generated will be that for which all $Y(\mathbf{hh'})$ are positive, provided that this is a possible solution of the equations (1).

(iv) In some instances we have used the subsidiary criterion that a set of signs is rejected unless, for each value of $\mathbf{h}$, the quantity $\sum\limits_{\mathbf{h'}} Y(\mathbf{hh'})$ is "not too negative". (See section 3 for a more precise definition.) This condition is used at this stage as an approximation to the condition that $U(\mathbf{h})$ is very probably of the same sign as $\sum\limits_{\mathbf{h'}} U(\mathbf{h'}) U(\mathbf{h}+\mathbf{h'})$.

(v) For each set of signs generated at (ii) and not subsequently rejected, the signs of additional (smaller) unitary structure factors are evaluated using the relation

$$s(\mathbf{h}_1) = s\left(\sum_{\mathbf{h}} U(\mathbf{h}) U(\mathbf{h}+\mathbf{h}_1)\right) \tag{2}$$

where the unitary structure factors appearing on the right are those for which signs have already been found, and $U(\mathbf{h}_1)$ is one of the smaller unitary structure factors. By continuing this process signs are found, as far as proves possible, for all unitary structure factors whose magnitudes exceed some specified limit, for example 0·15.

(vi) Each extended set of signs is now tested as follows. The machine evaluates

$$G(\mathbf{h}) = \sum_{\mathbf{h'}} U(\mathbf{h'}) U(\mathbf{h}+\mathbf{h'}) \tag{3}$$

which is proportional to the structure factor of the squared electron distribution (Sayre, 1952), and in separate zones of the reciprocal lattice a scaling factor,

$$\alpha = \sum \{|U(\mathbf{h})|/|G(\mathbf{h})|\}$$

The quantity

$$T = \sum \{\alpha|G(\mathbf{h})| - |U(\mathbf{h})|\}/|U(\mathbf{h})| \tag{4}$$

is next evaluated as a measure of the agreement between the U's and the G's, that is, between the electron distribution and its square. The ideal value of T is zero for a perfectly resolved distribution of equal atoms, and it had been anticipated that for an actual structure it would prove to be lowest for the correct set of signs.

(vii) Finally, electron density maps are evaluated for the various sets of signs, starting with that which has given the lowest value in the T-test,

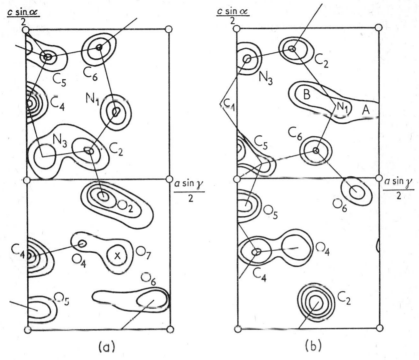

FIG. 1. (a) Projection of alloxantin down the b-axis, with incorrect signs. (b) The same, with the correct signs.

if this has been applied. These are produced in a form suitable for contouring (by hand) and examined for expected features.

The correct structural formula of alloxantin is

Crystals of the dihydrate contain one formula unit in a triclinic cell, space group $P\bar{1}$. The structure was determined in the b-axis projection starting from twenty-three of the largest unitary structure factors, two of which were given positive signs to fix the origin. In this instance the T-test was not at first used, and maps were evaluated (still using only twenty-three terms) for the first eight sets of signs produced. It is interesting to note that the molecule can be fitted to the electron density map of sign set No. 6 (Fig. 1 (a)) almost as well as to that of No. 7 (Fig. 1 (b)). Subsequent refinement showed No. 7 to be correct. Values of T (Eq. 4) were calculated later and $T_6 = 0.57$, $T_7 = 0.45$ were found,

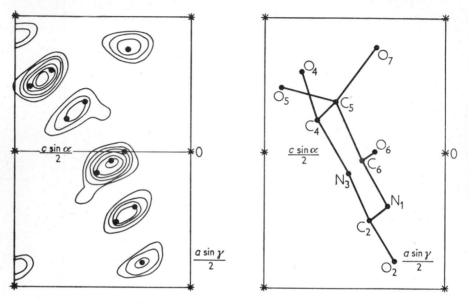

Fig. 2. The b-axis projection of alloxan.

so that this test indeed favoured No. 7. It should, however, be noted that set No. 8 gave the same value of T, 0.45. However, an inspection of the map prepared from the latter would have led to its rejection. The remaining steps of the structure determination were made by more conventional methods (Chatar Singh, 1961).

The formula of alloxan (aside from problems of hydrogen tautomerism) was known to be one of the following.

The space group is $P\bar{1}$ with two molecules per cell. The unit-cell dimensions and Patterson functions suggested that the molecules would be well resolved in the a- and c-axis projections, and poorly resolved in the b-axis projection. It was, however, only for the latter that the EDSAC method proved to be successful. Thirty unitary structure factors were used initially. The limits set on the number of Y's allowed to be negative resulted in twenty-three sets of signs being produced, of which No. 5 had $T = 0.38$, while the values for the others ranged from 0.46 to 0.58. The corresponding electron density map is shown in Fig. 2, and eventually proved to be correct. Attempts to determine the other projections directly were not successful and the y-co-ordinates were found by trial. The dihydroxy structure proved to be the correct one (Chatar Singh, 1961). Subsequently an instructive "post mortem" was held on the failure of the method for the other two projections. This was facilitated by the fact that it was at this stage that programming for EDSAC II was completed; some of the steps in the two investigations described above were in fact made by hand calculation. Results of the post-mortem are given in a later section.

The compound $C_6H_6N_4S$, prepared by Dr. Sorolla, was known to be a purine derivative with one of the following four structures.

(I)

(II)

(III)

(IV)

The space group was found to be $P2_1/a$, with four molecules per unit cell. The molecules should be well resolved in the c-axis projection ($c = 4.26$ Å) and there were twenty-seven unitary structure factors for which $|U(hk0)| \geqslant 0.25$. Three of these were found to be involved in comparatively few sign relations and were discarded. There were twenty-five sign relations of type (1), and the probability of their being positive ranged in this case from 0.99 to 0.83. Sets of signs were generated which satisfied the following conditions. (1) Not more than two of the first seventeen of the Y's should be negative, not more than one of the next four should be negative, and not more than one of the remaining four should be negative. In the notation of section 3, that is,

$$q = 17, \qquad u = 4, \qquad v = 4$$
$$q' = 2, \qquad u' = 1, \qquad v' = 1$$

(2) For each $\mathbf{h}$, the sum $\sum\limits_{\mathbf{h}'} Y(\mathbf{h}, \mathbf{h}')$ must not be negative.

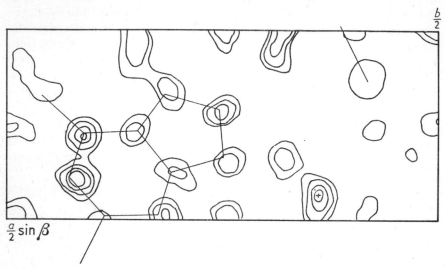

$\frac{b}{2}$

$\frac{a}{2}\sin\beta$

FIG. 3. First projection of 2-mercapto-6-methylpurine.

Sixty sets of signs were found to satisfy these conditions, including four sets for which no Y in the first seventeen was negative, and sixteen sets for which only one of these was negative. For each set of signs further signs were now evaluated using Eq. (2). Finally, the quantity T (Eq. 4) was evaluated for each. The lowest value was 0·50, others ranged from 0·56 to 0·80. This lowest value was for one of the first four sets of signs obtained. The corresponding electron density map is shown in Fig. 3. The molecule could be recognized, and subsequent refinement gave the map shown in Fig. 4, which includes a water molecule. The correct structural formula is therefore (II), 2-mercapto-6-methylpurine. A situation in which all Y's of the first set are positive is, of course, a very favourable one, the probability of its occurrence in this instance was calculated to be 36%.

§ 3. In order to understand the limitations of the method it is necessary to go into rather more algebraic detail. Let the number of signs involved, apart from those fixed by choice of origin, or already determined in some other way, be $(q+r)$. Let the total number of sign relations be $(q+u+v)$.

Of these, the $(q+r)$ having the highest probability of being positive are chosen to give a set of $(q+r)$ equations of type (1). Using the method already described elsewhere (Cochran and Douglas, 1955) these are converted to a set of *linear* equations

$$Y_i = \sum_j \alpha_{ij} s_j \qquad (5)$$

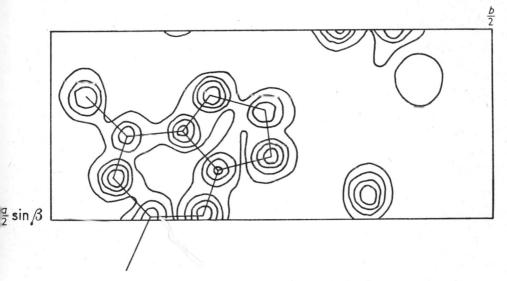

FIG. 4. Final projection of 2-mercapto-6-methylpurine.

in which a positive sign is represented by zero and a negative sign by unity. This is possible since

$$0+0 = 0, \qquad 0+1 = 1, \qquad 1+1 = 0 \quad (\text{mod } 2)$$

corresponds to

$$+ \times + = +, \qquad + \times - = -, \qquad - \times - = +$$

Equation (5) can be solved for a number q of the s's (those belonging to class Q_s) in terms of q of the Y's (those in class Q_y) and the remaining s's, which are r in number and which we describe as belonging to class R_s. This can be expressed by saying that the matrix whose elements are the α_{ij} is of order $(q+r)$ and of rank q.

The Y's which do not belong to class Q_y are now divided into classes U_y and V_y containing u and v members respectively, those in class U_y having higher probabilities of being positive than those in class V_y. (In practice we usually take $u = v$.) It is possible to express the Y's in these two classes in terms of those in class Q_y, and the signs in class R_s. Thus, to summarize, q of the signs are expressed in terms of q of the Y's, which are predominantly positive, and r of the signs, which are equally likely to be positive or negative. The remaining $(u+v)$ Y's, which are for convenience divided into two classes, are expressed in terms of the same q Y's and r s's. Now let us denote by q', u' and v' the maximum number of Y's which it is proposed to allow to be negative in classes Q_y, U_y and V_y respectively. The programme operates by generating those sets of signs, $\sum_{n=0}^{q'} 2^r q!/(q-n)!$ in number, which necessarily satisfy the condition that the number of negative Y's in class Q_y does not exceed q'. A set is rejected if it leads to more than u' negative Y's in class U_y, or more than v' in class V_y. It should, of course, be obvious that we do not know at the outset how many Y's will be negative in each class. The expected number can, however, be calculated, for example the number expected in class Q is

$$q'_{\text{ex}} = q - \sum_{i=1}^{q} p_i$$

where p_i is the probability that Y_i is positive, and in practice one begins by setting $q' = q_{\text{ex}}$ in the hope that the actual number of negative Y's in class Q, q'_{ac}, will not exceed q'_{ex}.

We have already mentioned, under (iv) in section 2, a further test which is applied to each set of signs, provided it has not already been rejected. We define a parameter C such that a set is rejected unless for each $\mathbf{h}$,

$$\sum_{\mathbf{h'}} Y(\mathbf{hh'}) \geqslant 0 \qquad \text{if } C \text{ is set equal to zero,}$$
$$\geqslant -1 \qquad \text{if } C \text{ is set equal to one.}$$

This parameter is supplied to the computer; q'_{ex}, u'_{ex} and v'_{ex} are evaluated by the computer from the magnitudes of the unitary structure factors involved.

We now discuss some of the considerations that govern the use of the program, and some of its limitations. The time taken to generate and test the sets of signs is roughly proportional to the number of sets of signs, and is therefore

$$t \sum_{n=0}^{q'} 2^r q!/(q-n)!$$

where t is the time required to generate and test one set of signs (about $0 \cdot 2$ sec). Thus the values of q' and of r have a very marked effect on the time taken. At first sight as large a value as possible for the number of signs, $(q+r)$, would appear to be advisable. However, this would mean that unitary structure factors of lower value would have to be included, thus increasing q' disproportionately and rapidly increasing the time required. If, however, too low a value of $(q+r)$ is used, there may not be enough signs initially for Eq. (2) to give further signs reliably. Various tests using different values suggest that $25 < q+r < 30$ is a suitable range. In the course of the post-mortem on the a-axis projection of

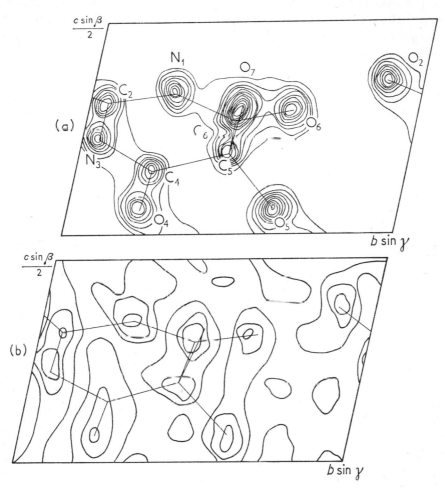

FIG. 5. The initial (b) and final (a) a-axis projections of alloxan.

alloxan it was found that with $q+r = 26$, 119 sets of signs were produced at the end of stage (iv). On eliminating five structure factors which were involved in few sign relations, the computer produced only twenty sets of signs. The correct set of signs was included in both cases, but obviously the time required for further tests—which are in any case not infallible— is much less in one instance and the fact that there are five fewer signs at this stage should not be of great importance. It is therefore advisable to study the matrix of sign relations (which can be put out by the computer) after stage (ii) with a view to eliminating structure factors which contribute to fewer than two sign relations. This could, of course, be programmed, but we have left it to the judgment of the investigator.

A serious pitfall of the method (or of any related method) is the possibility of bad luck. There is always a finite probability that the actual values of q', u' and v' for the correct set of signs may exceed their expected values. In the course of the post-mortem on the c-axis projection of

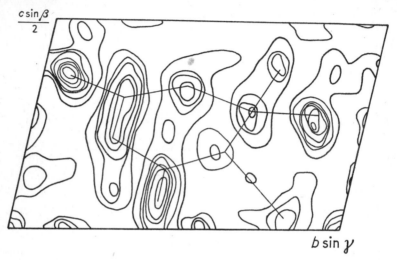

$$\frac{c \sin \beta}{2}$$

$$b \sin \gamma$$

FIG. 6. The a-axis projection of alloxan made with an incorrect set of signs.

alloxan an attempt to produce the correct set of signs, using $(q+r) = 25$, was not successful. Substitution of the correct set of signs showed that

$$q'_{ac} = 8, \qquad u'_{ac} = 3, \qquad v'_{ac} = 6$$

with $q = 21$, $u = 14$, $v = 14$ (and $r = 4$).

From the probabilities involved, however,

$$q'_{ex} = 3, \qquad u'_{ex} = 3, \qquad v'_{ex} = 4$$

The probability of eight negative Y's in the first twenty-one is in this case only 2%, so this is an example of bad luck. However, the probability that q'_{ac} exceeds q'_{ex} in this case is 42%, and it is clear that setting $q' = q'_{ex}$ is optimistic. Larger values of q', u' and v' can always be tried, at the expense of producing more sets of signs for subsequent testing.

Although the T-test works in accordance with expectation in some instances, this is not always so. For example, in investigating the a-axis projection with $(q+r) = 21$, we have already noted that twenty sets of signs were produced. The correct set had $T = 0.54$ but fourteen others had values between 0.47 and 0.54. With $(q+r) = 26$, the correct set gave $T = 0.50$. The corresponding map is shown in Fig. 5. There were forty-eight sets having $T < 0.50$, and the minimum value was 0.41. The corresponding map (Fig. 6) could be fitted quite well by a possible molecular structure, and in fact this was true of several maps which corresponded to low values of T. The structure in this projection is an open one and the molecules fairly symmetrical. It appears that there are a number of pseudo-homometric structures, but we do not fully understand why the correct set of signs should give a relatively high value of T.

In conclusion, the method has not come up to our best expectations, but we believe it contains features which would be worth incorporating in future programs for faster computers using three-dimensional data.

REFERENCES

Chatar Singh (1961). Thesis, University of Cambridge.

Cochran, W. (1961). In *Computing Methods and the Phase Problems in X-ray Crystal Analysis* (R. Pepinsky, J. M. Robertson and J. C. Speakman, eds.). Pergamon Press, Oxford.

Cochran, W. and Douglas, A. S. (1955). *Proc. roy. Soc.* **A227**, 486.

Sayre, D. (1952). *Acta cryst.* **5**, 60.

Woolfson, M. M. (1961). *Direct Methods in Crystallography*. Clarendon Press, Oxford.

DISCUSSION

H. JAGODZINSKI: Sometimes quite a few signs of triple products come out to be negative. I wonder whether your programme brings the signs of triple products to the best agreement possible.

R. SRINIVASAN: This is simply incorporated into the programme by the fact that we allow a certain number of possible failures to occur. Though this increases the number of possible sets of signs, we finally depend on some criterion such as the T-test to pick out the correct structure.

The Patterson Approach to Phase Problem

S. Raman† and W. N. Lipscomb

*Department of Chemistry, Harvard University, Cambridge,
Massachusetts, U.S.A.*

ABSTRACT

The phase problem of crystallography is studied via both the minimum function
and the sum function. Methods are proposed for better sharpening of the Patterson
function and properties of the MA-function are also discussed.

INTRODUCTION

The phase problem in crystallography is most conveniently tackled via
the Patterson function

$$P(\mathbf{u}) = \frac{1}{V} \sum_{\mathbf{H}} |F(\mathbf{H})|^2 \exp - 2\pi i \mathbf{H} \cdot \mathbf{u}$$

In the language of the image theory, the problem is to find the funda-
mental set $\mathbf{r}_i$ given the vector set $\mathbf{r}_i - \mathbf{r}_j$ where $\mathbf{r}_i$ is the position vector of
the ith atom in the unit cell and $i = 1, N$. In the language of Fourier
transform theory, the problem is to find that function $\rho(\mathbf{r})$ whose self-
convolution is the Patterson function available from the finite set of
intensity data $|F(\mathbf{H})|^2$ where the self-convolution is defined by

$$P(\mathbf{u}) = \int \rho(\mathbf{r}) \rho(\mathbf{u} + \mathbf{r}) \, d\mathbf{r}$$

In this paper, we try to analyse the problem by both mathematical
techniques and propose methods for the solution.

SHARPENING OF THE PATTERSON FUNCTION

Since most of the ideas suggested here are exactly valid only under the
assumption of point-atoms it is essential that the starting point should
be a very good sharpened Patterson function. In actuality, the scattering
atoms are not points but have a finite shape arising out of the inherent
quantum mechanical shape as well as the disturbing influences of thermal
vibrations of the nuclei. The sharpening procedure first adopted approxi-
mates the dynamics by an isotropic factor of Debye-Waller type leading

† Present address: Chemistry Department, Brookhaven National Laboratory, Upton,
L.I., New York.

to normal-sharpening of the Patterson function. It was subsequently pointed out (Jacobson *et al.*, 1961) that self-convolutions of the first derivative of $\rho(\mathbf{r})$ are more sharpened than self-convolutions of $\rho(\mathbf{r})$, thus attempting to reduce the quantum-mechanical shape of the atoms. Such first-derivative sharpened functions, however, suffer from the fact that the sharpening is inevitably accompanied by second-order negative peaks which are over and above the negative ripples already present owing to the finiteness of the transform. The attempt to overcome this difficulty by adding a constant amount (say 18%) of the unsharpened Patterson function is not really very satisfactory. A better procedure involves extension of the finite data and uses not just the self-convolution of the first derivative of $\rho(\mathbf{r})$ but instead a linear combination of self-convolutions of higher derivatives of $\rho(\mathbf{r})$. This combination, called $BP(\mathbf{r})$ is given by

$$BP(\mathbf{r}) = \sum_{i=0}^{n} a_i S^{(i)}(\mathbf{r})$$

where $S^{(i)}(\mathbf{r})$ is the self-convolution of the ith derivative and a_i are the coefficients. It is not clear what the minimum value of n should be but obviously, the larger the value of n, the higher the quality of $BP(\mathbf{r})$. The transforms of such self-convolutions of the ith derivative are simply given by the convolution integral theorem of Fourier transform theory as $|F(\mathbf{H})|^2 \sin^{2i}(\theta)/\lambda^{2i}$ so that their calculation is simply achieved through Fourier syntheses. The next question is how the data should be extended. An obvious way is to use numerical relations between magnitudes of crystal structure factors that can be derived either by algebraic methods or by joint probability distributions. For instance, a typical relation (Hauptman and Karle, 1955) is

$$|E(\mathbf{H}+\mathbf{K})|^2 - 1 = N\langle(|E(\mathbf{H})|^2 - 1) \times (|E(\mathbf{K})|^2 - 1)\rangle_{\mathbf{H}+\mathbf{K}}$$

Such relations are exactly valid only if the corresponding Patterson function shows no overlap; further, the range of data needed for valid extrapolation is not clear. Instead it is an equally feasible, if not better, procedure to use the Patterson function itself to obtain the extrapolation since we have

$$|F(\mathbf{H})|^2 = K \int P(\mathbf{r}) \exp 2\pi i \mathbf{H}\cdot\mathbf{r}\, d\mathbf{r}$$

where K is a scale factor which is easily known from a calculation of some known intensities. The extrapolation can be achieved in a finite number of stages by increasing the radius of the sphere in reciprocal space by small amounts, extrapolating the data and recalculating the P-function to be used for the next cycle. Note that this extrapolation seems to be a valid procedure even under the presence of heavy overlap in the P-function.

THE APPROACH VIA M-FUNCTION AND MA-FUNCTION

The M-function (Buerger, 1951) and the MA-function (Raman and Lipscomb, 1961) can be jointly used to unravel the P-function. In principle, the MA-function offers a complete solution but in practice, structure-determining methods have to exploit the different properties of not only $M(r)$, $MA(r)$ but other functions as well. To start with, we shall demonstrate how the generalized MA-function theoretically solves the phase problem. As a preliminary we define the functions

$$\mathbf{u}_{ab}^{(ij)} = \mathbf{r}_{ai} - \mathbf{r}_{bj} \quad (a_i = 1, N; b_j = 1, N) \tag{1}$$

$$1M(\mathbf{r}) = \text{Min}\{P(\mathbf{r}), P(\mathbf{r} + \mathbf{u}_{ab})\} \tag{2}$$

$$cM(\mathbf{r}) = \text{Min}\{P(\mathbf{r}), P(\mathbf{r} + \mathbf{u}_{ab}^{(i)})\} \quad (i = 1, c) \tag{3}$$

$$1MA(\mathbf{u}_{ab}) = \int_{\mathbf{r}} M(\mathbf{r}) \, d\mathbf{r} \tag{4}$$

$$cMA(\mathbf{u}_{ab}^{(i)}) = \int_{\mathbf{r}} cM(\mathbf{r}) \, d\mathbf{r} \tag{5}$$

for a non-centrosymmetric structure containing N atoms per unit cell, the jth one of scattering power f_j being defined by the position-vector $\mathbf{r}_j$. The expression Min implies the operation of taking the minimum of the relevant P-function values. Equation (1) defines the N^2 interatomic vectors of the structure. These are the content of the P-function and offer the starting point for finding the fundamental set $\mathbf{r}_i$ through the succeeding equations. Equation (2) defines the Buerger minimum function and implies the result that $1M(\mathbf{r})$ drawn for interatomic vector $\mathbf{u}_{ab}$ has $(2N-2)$ peaks at $\pm(\mathbf{r}_i - \boldsymbol{\Delta}_{ab})$ of strength $f_i \, \text{Min} \, (f_a, f_b)$. Here $\boldsymbol{\Delta}_{ab} = \frac{1}{2}(\mathbf{r}_a + \mathbf{r}_b)$ and $i = 1, N$ but $i \neq a$ or b. If $i = a$ or b, the strength is $f_a f_b$. A geometrical interpretation of the result is that $1M(\mathbf{r})$ yields the structure duplicated by inversion about the mid-point of the shift-vector $\mathbf{u}_{ab}$.

The duplication, inevitable when image-seeking is performed by a single vector (i.e. a 2-gon) can be eliminated by increasing the order of the image-seeking configuration, a result implied in equation (3) where the minimum is taken of the P-function values at the vertices of a $(C+1)$-gon as this $(C+1)$-gon roams the full unit cell. However, the computed $cM(\mathbf{r})$ function is meaningful if and only if the image-seeking $(C+1)$-gon is part of one and the same image in the Patterson space, i.e. the set of vectors $\mathbf{u}_{ab}^{(i)} = \mathbf{r}_a - \mathbf{r}_{bi}$ must have one atom in common and just not any set of c vectors out of the total of N^2 vectors $\mathbf{r}_i - \mathbf{r}_j$. If so, how do we know that a given set of vectors belong to one and the same image? The answer to this important question is given by Eqs. (4) and (5). Equation (4) answers the question whether a given vector is an interatomic vector or not. In fact, the 1MA-function can maximize only if the shift-vector $\mathbf{u}$ is an interatomic vector $\mathbf{u}_{ij}$. Equation (5) implies that the cMA-function can maximize if and only if the corresponding $(C+1)$-gon is part of one and the same image. Therefore, the cM($\mathbf{r}$) function followed by a cMA-calculation, where one starts with $C = 1$ and increases the value of C in steps of unity, leads to a systematic structure determining procedure, which procedure becomes less tedious and more powerful when stereochemical considerations are also employed. This technique has already been discussed by us (Raman and Lipscomb, 1961) and attempts are under way to adapt the ideas for automatic computers. But here we generalize the ideas and point out their applications. Hitherto, it has been explicitly assumed that we are concerned with just one particular set $\mathbf{u}_{ab}^{(i)}$ in the evaluation of the cMA function. Now we investigate the properties of the function calculated for all the sets. It is obvious that the function gives all the possible $(C+1)$-gons in the structure where by a possible $(C+1)$-gon we mean a $(C+1)$-gon which is part of any one of the N-images of the fundamental set (or the homometric mates). In particular, we will study the two extremes, the 1MA and the GMA-function. The 1MA-function is equation (4) calculated for all possible vectors $\mathbf{u}$ in the unit cell (the unit cell dimensions having been divided by suitable grid intervals, like say $120 \times 120 \times 60$) and gives back the interatomic vectors $\mathbf{r}_i - \mathbf{r}_j$. Therefore it resembles the P-function and obviously fails to solve the phase problem, but there are certain subtle differences. Firstly the 1MA-function might be more sharpened than the P-function, thereby offering a better starting point for running superpositions. Secondly, the peak strengths are different from those in the P-function. This enables us to eliminate light atom to light atom vectors from the Patterson of a complicated structure containing, say, L light atoms of strength f_{Li} and H heavy atoms of strength f_{Hj}. The reason is that, whereas in the P-function the strength at $H_i L_j$ vectors is $f_{Hi} f_{Lj}$ and that at $L_i L_j$ vectors is $f_{Li} f_{Lj}$, in the 1MA function the strength at $H_i L_j$ vectors is $f_{Lj} \Sigma' f_j + 2 f_{Hi} f_{Lj}$ and the strength at $L_i L_j$ is $f_{Li} \Sigma' f_j + 2 f_{Li} f_{Lj}$. [In general, the strength at $\mathbf{r}_a - \mathbf{r}_b$ is $2\text{Min}\,(f_a, f_b) \Sigma' f_j + 2 f_a f_b$, where the prime implies $j \neq a$ or b.] This result implies that in the 1MA-function the strengths at $H_i L_j$ is more or less the same as the strength at $L_i L_j$, whereas in the P-function the strength at $H_i L_j$ is much greater than that at $L_i L_j$. If the 1MA-function is suitably scaled and subtracted from the P-function, one may hopefully be left with just the HH and HL vectors. Thus, we have here an attractive method of identifying and eliminating the LL vectors. The result is valid whether there is or is not overlap in the P-function. There are a number of other applications of the 1MA-function, like the facts that the P_s-function (Pepinsky and Okaya, 1956) of anomalous dispersion on minimum accumulation gives the anomalously scattering atom to anomalously scattering atom-vectors and the DP-function of isomorphous replacement (Kartha and Ramachandran, 1955), on minimum-accumulation gives the replaceable atom to replaceable atom vectors, a result independently arrived at by Sarma and Srinivasan, (1962). These and other applications have been discussed by us in greater detail elsewhere (Raman and Lipscomb, 1961). The generalization of the 1MA-function to GMA-function through cMA-function is quite straight-forward. The GMA-function is calculated by taking an N-gon in Patterson space, examining the minimum of the P-function values at the vertices of the N-gon and accumulating the minima as the N-gon roams the full cell. The resultant sum (or integral) is a pure real number associated with the set $\mathbf{u}_i$ of N-vectors defining the N-gon. If we denote the entire set by a single vector U in N-space and repeat the operation for different values of the N-space vector U then the complete GMA-function is obtained. The GMA-function gives the fundamental set and its homometric mates and therefore completely solves the phase problem. However, it is unfortunate that calculation of GMA-function is impractical at the present stage of computing.

The Sum-function Approach to the Phase Problem

This approach was initiated by many workers (McLachlan, 1951) but has received considerable development in recent years (Ramachandran and Raman, 1959; Raman, 1959). The basic idea is that once the positions $\mathbf{r}_{Pj}$ of a small number of atoms, say P, are known, it is possible to superimpose and add the values of P such Patterson functions, the origin of each one of which has been shifted by each one of the $\mathbf{r}_{Pj}$ in turn. The resultant sum-function purports to give a P-fold accumulation at the required atomic sites $\mathbf{r}_{Qj}(Q = N - P)$. Instead of just shifting the origin by $\mathbf{r}_{Pj}$ and adding, one may as well multiply the P-function value by f_{Pj} and then add up. Such a procedure immediately brings the problem within the purview of Fourier transform theory and the tedious operation of shifting and adding is replaced by the elegant Fourier synthesis:

$$\alpha_{\text{gen}} = \frac{1}{V} \sum |F(\mathbf{H})|^2 \, F_P(\mathbf{H}) \exp - 2\pi i \mathbf{H} \cdot \mathbf{r}$$

where F_P is the calculated contribution from the atoms P given by

$$F_P(\mathbf{H}) = \sum_{j=1}^{P} f_{Pj} \exp 2\pi i \mathbf{H} \cdot \mathbf{r}_{Pj}$$

Both the strengths and positions of the peaks given by syntheses like α_{gen} are now well-known (Raman, 1959), but the important point is that such syntheses give major accumulations at the required sites $\mathbf{r}_{Qj}$

only at the expense of the introduction of a huge number of unwanted minor background peaks, which peaks superpose by accident and produce strong peaks competing with the genuine accumulations for choice of possible atomic positions. Therefore it is imperative that the background should be reduced, if not eliminated, to make the syntheses more powerful. We have tackled this problem via the Fourier transform theory, as well as geometrical operations performed on the α-synthesis itself. Here, we will describe the geometrical method, while the Fourier formulation will be presented elsewhere (Raman and Lipscomb, 1963). We consider the α_{is}-synthesis calculable when a pair of isomorphous crystals are available, though our results are more general. Consider the case when crystal 1 has atoms Q of strength 1 at $\mathbf{r}_{Qj}$, while crystal 2 has atoms $(Q+P)$ of strength 1 at $\mathbf{r}_{Qj}$ and $\mathbf{r}_{Pj}$. The α_{is}-synthesis calculable when the positions of P are known is a Fourier synthesis involving the coefficient $(|F^{(1)}|^2 - |F^{(2)}|^2 - |F_P|^2) F_P$, and gives strength P at the wanted sites $\mathbf{r}_{Qj}$ against background peaks of strength 1 at $\mathbf{r}_{Qi} - \mathbf{r}_{Qj} + \mathbf{r}_{Pk}$, and also at $2\mathbf{r}_{Pi} - \mathbf{r}_{Qj}$, but peaks of strength 2 at $\mathbf{r}_{Pi} + \mathbf{r}_{Pj} - \mathbf{r}_{Qk}(i \neq j)$. The α_{is}-map may be solved for the structure using the following three criteria.

1. Peak-strength criterion: A peak strength considerably less than P is not a genuine peak.
2. Criterion of coincidence: A peak is a good peak only if it coincides with another peak after vector-shifting the α_{is}-synthesis by each one, in turn, of the vectors $\mathbf{r}_{Pi} - \mathbf{r}_{Pj}$ of the replaceable group.
3. Criterion of non-coincidence: A peak is a good peak only if it does not coincide with another peak after vector-shifting the α_{is}-synthesis by each one, in turn, of the vectors $2\mathbf{r}_{Pi}$ and $\mathbf{r}_{Pi} + \mathbf{r}_{Pj}$ of the "squared" structure of the replaceable group. Note that criterion 3 loses validity if the replacement group is centrosymmetric, because the squared structure and the Patterson then become identical.

Acknowledgement

We would like to thank the National Institutes of Health for supporting this project.

REFERENCES

Buerger, M. J. (1951). *Acta cryst.* **4**, 531.
Hauptman, H. and Karle, J. (1955). *Acta cryst.* **8**, 355.
Jacobson, R. A., Wunderlich, J. A. and Lipscomb, W. N. (1961). *Acta cryst.* **14**, 598.
Kartha, G. and Ramachandran, G. N. (1955). *Acta cryst.* **8**, 195.
McLachlan, D. (1951). *Proc. nat. Acad. Sci., Wash.* **37**, 115.
Pepinsky, R. and Okaya, Y. (1956). *Proc. nat. Acad. Sci., Wash.* **42**, 286.
Ramachandran, G. N. and Raman, S. (1959). *Acta cryst.* **12**, 957.
Raman, S. (1959). *Acta cryst.* **12**, 964.
Raman, S. and Lipscomb, W. N. (1961). *Z. Kristallogr.* **116**, 314.
Raman, S. and Lipscomb, W. N. (1963). *Z. Kristallogr.* (in press).
Sarma, V. R. and Srinivasan, R. (1962). *Acta cryst.* **15**, 457.

Statistical Tests for Isomorphism

R. Srinivasan, V. Raghupathy Sarma and G. N. Ramachandran

Department of Physics, University of Madras, Madras, India

ABSTRACT

The paper deals with the results of the probability distribution of the differences and the products of the structure amplitudes of two crystals, containing N atoms and P atoms respectively ($P < N$). Two cases are considered: (a) When P forms a part of N (related case) and (b) when the two sets are entirely independent (un-related case), both when the crystals are centrosymmetric and non-centro-symmetric. The theoretical results have been tested out in a practical case of a structure containing eighteen atoms in the unit cell and good agreement has been found with theory. The theory for the related case is directly applicable to a pair of isomorphous crystals and leads to various tests for isomorphism and to the possibility of putting the data of the two crystals on the same scale. These results have been tested in the case of the pair, caffeine and theophylline.

INTRODUCTION

The theory of the isomorphous replacement method rests essentially on the assumption that ideal isomorphism exists between the structures concerned. However, it is a common experience that, in practice, such an ideal situation rarely exists, the lack of isomorphism varying to different extents depending on the circumstances. It would therefore be useful if one could have a criterion, preferably based on statistical considerations, by which one can assess how close the isomorphism is between the two compounds under study. The present paper describes two or three criteria which seem to fulfil such a requirement. These are based on certain basic results that have been obtained as a consequence of a systematic study of a more general problem, namely, that of the distribution of structure amplitudes of two related crystals. The details of this latter work are being published elsewhere in a series of papers and only the main results are given here, in so far as they pertain to our problem. They lead to the interesting result that the probability distribution of the *difference* between the structure amplitudes $|F^{(1)}|$ and $|F^{(2)}|$ of the two crystals are widely different, according as they are isomorphous or not. In particular, the R-value between the structure amplitudes of the two crystals, defined by

$$R = \frac{\sum ||F^{(1)}| - |F^{(2)}||}{\sum |F^{(1)}|}$$

85

is also very different, according as the two crystals form an isomorphous pair or an independent pair. A third criterion is based on the probability distribution of the *product* of $|F^{(1)}|$ and $|F^{(2)}|$ and is described below. The theoretical predictions have been tested out in some actual cases and these are also described in this paper.

PROBABILITY DISTRIBUTION OF THE DIFFERENCE

We consider a pair of crystals, one containing P and the other $N(= P+Q)$ atoms respectively ($P < N$), all atoms being assumed to be alike. The latter assumption is not essential, but it is enough if the probability distributions of both crystals follow the asymptotic distributions for a large number of atoms, which is true if a small number of atoms in the structure is not distinguished from the rest by having a large scattering factor. We thus assume that the number of atoms in each crystal is sufficiently large so that the distribution of intensities would follow the ideal centrosymmetric or non-centrosymmetric one, as the case may be. There are two situations to be considered, one in which the P atoms of the first crystal occupy identical positions in the second crystal, so that the two crystals may be considered to be ideally isomorphous, with the Q atoms forming the additional group in the latter. To talk of this situation in a more general sense, we shall refer to it as the "related case". The other situation is one in which the P atoms in the first crystal have no relation to the N atoms in the second. In other words, the positions of the atoms in the two crystals are completely independent of each other. We shall refer to this as the "unrelated case". It is clear that the latter situation can also be described as one in which isomorphism is completely lacking.

In order to talk about "related" and "unrelated" crystals, it is necessary that the two crystals should have a geometrical similarity. That is to say, they should have approximately the same cell dimensions and have the same crystallographic symmetry, etc., so that it would be possible to talk of corresponding reflections in the two crystals. It is interesting to note that occasionally, two crystals with closely related chemical formulae may have similar cell dimensions, but their structures may not be isomorphous.

We shall first consider the probability distribution of the difference in structure amplitudes of two crystals. Denoting the two structure amplitudes by $|F_N|$ and $|F_P|$, it is possible to work out from first principles the distribution of their difference (Ramachandran *et al.*, 1962). For convenience, we shall consider the distribution $P(w)$ for the normalized difference, w, defined by

$$w = \frac{(|F_N| - |F_P|)}{\sigma_N} \tag{1}$$

where σ_N is the root mean square value of $|F_N|$. We give below the expressions for $P(w)$ for the different cases, omitting the proofs.

Related case
Non-centrosymmetric crystal

$$P(w) = \frac{2}{\sigma_1^2}\left\{\exp-\frac{w^2}{\sigma_2^2}\right\} \int_0^\infty p\,e^{-p}\,I_0(p)\exp-\frac{x^2}{\sigma_1^2}\,dx \qquad \text{for } w > 0 \qquad (2a)$$

$$P(w) = \frac{2}{\sigma_1^2}\left\{\exp-\frac{w^2}{\sigma_2^2}\right\} \int_{|w|}^\infty p\,e^{-p}\,I_0(p)\exp-\frac{x^2}{\sigma_1^2}\,dx \qquad \text{for } w < 0 \qquad (2b)$$

where $\qquad\qquad p = 2x(w+x)/\sigma_2^2, \quad x = |F_P|/\sigma_N \qquad\qquad (3)$

and $\qquad\qquad\qquad \sigma_1^2 = \sigma_P^2/\sigma_N^2, \quad \sigma_2^2 = \sigma_Q^2/\sigma_N^2$

with $\qquad\qquad\qquad \sigma_1^2 + \sigma_2^2 = 1 \qquad\qquad\qquad\qquad (4)$

Centrosymmetric crystal

$$P(w) = \frac{\exp-\dfrac{w^2}{2\sigma_2^2}}{\sqrt{(2\pi\sigma_2^2)}} + \frac{\exp-\dfrac{w^2}{2\sigma'^2}}{\sqrt{(2\pi\sigma'^2)}}\left[1-\mathrm{erf}\frac{\sqrt{(2)}\,\sigma_1 w}{\sigma'\sigma_2}\right] \qquad \text{for } w > 0 \qquad (5a)$$

$$P(w) = \frac{\exp-\dfrac{w^2}{2\sigma_2^2}}{\sqrt{(2\pi\sigma_2^2)}}\left[1-\mathrm{erf}\frac{|w|}{\sigma_1\sqrt{2}}\right]$$

$$+\frac{\exp-\dfrac{w^2}{2\sigma'^2}}{\sqrt{(2\pi\sigma'^2)}}\left[1-\mathrm{erf}\frac{(\sigma_2^2+2\sigma_1^2)\,|w|}{\sqrt{(2)}\,\sigma_1\sigma_2\sigma'}\right] \qquad \text{for } w < 0 \qquad (5b)$$

where $\qquad\qquad\qquad \sigma'^2 = \sigma_2^2 + 4\sigma_1^2 \qquad\qquad\qquad (6a)$

and $\qquad\qquad\qquad \mathrm{erf}\,x = \frac{2}{\sqrt{\pi}}\int_0^x e^{-t^2}\,dt \qquad\qquad (6b)$

Unrelated case
Non-centrosymmetric crystal

$$P(w) = \frac{2\sigma_1}{\Sigma^3}\left\{\exp-\frac{w^2}{\Sigma^2}\right\}\left\{\sqrt{\left(\frac{\pi}{2}\right)}\left[1-I\left(\sqrt{\left(\frac{2}{3}\right)}\frac{k^2 w^2}{\Sigma^2};\frac{1}{2}\right)\right]\right.$$

$$+\frac{(\sigma_1^2-1)\,w}{\Sigma\sigma_1}\left[1-I\left(\frac{k^2 w^2}{\Sigma^2};0\right)\right]$$

$$\left.-\frac{\sqrt{(\pi)}\,w^2}{\Sigma^2}\left[1-I\left(\frac{\sqrt{(2)}\,k^2 w^2}{\Sigma^2};-\frac{1}{2}\right)\right]\right\} \qquad (7)$$

with $k^2 = 1/\sigma_1^2$ for $w > 0$ and $k^2 = \sigma_1^2$ for $w < 0$.

4

Here $$\sigma_1^2 + 1 = \Sigma^2 \qquad (8a)$$

and $I(x;p)$ is the incomplete gamma-function (Pearson, 1922) defined by

$$I(x;p) = \int_0^{x\sqrt{(p+1)}} \frac{e^{-t}t^p}{\Gamma(p+1)}\,dt \qquad (8b)$$

Centrosymmetric crystal

$$P(w) = \sqrt{\left(\frac{2}{\pi\Sigma^2}\right)}\left\{\exp - \frac{w^2}{2\Sigma^2}\right\}\left\{1 - \mathrm{erf}\frac{\sigma_1 w}{\sqrt{2}}\right\}$$
$$\text{for } w > 0 \qquad (9a)$$

$$P(w) = \sqrt{\left(\frac{2}{\pi\Sigma^2}\right)}\left\{\exp - \frac{w^2}{2\Sigma^2}\right\}\left\{1 - \mathrm{erf}\frac{w}{\sigma_1\sqrt{2}}\right\}$$
$$\text{for } w < 0 \qquad (9b)$$

where $\Sigma^2 = \sigma_1^2 + 1$ as above.

The results are given in Tables I and II, for a centrosymmetric and a non-centrosymmetric crystal respectively. In addition to the value of $P(w)$ for different values of w these tables also contain the values of P_+ and R defined by

$$P_+ = \int_0^\infty P(w)\,dw \qquad (10)$$

and $$R = \frac{\Sigma\,||F_N| - |F_P||}{\Sigma\,|F_N|} \qquad (11)$$

It is readily shown that

$$R = \frac{\int_{-\infty}^\infty |w|\,P(w)\,dw}{\int_{-\infty}^\infty yP(y)\,dy} \qquad (12)$$

Here, $P(y)$ is the distribution function of the structure amplitude for a single crystal (centrosymmetric or non-centrosymmetric as the case may be (Ramachandran and Srinivasan, 1959; Srinivasan, 1960). It is well known that $\int_{-\infty}^\infty yP(y)\,dy$ is $\sqrt{(2/\pi)} = 0\cdot798$ for a centrosymmetric and $\sqrt{(\pi)}/2 = 0\cdot886$ for a non-centrosymmetric crystal.

A comparison of the corresponding related and unrelated probability distributions shows that the two are markedly different, particularly for large values of σ_1^2, i.e. when the number of atoms in the two crystals are nearly the same. This is shown in a particularly striking manner in Figs. 1 (a) and 1(b). The sharp curve in either case corresponds to an isomorphous pair and the broad curve to an independent pair of crystals. This marked difference in the distribution functions is also reflected in the

TABLE I. Calculated values of $P(w)$ versus w and of P_+, R and $\langle Z \rangle$ for various values of σ_1^2. The data are for a centrosymmetric pair of related and unrelated crystals

Column group: σ_1^2

w	0·0 Rel. and Unrel.	0·2 Rel.	0·2 Unrel.	0·4 Rel.	0·4 Unrel.	0·5 Rel.	0·5 Unrel.	0·6 Rel.	0·6 Unrel.	0·7 Rel.	0·7 Unrel.	0·8 Rel.	0·8 Unrel.	0·9 Rel.	0·9 Unrel.	1·0† Unrel.
−3·2													0·000		0·000	0·001
−3·0											0·000		0·001		0·001	0·002
−2·8									0·000		0·001		0·001		0·002	0·004
−2·6									0·001		0·002		0·003		0·005	0·007
−2·4							0·000		0·002		0·003		0·006		0·008	0·012
−2·2					0·000		0·001		0·003		0·006		0·010		0·015	0·020
−2·0					0·001		0·004		0·008		0·013		0·019		0·026	0·033
−1·8				0·000	0·003	0·000	0·008		0·015	0·000	0·023		0·032		0·042	0·051
−1·6				0·001	0·009	0·001	0·018	0·000	0·029	0·001	0·041	0·000	0·053		0·065	0·077
−1·4		0·000		0·005	0·021	0·005	0·035	0·001	0·052	0·003	0·068	0·001	0·084		0·098	0·111
−1·2		0·002		0·013	0·044	0·016	0·067	0·016	0·089	0·012	0·108	0·005	0·127	0·000	0·142	0·156
−1·0		0·013		0·037	0·086	0·045	0·116	0·046	0·142	0·039	0·163	0·022	0·182	0·003	0·198	0·211
−0·8		0·038		0·091	0·153	0·105	0·187	0·111	0·214	0·104	0·234	0·077	0·251	0·022	0·264	0·275
−0·6		0·107		0·192	0·250	0·216	0·282	0·230	0·304	0·233	0·320	0·212	0·332	0·114	0·341	0·346
−0·4		0·251		0·352	0·441	0·334	0·398	0·415	0·410	0·441	0·416	0·461	0·420	0·420	0·422	0·421
−0·2		0·483		0·561	0·525	0·508	0·526	0·676	0·522	0·704	0·516	0·799	0·510	0·966	0·503	0·496
−0·0	0·798	0·761	0·728	0·784	0·674	0·817	0·651	0·782	0·631	0·955	0·612	1·109	0·595	1·469	0·579	0·564
0·2	0·780	0·707	0·669	0·718	0·608	0·742	0·554	0·646	0·562	0·845	0·543	0·680	0·526	1·144	0·510	0·496
0·4	0·735	0·629	0·592	0·622	0·529	0·633	0·526	0·487	0·480	0·665	0·465	0·402	0·449	0·611	0·434	0·421
0·6	0·662	0·535	0·506	0·507	0·443	0·499	0·421	0·335	0·402	0·463	0·386	0·196	0·371	0·221	0·358	0·346
0·8	0·580	0·435	0·415	0·391	0·359	0·367	0·389	0·209	0·323	0·284	0·308	0·079	0·295	0·054	0·284	0·275
1·0	0·485	0·338	0·328	0·282	0·280	0·250	0·263	0·119	0·249	0·154	0·238	0·026	0·227	0·009	0·218	0·211
1·2	0·390	0·250	0·250	0·191	0·210	0·158	0·197	0·061	0·186	0·073	0·177	0·007	0·169	0·001	0·162	0·156
1·4	0·298	0·176	0·183	0·122	0·152	0·083	0·142	0·029	0·134	0·030	0·127	0·002	0·121	0·000	0·116	0·111
1·6	0·225	0·119	0·129	0·073	0·106	0·050	0·099	0·012	0·093	0·011	0·088	0·000	0·084		0·080	0·077
1·8	0·158	0·077	0·087	0·041	0·071	0·025	0·066	0·005	0·062	0·004	0·059		0·056		0·053	0·051
2·0	0·108	0·047	0·058	0·021	0·043	0·012	0·043	0·002	0·040	0·001	0·038		0·036		0·034	0·033
2·2	0·074	0·027	0·036	0·011	0·029	0·005	0·026	0·001	0·025	0·000	0·023		0·022		0·021	0·020
2·4	0·045	0·015	0·022	0·005	0·017	0·003	0·016	0·000	0·015		0·014		0·013		0·013	0·012
2·6	0·025	0·008	0·015	0·002	0·012	0·001	0·011		0·010		0·009		0·008		0·007	0·007
2·8	0·008	0·004	0·007	0·001	0·006	0·000	0·005		0·005		0·004		0·004		0·004	0·004
3·0	0·000	0·002	0·004	0·000	0·003		0·002		0·003		0·002		0·002		0·002	0·002
3·2		0·000	0·002		0·002		0·001		0·001		0·001		0·001		0·001	0·001
3·4			0·001		0·001		0·000		0·000		0·000		0·000		0·000	0·000
3·6			0·000		0·000											
P_+	1·000	0·750	0·731	0·675	0·634	0·645	0·610	0·621	0·580	0·601	0·555	0·578	0·536	0·553	0·517	0·500
R	1·000	0·704	0·739	0·619	0·736	0·572	0·740	0·526	0·750	0·464	0·766	0·387	0·782	0·278	0·801	0·824
$\langle Z \rangle$	0·637	0·695		0·770		0·805		0·845		0·925		0·925		0·965		

† $P(w)$ for $\sigma_1^2 = 1\cdot0$ in the related case is just a delta function, $\delta(0)$.

TABLE II. Calculated values of $P(w)$ versus w and of P_+, R and $\langle Z \rangle$ for various values of σ_1^2. The data are for a non-centrosymmetric pair of related and unrelated crystals

Column group header: σ_1^2

w	0·0	0·2		0·4		0·5		0·6		0·7		0·8		0·9		1·0†
	Rel. and Unrel.	Rel.	Unrel.	Rel.	Unrel.	Rel.	Unrel.	Rel.	Unrel.	Rel.	Unrel.	Rel.	Unrel.	Rel.	Unrel.	Unrel.
-2·6																0·000
-2·4															0·000	0·001
-2·2													0·000		0·001	0·003
-2·0									0·000		0·000		0·001		0·002	0·007
-1·8							0·000		0·001		0·001		0·002		0·004	0·015
-1·6							0·002		0·005		0·003		0·006		0·011	0·032
-1·4					0·000		0·006		0·013		0·009		0·015		0·023	0·063
-1·2			0·000	0·000	0·001	0·000	0·018	0·000	0·033	0·000	0·022		0·035		0·048	0·111
-1·0		0·000	0·001	0·001	0·008	0·001	0·048	0·001	0·076	0·004	0·051	0·000	0·072		0·090	0·184
-0·8		0·001	0·009	0·004	0·025	0·006	0·111	0·030	0·152	0·024	0·102	0·001	0·134		0·160	0·280
-0·6		0·005	0·043	0·021	0·071	0·028	0·221	0·112	0·269	0·108	0·189	0·012	0·226	0·000	0·258	0·399
-0·4		0·024	0·146	0·081	0·165	0·103	0·376	0·312	0·419	0·335	0·309	0·079	0·345	0·020	0·366	0·503
-0·2		0·109	0·352	0·231	0·319	0·278	0·546	0·639	0·569	0·722	0·452	0·328	0·477	0·214	0·487	0·589
0·0	0·000	0·316	0·603	0·487	0·509	0·560	0·682	0·941	0·679	1·078	0·582	0·838	0·589	0·970	0·592	0·627
0·2	0·390	0·603	0·758	0·761	0·677	0·842	0·714	1·024	0·688	1·115	0·669	1·312	0·656	1·825	0·642	0·589
0·4	0·680	0·798	0·779	0·891	0·738	0·949	0·655	0·854	0·619	0·839	0·662	1·259	0·638	1·418	0·614	0·503
0·6	0·840	0·844	0·705	0·846	0·694	0·855	0·545	0·569	0·507	0·473	0·587	0·767	0·561	0·475	0·529	0·399
0·8	0·844	0·760	0·568	0·677	0·590	0·634	0·408	0·305	0·374	0·200	0·473	0·308	0·444	0·070	0·411	0·280
1·0	0·736	0·597	0·412	0·462	0·449	0·393	0·278	0·133	0·252	0·064	0·344	0·082	0·323	0·002	0·299	0·184
1·2	0·570	0·416	0·270	0·272	0·312	0·205	0·174	0·047	0·156	0·015	0·231	0·014	0·216	0·000	0·200	0·111
1·4	0·394	0·268	0·161	0·139	0·197	0·110	0·100	0·013	0·089	0·003	0·142	0·001	0·183		0·118	0·063
1·6	0·240	0·143	0·089	0·061	0·114	0·034	0·053	0·003	0·047	0·000	0·080	0·000	0·075		0·047	0·032
1·8	0·140	0·071	0·045	0·024	0·061	0·014	0·026	0·001	0·023		0·042		0·039		0·035	0·015
2·0	0·070	0·040	0·023	0·008	0·030	0·004	0·012	0·000	0·010		0·020		0·019		0·016	0·007
2·2	0·035	0·013	0·009	0·000	0·013	0·000	0·005		0·004		0·009		0·008		0·008	0·003
2·4	0·015	0·005	0·003		0·006		0·002		0·002		0·004		0·004		0·002	0·001
2·6	0·001	0·002	0·001		0·001		0·001		0·001		0·001		0·001		0·001	0·000
2·8	0·000	0·000	0·000		0·000		0·000		0·000		0·000		0·000		0·000	
P_+	1·000	0·852	0·731	0·757	0·634	0·726	0·610	0·685	0·580	0·652	0·557	0·620	0·536	0·582	0·517	0·500
R	1·000	0·612	0·624	0·481	0·557	0·441	0·546	0·383	0·544	0·328	0·547	0·255	0·563	0·183	0·567	0·583
$\langle Z \rangle$	0·785	0·822		0·865		0·888		0·910		0·930		0·950		0·975		

† $P(w)$ for $\sigma_1^2 = 1\cdot0$ in the related case is just a delta function, $\delta(0)$.

"discrepancy factor" R. For $\sigma_1^2 = 0.9$, $R = 0.278$ and 0.183 for a centro-symmetric and non-centrosymmetric pair of isomorphous or related crystals, while they are as large as 0.801 and 0.567 respectively if the crystals are unrelated. Thus, by finding the value of the discrepancy factor between two crystals, it is possible to estimate what may be

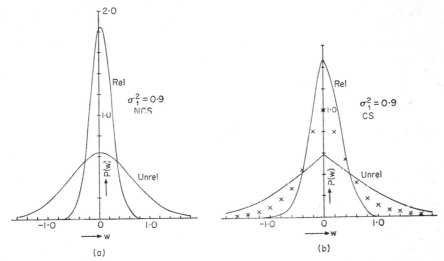

Fig. 1. (a) Theoretical probability distribution function $P(w)$ for the related and unrelated cases in a non-centrosymmetric crystal, corresponding to $\sigma_1^2 = 0.9$. (b) Theoretical probability distribution function $P(w)$ for the related and unrelated case in a centrosymmetric crystal, corresponding to $\sigma_1^2 = 0.9$. The crosses are the observed data for the pair of crystals, caffeine and theophylline (see p. 96).

termed the "degree of isomorphism" γ between two crystals. This may be defined by

$$\gamma_R = \frac{R_{\text{obs}} - R_{\text{unrel}}}{R_{\text{rel}} - R_{\text{unrel}}} \tag{13}$$

where the notation is obvious. In order to indicate that the value of γ has been obtained from the R-value, the subscript R is used in γ_R for another method of obtaining γ is indicated below.

The quantity R, as defined by Eq. (11) has other interesting applications as well. Suppose we determine the heavy atom positions from the Patterson synthesis of a crystal, in which their interactions are not particularly clear. It is then possible to verify that the positions so determined are correct, by calculating the contribution $|F_P|$ to the structure amplitudes from the heavy atoms (P) alone, and evaluating R, given by Eq. (11). If this is close to R_{rel} then the positions determined are correct, and *vice versa*. Usually, when $\sigma_1^2 < 0.9$ both R_{rel} and R_{unrel} are much larger than the errors of observations, and the effect of the latter can generally be neglected in evaluating R_{obs}.

PROBABILITY DISTRIBUTION OF THE PRODUCT

We shall now consider the probability distribution of another important variable connecting the intensities of two crystals, namely the product $q = |F_N||F_P|$. The quantity q can be considered to be the "correlation intensity" of the two crystals. For convenience, we deal with the normalized correlation intensity, defined by

$$Z = |F_N||F_P|/\sigma_N \sigma_P \tag{14}$$

We observe that when P tends to N, the right-hand side of Eq. (14) becomes $|F_N|^2/\langle I_N \rangle = z$, which is the familar normalized intensity for a single crystal. In other words, Z is the generalized form of z for the case of a pair of crystals.

It is possible to work out the distribution function for Z (Srinivasan *et al.*, 1962) and the following are the expressions for $P(Z)$ for the different cases.

Related case

Non-centrosymmetric crystal

$$P(Z) = \frac{4Z}{\sigma_2^2} I_0\left(\frac{2Z\sigma_1}{\sigma_2^2}\right) K_0\left(\frac{2Z}{\sigma_2^2}\right) \tag{15}$$

Centrosymmetric crystal

$$P(Z) = \frac{2}{\pi\sigma_2} \cosh\left(\frac{Z\sigma_1}{\sigma_2^2}\right) K_0\left(\frac{Z}{\sigma_2^2}\right) \tag{16}$$

where I_0 and K_0 are the Bessel functions with imaginary argument (Watson, 1944).

Unrelated case

Non-centrosymmetric crystal

$$P(Z) = 4Z K_0(2Z) \tag{17}$$

Centrosymmetric crystal

$$P(Z) = \frac{2}{\pi} K_0(2Z) \tag{18}$$

It can be seen from the above expressions that the Eqs. (17) and (18) for the unrelated case may be obtained by just substituting $\sigma_1^2 = 0$

$(\sigma_2^2 = 1)$ in the corresponding Eqs. (15) and (16) for the related case. In fact, in the unrelated case, $P(Z)$ is independent of σ_1^2. Hence, it is understandable that $P(Z)$ for the unrelated case should be the same as $P(Z)$ for the related case when $\sigma_1^2 = 0$, for this condition is equivalent to saying that the common part between the two structures (of which σ_1^2 is a measure) vanishes, and therefore the two crystals are unrelated to each other.

Analogous to γ_R we may define a parameter by the equation

$$\gamma_Z = \frac{\langle Z \rangle_{\text{obs}} - \langle Z \rangle_{\text{unrel}}}{\langle Z \rangle_{\text{rel}} - \langle Z \rangle_{\text{unrel}}} \tag{19}$$

where $\langle Z \rangle$ is the expectation value of Z and the significance of the different subscripts are obvious. The values of $\langle Z \rangle_{\text{rel}}$ and $\langle Z \rangle_{\text{unrel}}$ have been calculated by numerical integration of the corresponding expressions and the results are also given in Tables I and II.

Practical Test of the Results and Discussion

Most of the results described above have been tested with a structure containing 18 atoms in the unit cell. The structure used for this purpose was that of phosphorus sulphide (P_4S_5) (van Houten and Wiebenga, 1957), which has the cell dimensions $a = 6 \cdot 41$ Å, $b = 10 \cdot 94$ Å, $c = 6 \cdot 69$ Å, $\beta = 111 \cdot 7°$ and the space group $P2_1$. However, all the atoms were taken to be the same and to have the scattering factor of a sulphur atom, with an isotropic temperature factor $B = 3 \cdot 0$ Å^2. The data of both the centrosymmetric projection ($h0l$ reflections) and the non-centrosymmetric projection ($0kl$ reflections) were used for the study. The atoms of both the structures are plotted in Fig. 2, in which P represents the fraction

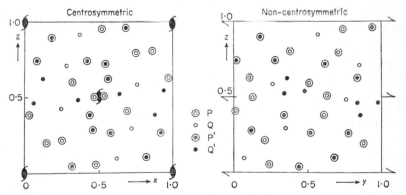

Fig. 2. The positions (fractional co-ordinates) of centrosymmetric and non-centrosymmetric projections of the 18-atom structure used in the related and unrelated cases.

of the structure $N (= P+Q)$, which was used for testing the related case. For testing the unrelated case, another set of 9 atoms $(6+3)$ was taken in locations different from those of the true structure, and P' and Q' represent these atoms in the second structure based on the same unit cell. The following pairs were studied in relation to $P(w)$, R, P_+ and $\langle Z \rangle$:

    (i) N and P (related) $\sigma_1^2 = 0.67$
    (ii) N and P' (unrelated) $\sigma_1^2 = 0.67$
    (iii) N and N' (unrelated) $\sigma_1^2 = 1.0$

The results are shown in Fig. 3 (a)—(f) and Table III.

In Fig. 3 (a)—(f), the observed (calculated) data of $P(w)$ are plotted against the theoretical curve for each of the six cases. In determining

TABLE III. Observed and theoretical values of P_+, R and $\langle Z \rangle$ for $\sigma_1^2 = 0.67$ in the related and unrelated cases of a pair of centrosymmetric and non-centrosymmetric crystals

	P_+		R		$\langle Z \rangle$	
	Theory	Observed	Theory	Observed	Theory	Observed
Related:						
Centrosymmetric	0·607	0·659	0·482	0·494	0·872	0·878
Non-centrosymmetric	0·662	0·683	0·345	0·388	0·924	0·900
Unrelated:						
Centrosymmetric	0·564	0·581	0·761	0·650	0·637	0·555
Non-centrosymmetric	0·599	0·641	0·546	0·568	0·815	0·820

$w = (|F_N| - |F_P|)/\sigma_N$, σ_N^2 was taken to be equal to $\sum_1^N f_j^2$, which is the ideal value. Further, in order to reduce the statistical fluctuations, the data were divided into intervals of 0·4 for w and the value of $P(w)$ for each interval has been plotted at the abscissa corresponding to the middle of the interval. Although $\sigma_1^2 = 0.67$, the theoretical curve shown is that for $\sigma_1^2 = 0.7$. It will be seen that there is good agreement between the theoretical curve and the statistical data for the various pairs of structures. In particular, the agreement between theory and observation as regards the quantities P_+, R and $\langle Z \rangle$ is even better than for the distribution curves $P(w)$, as is readily seen from Table III.

From the agreement between the actual value of P_+, i.e. the fraction of reflections for which $|F_N| > |F_P|$, and the theoretical value, it is evident that this statistic can be confidently used for putting the data of two isomorphous crystals on the same relative scale. In fact, on varying the relative scale factor either way by 10 to 20%, P_+ also varied

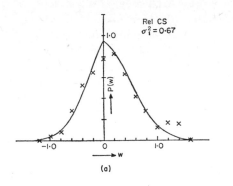

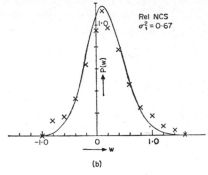

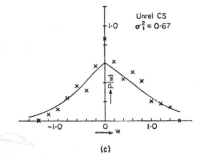

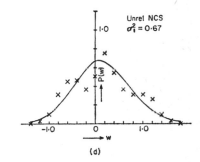

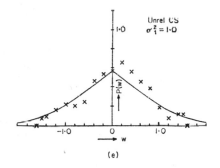

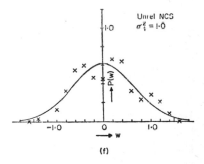

FIG. 3. Probability distribution functions $P(w)$ for the following cases:

(a) Related centrosymmetric $\qquad\qquad\sigma_1^2 = 0 \cdot 67$

(b) Related non-centrosymmetric $\qquad\sigma_1^2 = 0 \cdot 67$

(c) Unrelated centrosymmetric $\qquad\quad\sigma_1^2 = 0 \cdot 67$

(d) Unrelated non-centrosymmetric $\quad\sigma_1^2 = 0 \cdot 67$

(e) Unrelated centrosymmetric $\qquad\quad\sigma_1^2 = 1 \cdot 0$

(f) Unrelated non-centrosymmetric $\quad\sigma_1^2 = 1 \cdot 0$

The continuous curves are from theory and the crosses are the observed data.

4*

by an appreciable amount, and the value of the scale factor deduced from P_+ varies from the true value by only 5% (see Table IV).

Since our formulae hold not only for a pair of isomorphous crystals, but also for a whole crystal and its part, the above test suggests a good method of putting the observed data of a crystal on the correct scale when the heavy atom positions (say the P atoms) have been located. It is only necessary to calculate $|F_P|$ for the various reflections, and find the fractional number of reflections for which this is less than $|F_N|$ for various values of the scale factor. That value for which this agrees with P_+ from theory for the particular crystal (i.e. corresponding to its value of σ_1^2) will give the correct scale factor. When the number of heavy atoms is small, one should be careful when applying this method.

TABLE IV. Variation of P_+ with change in relative scale factor. The scale of intensities of the P atoms was changed with respect to that of the N atoms over the range 0·8 to 1·2

		Relative scale factor				
		0·8	0·9	1·0	1·1	1·2
P_+	Related Centrosymmetric	0·736	0·703	0·659	0·585	0·561
	Related Non-centrosymmetric	0·782	0·752	0·683	0·594	0·515

We shall now consider the test in a case in which there was isomorphism, but this was not good. The crystals chosen were caffeine ($C_8H_{10}N_4O_2$, H_2O; Sutor, 1958b, c) and theophylline ($C_7H_8N_4O_2$, H_2O; Sutor, 1958a, c). The space group is $P2_1/a$ and the cell dimensions are as follows:

	a	b	c	β
Caffeine	14·8 Å	16·7 Å	3·97 Å	97°
Theophylline	13·3 Å	15·3 Å	4·5 Å	99·5°

In this case, $\sigma_1^2 = 0.95$, and the values of $P(w)$ found in the same way as before are plotted against the theoretical curves for both the related and the unrelated cases for $\sigma_1^2 = 0.90$ in Fig. 1 (b). The true related curve should be even sharper than the one shown, while the unrelated curve would be affected very little by a change from $\sigma_1^2 = 0.90$ to 0.95.

The data for both the zero and first layers were used and the average of the two was plotted in Fig. 1 (b). The observed data lay in between the two theoretical curves, showing that the isomorphism was not perfect. In view of this, the values of γ_R and γ_Z were calculated from Eqs. (13) and (19). The theoretical values of R were $R_{rel} = 0.15$; $R_{unrel} = 0.81$, while the observed value was 0·56, giving $\gamma_R = 38\%$. Similarly,

$\langle Z \rangle_{\text{rel}} = 0.98$, $\langle Z \rangle_{\text{unrel}} = 0.64$ and $\langle Z \rangle_{\text{obs}} = 0.83$, giving $\gamma_Z = 55\%$. The values of γ_Z for the zero level and the first level separately were 50% and 60%. The larger value for the latter is due to the larger variations in the z-co-ordinates than the x- and y-co-ordinates between the two structures (Sutor, 1958a, b, c).

It will be seen from this test that γ_R and γ_Z may differ appreciably. The latter is larger because the low-angle reflections are given a larger weight in finding $\langle Z \rangle$ than in calculating R. Incidentally, it may be mentioned that no correction has been made for experimental errors in obtaining R_{obs} or $\langle Z \rangle$. However, since R_{exp} is of the order of 0.10 for both the structures, this only changes R_{obs} between caffeine and theophylline by a few per cent from the value 0.56 used above. Here, again, experimental errors are likely to affect R more than $\langle Z \rangle$.

The value of P_+ was also found to be intermediate between the related and unrelated cases, with an observed value of 0.515 for both zero and first levels together, as against 0.53 and 0.51 for the related and unrelated cases.

Acknowledgements

A part of the work reported here was completed while one of the authors (R.S.) was working in the Cavendish Laboratory, University of Cambridge. He wishes to thank Professor N. F. Mott and Dr. W. H. Taylor for the provision of facilities and Dr. J. C. P. Miller for helpful discussions regarding numerical integrations. His thanks are also due to the Commonwealth Scholarship Commission for the award of a scholarship during the tenure of which part of the work was done.

REFERENCES

Pearson, K. (1922). *Tables of Incomplete Gamma Functions*. London.
Ramachandran, G. N. and Srinivasan, R. (1959). *Acta cryst.* **12**, 410.
Ramachandran, G. N., Srinivasan, R. and Raghupathy Sarma, V. (1962). *Acta cryst.* (in press).
Srinivasan, R. (1960). *Acta cryst.* **13**, 388.
Srinivasan, R., Raghupathy Sarma, V. and Ramachandran, G. N. (1962). (in press).
Sutor, D. J. (1958a). *Acta cryst.* **11**, 83.
Sutor, D. J. (1958b). *Acta cryst.* **11**, 453.
Sutor, D. J. (1958c). Ph.D. Thesis, University of Cambridge.
van Houten, S. and Weibenga, E. H. (1957). *Acta cryst.* **10**, 156.
Watson, G. N. (1944). *A Treatise on the Theory of Bessel Functions*. Cambridge University Press.

DISCUSSION

G. N. RAMACHANDRAN: One of the problems that often occurs in protein structure work is the question of finding out if the substitution of a heavy atom leaves the structure still isomorphous with the parent compound or not. For this, I think the present tests can be applied effectively. We know, for instance, the R values corresponding to the two extreme cases, viz. the case when the other atoms in the two structures occupy exactly the same positions, and the case when the atoms in the second crystal have completely moved away from the original positions. The test would therefore reveal roughly by how much the atoms have moved. The example of the pair, caffeine and theophylline, cited in the paper, illustrates this point well.

G. KARTHA: I was interested in knowing whether any quantitative study has been made regarding the "relatedness" as a function of the scattering angle when the atoms are slightly shifted.

G. N. RAMACHANDRAN: A study like this is actually being undertaken in our laboratory.

D. HARKER: I wonder whether the use of $\langle|F|^2\rangle$ rather than Σf_j^2 weakens the method described here. These two quantities are far from equal in the case of proteins.

G. N. RAMACHANDRAN: This question actually arose while applying the test in a practical case, and we have used so far only $\langle I \rangle$. I think we can try both and test which one gives the better result.

A. J. C. WILSON: I feel that the meaning of the already maltreated word "isomorphism" is being stretched too far in this paper. Would not "relatedness" express precisely what is meant by the authors?

Several years ago I got as far as calculating the R value for completely unrelated centrosymmetric and non-centrosymmetric structures. I wonder if they are in agreement with the limiting values obtained by the authors.

G. N. RAMACHANDRAN: Yes. As regards the first question, we agree that the term "relatedness" would be a more suitable term than "isomorphism".

SECTION II
Crystal Perfection

Some Problems of X-Ray Optics:
Partial Reflection and Superposition of Wavefields

G. BORRMANN AND K. LEHMANN

Fritz-Haber-Institut der Max-Planck-Gesellschaft, Berlin-Dahlem, Germany

ABSTRACT

One part of a low absorption X-ray fan traverses the plane parallel crystal plate directly, the other part indirectly being (partially) reflected at a side face of the plate. Interference fringes resulting from the superposition of both fans at the exit surface are observed on a film set up close to the crystal. The geometry of the beams within the crystal resembles that of Lloyd's mirror experiment, but the phase difference of the interfering waves is not determined by the path difference of the beams alone. Each beam of the fan is given by the Poynting vector of a wavefield, which is described by two wave vectors. Poynting's vector and wave vectors being tied together by the dispersion surface, the phase difference and the fringe distance can be calculated. Fringe systems produced by silicon crystals free from dislocations turn out as correctly described by the theory, within a still rather large limit of error.

1. INTRODUCTION

Let the beam P (Fig. 1) satisfy Bragg's law at the net plane N of the perfect crystal C. In general, four X-ray "fans" will be formed at A, each of them covering the angle 2θ (roughly, i.e. neglecting refraction) (von Laue, 1960). Let us consider one of them, that of the weakest absorption.

One part of the fan, including the beam 3, will arrive at the exit surface E_2E_3. Here each beam will be divided into its two components, which will produce the two "reflexes" R_0 and R_h on the film. The other part, including the beam 1, will arrive at the surface E_1E_2. Here the phenomenon of partial reflection, as theoretically derived in the Bragg case by Wagner (1956), is expected. A second fan will be produced, the angles ϵ_1 and ϵ_2 being equal when the surface is parallel to the net plane. Part of the radiation will be transmitted through the surface in the direction given by the angle θ and will produce R'_h. The reflected fan arrives at the surface E_2E_3 between E_2 and B, where again each beam will be decomposed.

Thus at each point W between E_2 and B a beam 1–2 and a beam 3 will meet each other. Two pairs of waves will leave the crystal in two directions of $\pm \theta$. The waves being coherent, the intensity in R_0 and R_h will depend on their phase angles at the exit surface. Variation within E_2 and B of the phase angles will effect a modulation of the intensity. In fact, interference fringes have been observed (Borrmann and Lehmann, 1962).

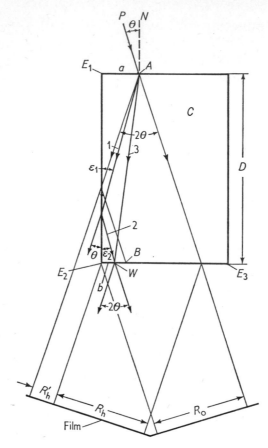

FIG. 1. Geometry of beams.

$$N \| E_1 E_2, \; \epsilon_2 = -\epsilon_1, \; E_1 A = a, \; E_2 W = b, \; \tan \epsilon_1 = \frac{a+b}{D}, \; \tan \epsilon_3 = \frac{a-b}{D}$$

The purpose of this paper is to give some results of the theory and to compare them with diagrams of a better crystal used in some more experiments.

2. THEORETICAL RESULTS

A. *Partial reflection*

Let S_1 be the Poynting vector (mean value) of the beam 1 at the surface $E_1 E_2$. S_1 will be constant along the element df of the surface. Let S_2 be valid for the beam 2 at the same spot. Let $I_h'^d$ be the intensity of the wave which leaves the crystal. From Wagner's paper results

$$S_2 = \frac{1 - q_1}{1 + q_1} S_1 \tag{1}$$

where

$$q_1 = \frac{\tan \epsilon_1}{\tan \theta}$$

$$I_h'^d = \frac{2 q_1 \sin \epsilon_1}{(1 + q_1) \sin \theta} S_1 \tag{2}$$

and

$$I_h'^d = \frac{2 q_1^2}{1 + q_1} S_1 \tag{3}$$

if θ is small.

The conservation of energy requires

$$S_1 \sin \epsilon_1 = S_2 \sin \epsilon_1 + I_h'^d \sin \theta \quad \text{for } df \tag{4}$$

Equation (4) is verified by (1) and (2).

Therefore at the boundary of the fan ($\epsilon_1 \approx \theta$) the greater part of the energy flow is transmitted through the surface, whereas in the centre of the fan ($\epsilon_1 \ll \theta$) the greater part is reflected.[†] Obviously the result is independent of polarization.

B. *Superposition of two low absorption wavefields: the fringe distance*

The variables of a wave field are the wave vectors $\mathbf{K}_0$, $\mathbf{K}_h$ and the intensities I_0, I_h of the two waves forming the field, the Poynting vector of the field (the "beam") and the absorption coefficient related to the direction of Poynting's vector. The question is how to find $\mathbf{K}_0$, $\mathbf{K}_h$ of the beams 1, 2, 3 because these vectors are needed for the calculation of the fringe distance.

When $I_0/I_h = \alpha$ is given, all the other quantities are fixed, with the obvious reservation that it is only the direction of the Poynting vector that will be obtained, and that the fact of low absorption is understood. By α the tiepoint of the wave vectors on the dispersion surface is fixed. A line drawn at right angles to this surface through the tiepoint is parallel to the Poynting vector (Kato, Ewald and E. H. Wagner). Disregarding the dispersion surface, Poynting's vector is obtained according to von Laue by simply adding I_0 and I_h vectorially. From this relation one gets (see e.g. von Laue, 1960, § 34):

$$\alpha = \frac{1 - q}{1 + q} \tag{5}$$

† As for the energy flow in the fan, it strongly depends on ϵ. Without absorption the intensity is high at the boundaries, whereas the absorption coefficient is the smallest in the centre (Borrmann, Hildebrandt and Wagner, 1955; Wagner, 1956; Kato, 1960).

where $$q = \frac{\tan \epsilon}{\tan \theta} \quad \text{(see Eq. (1))}$$

The ϵ values of the beams 1, 2, 3 are known from the experimental conditions (Fig. 1). Thus the wave vectors $\mathbf{K}_0$, $\mathbf{K}_h$ of each beam finally depend on ϵ.

Let $\mathbf{r}$ be the path of a beam inside the crystal. The number of waves counted along this path is given by $(\mathbf{K}_0 \cdot \mathbf{r})$ (and $(\mathbf{K}_h \cdot \mathbf{r})$ respectively).

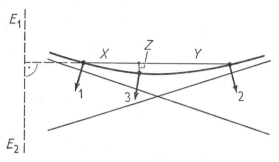

FIG. 2. Upper branch of the dispersion surface with three tiepoints and three directions of wave propagation.

Along the two paths running from A to W there will be the difference n between the numbers of waves according to

$$n = (\mathbf{K}_{03} \cdot \mathbf{r}_3) - (\mathbf{K}_{01} \cdot \mathbf{r}_1) - (\mathbf{K}_{02} \cdot \mathbf{r}_2) \tag{6}$$

By means of $\mathbf{K}_0 = \mathbf{K}_{0x} + \mathbf{K}_{0z}$, wherein $\mathbf{K}_{0x}$ stands for the component perpendicular to the net plane, $\mathbf{K}_{0z}$ for the parallel one, and $\mathbf{K}_{01z} = \mathbf{K}_{02z}$ (see Fig. 2) one gets

$$n = a(\mathbf{K}_{01x} - \mathbf{K}_{03x}) + b(\mathbf{K}_{03x} - \mathbf{K}_{02x}) - D(\mathbf{K}_{01z} - \mathbf{K}_{03z}) \tag{7}$$

or abbreviated

$$n = aX + bY - DZ \tag{8}$$

(The same result is valid for $\mathbf{K}_h$.) The distances a, b, D are taken from Fig. 1; X, Y, Z are drawn in Fig. 2. By means of Eqs. 27.10 and 27.12 of von Laue (1960) one calculates:

$$n = \frac{C|\chi_h| D}{2\lambda \cos \theta} [(1 - q_3^2)^{1/2} - (1 - q_1^2)^{1/2}] \tag{9}$$

where $C = 1$ or $\cos 2\theta$ if $\mathbf{E}$ is $\perp$ or $\parallel$ to the fan, λ is the wavelength of the incident beam and

$$|\chi_h| = \frac{|F_h|}{F_0} \lambda^2 \mathcal{N} \frac{e^2}{\pi m c^2}$$

$|F_h|$ is the structure factor, F_0 the number of electrons in the unit cell, $\mathcal{N}$ the number of electrons per cm^3, e the charge and m the mass of the electron, c the velocity of light, $e^2/(\pi m c^2) = 8 \cdot 95 \times 10^{-14}$ cm.

If $q \leqq 1/2$, n is approximately proportional to the distance b. Therefore the maxima of the intensity given by whole numbers of $n(0, 1, 2, \ldots)$ follow each other at almost constant distances. The fringe distance (distance of adjacent maxima) proves to be

$$d_M = \frac{\lambda}{C|\chi_h|} \sin \theta \tan \theta \frac{D}{a} \qquad (10)$$

This is valid for the exit surface. On a film set up perpendicular to the rays, the fringe distance is $d_M \cos \theta$.

The result is the same for $\mathbf{K}_0$ and $\mathbf{K}_h$. Moreover, a maximum in R_0 corresponds to a maximum in R_h, because the two interfering wavefields are of the same type, i.e. their tiepoints are placed on the same branch of the dispersion surface and this implies that their nodal planes coincide. The "Pendellösung", on the contrary, means superposition of two wavefields of different types, i.e. one of strong and one of weak absorption, represented by tiepoints on different branches. Their nodal planes are separated by half the nodal plane's spacing, which means that wherever the two $\mathbf{K}_0$ waves have equal phases, those of the two $\mathbf{K}_h$ waves will be different by π.

Example

$\lambda = 0 \cdot 71$ Å (Mo $K\alpha$), $C = 1$, (220) net plane of Si, $\theta = 10° \ 40'$, $F_{220}/F_0 = (f/z)e^{-M}$ ($f =$ atomic scattering factor, z the number of electrons of the Si atom, e^{-M} Debye factor), $|\chi_h| = 2 \times 10^{-6}$; $D = 1 \cdot 2$ cm, $a = 0 \cdot 05$ cm; $d_M = 0 \cdot 003$ cm. On a diagram 20 times enlarged the fringe distance is expected to be $0 \cdot 6$ mm (see Fig. 3).

3. EXPERIMENTS

A. *Conditions due to absorption*

The absorption coefficient μ of the Mo $K\alpha$-radiation in Si amounts to 15 cm^{-1}. The minimum coefficient μ_{min}, valid for a wavefield the Poynting vector of which is parallel to the net plane, was found to be about $0 \cdot 05 \ \mu$ in the case of (220) (preliminary measurement by G. Hildebrandt).

From this value result the following coefficients of the four wavefields produced at A (Fig. 1), travelling along the net plane (see e.g. von Laue, 1960, p. 417):

$$\mu_{min}^{\perp} = 0 \cdot 8 \ cm^{-1}$$
$$\mu_{min}^{\parallel} = 1 \cdot 8 \ cm^{-1}$$
$$\mu_{max}^{\parallel} = 29 \ cm^{-1}$$
$$\mu_{max}^{\perp} = 28 \ cm^{-1}$$

A crystal plate 0·1 cm thick would attenuate the field of the weakest absorption by the factor $e^{-0.1}$, the field of the strongest absorption by e^{-3}. The intensity of the four fields would not differ much, even less would their amplitude, being crucial in the case of their superposition. The "Pendellösung fringes" as observed and calculated by Kato and Lang (1959) and Kato (1961a, 1961b) arise under these conditions.

A crystal plate 1·2 cm thick will attenuate both fields of strong absorption practically to zero. However, it will reduce the field of the weakest absorption, only by the factor e^{-1} and the field of weak absorption and unfavourable plane of vibration by e^{-2}.

The remaining two fields will not interfere because their planes of vibration are different. By means of partial reflection both fields will produce interference fringes according to Eq. (10); because of the factor C the values d_M will differ by 7%. Since the field of the weakest absorption is three times stronger than the other one, its fringe system will not be seriously disturbed by that of the other field. The disturbance will be even less in the case of (440).

As Wagner (1956) has already pointed out, partial reflection does not alter the character of absorption, i.e. if the fan arriving at the surface shows reduced absorption, the reflected fan will do so too. This is evident, since all the tiepoints involved are situated on the same branch of the dispersion surface.

B. *Diagrams*

Figures 3 and 4 show R'_h, R_h, R_0, cast from the reflecting lattice-plane (220) of a Si crystal, and Fig. 5 shows R'_h, R_h of (440). On all the pictures the modulation of intensity is seen, beginning at the left border of R_h and R_0 and extending more or less far to the right.

(a) The fringes are equidistant. (Note in comparison with this that the "Pendellösung fringes" of the plane parallel plate are not equidistant.) In Fig. 5, slight deviations are to be noticed. In this case, the entrance and the exit surface were not parallel but parts of the cylindrical surface of the original crystal from which the sample had been cut. Therefore, equal spacing of the stripes is not to be expected. These pictures, however, reproduce the best series of fringe systems hitherto obtained.

(b) The fringe distances in R_0 and R_h are the same. (They are different when the exit surface and the net plane are not at right angles.)

(c) The fringe distance increases with a (Fig. 1) decreasing, in accordance with Eq. (10).

(d) The fringe distance increases when a is kept constant and (220) exchanged for (440), although D is halved—in accordance with Eq. (10). ($|\chi_h|$ decreases from 2 to 1.3×10^{-6}.)

FIG. 3. Diagram of a Si crystal, enlarged about $20\times$. Net plane (220), Mo $K\alpha_1$-radiation, $D = 12$ mm, $a = 0.5$ mm.

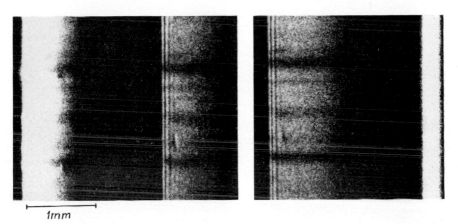

1mm

FIG. 4. The same as Fig. 3, but $a = 0.2$ mm.

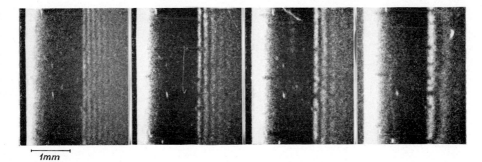

1mm

FIG. 5. The same crystal, turned by $90°$; $\times 10$; (440), $D \approx 5.6$ mm; a values about 0.6, 0.4, 0.3, 0.2 mm.

Seventeen diagrams, obtained from different partially reflecting surfaces of the same crystal, yielded the mean value

$$\frac{d_M(\text{exp})}{d_M(\text{theor})} = 0{\cdot}95 \pm 0{\cdot}25$$

(mean error). The rather wide spread of the results is not surprising, because the distance a amounts to some tenths of a millimetre only and therefore is not known accurately. Besides, the fringe system is sensible to crystal defects (see Borrmann and Lehmann, 1962). It is true that the good diagrams prove the interior of the crystal to be rather homogeneous, but the surface after having been ground and etched is often not well suited for regular partial reflection. The crystal edge is another source of trouble.†

One of the questions not yet sufficiently answered is where in R_0 and R_h the edge E_2 of the crystal will be projected. If this were known three results could be gained. The distance a could be found out of the distance between E_2 and the clearly visible edge of the fan. Secondly, the correlation of the R_0 and R_h fringes could be checked up. Thirdly, the claim of the theory not yet mentioned might be tested, that both waves of a field, when it is partially reflected, change their phases by π. Consequently the left edges of R_0 and R_h should be defined by a minimum of intensity, not by the maximum $n = 0$ as described above. (In fact the diagrams have been evaluated on the supposition that this is true.‡)

Let us state as a brief survey: the interference fringes, especially their spacing, are correctly described by the Ewald–von Laue theory of wavefields, including the theory of the energy flow and H. Wagner's partial reflection; numerous details, however, are still to be examined, and higher accuracy in measurements is desirable.

Acknowledgements

We thank Dr. R. H. Gillette (European Research Associates, Brussels) for a scholarship, and Dr. W. C. Dash (Schenectady) for his kind gift of crystals.

† Partial reflection was first observed by means of a calcite crystal, which evidently was not flawless. The patterns found on the diagrams looked like interference fringes (see Borrmann, Hildebrandt and Wagner, 1955, Fig. 13). A re-examination proved that they were not so. So it must be concluded that, although partial reflection did occur, the surface not being transparent, it is the imperfections of the crystal that prevented the formation of fringes.

‡ Trying to have some fine furrows (3μ large), drawn with a diamond point on the surface E_1E_2, projected onto the diagram as marks was a complete failure. The lattice must have been deformed to a remarkably great depth (some tenths of a mm at least), as judged from the vanishing of the fringes. Fortunately the perfect lattice was restored by slightly etching the surface. As Renninger (1962) reports, he observed similar effects by means of a different method.

REFERENCES

Borrmann, G., Hildebrandt, G. and Wagner, H. (1955). *Z. Phys.* **142**, 406.

Borrmann, G. and Lehmann, K. (1962). In *Direct Observation of Imperfections in Crystals*, p. 409. Interscience, New York.

Kato, N. (1960). *Acta cryst.* **13**, 349.

Kato, N. (1961a). *Acta cryst.* **14**, 526.

Kato, N. (1961b). *Acta cryst.* **14**, 627.

Kato, N. and Lang, A. R. (1959). *Acta cryst.* **12**, 787.

Laue, M. von (1960). *Röntgenstrahl-Interferenzen*, 3. Aufl. Akademische Verlagsgesellschaft, Frankfurt/Main.

Renninger, M. (1962). *Physics Letters* **1**, 104; 106.

Wagner, H. (1956). *Z. Phys.* **146**, 127.

Role of X-Ray Intensities in Crystal Perfection Studies

Leonid V. Azároff

Illinois Institute of Technology, Chicago, Illinois, U.S.A.

ABSTRACT

Present X-ray diffraction theory is based on an artificial "mosaic" crystal proposed by Darwin. In terms of this model, crystal perfection can be related to the intensity of an X-ray reflection via two factors called primary and secondary extinction. It is possible to evaluate these two terms independently either by comparing the reflecting powers of a single reflection at different X-ray wavelengths or by comparing several *hkl* reflections using the same wavelength. This analysis yields an effective thickness for the "mosaic" blocks and an average value for their relative tilts. It is then possible to interpret Darwin's model of a crystal in terms of dislocation theory.

Relatively large concentrations of point defects in a crystal modify its electron density distribution sufficiently to affect the X-ray intensities. If the intensities are measured accurately and are suitably processed, they can be used to synthesize "difference" electron densities capable of disclosing the imperfections present. Both of the above procedures have been used successfully and are illustrated by applications to silicon and zinc oxide crystals. The possible limitations of electron density methods are illustrated by a study of indium antimonide.

INTRODUCTION

The growing appreciation of the role that imperfections present in crystals play in determining a crystal's properties has led to the development of a variety of tools for their observation and study. The X-ray methods can be classified into three main categories: topographic studies, extinction measurements, and electron density syntheses. Imperfections extending through relatively large regions of a crystal, such as dislocations and small-angle boundaries, can be observed directly by topographic examinations of surface layers or bulk crystals (Berg, 1931, 1934; Ramachandran, 1944; Barrett, 1945; Guinier and Tennevin, 1949; Schulz, 1954; Newkirk, 1958; Borrmann *et al.*, 1958; Lang, 1958, 1959). Topographic methods depend on intensity contrasts produced in the photographically recorded reflections by the presence of dislocations in crystals. They do not at present include quantitative evaluations of the observed intensity variations because the effect of such imperfections on the intensity of an X-ray reflection has not been rigorously formulated as yet (cf. Webb, 1961; Azároff, 1963).

In the development of the theory of X-ray diffraction (Darwin, 1914, 1922; Ewald, 1916, 1917) two distinct cases were considered: the "ideally perfect crystal" and the "ideally imperfect crystal". According to the model used by Darwin (1922) a crystal can be considered to consist of coherent regions that are optically independent, i.e. no definite phase relationships exist between X-rays scattered from the different regions of a crystal. For convenience, the independent regions are usually grouped into blocks to form a so-called "mosaic" crystal but the diffraction theory of an imperfect crystal does not actually require such grouping. The sizes and relative orientations of the coherent regions determine the magnitudes of two attenuation factors called primary and secondary extinction while the nature of the regions themselves is determined by the imperfections present in a crystal. Thus it is possible to use X-ray intensities to measure extinction effects and to deduce from them the "perfection" of a crystal. While it is not possible to determine the exact nature of the imperfections by this means, extinction measurements afford a quantitative evaluation of crystal perfection. Methods for measuring total extinction by using polarized X-rays, based on a theoretical analysis by Ramaseshan and Ramachandran (1953, 1954), has been described by Chandrasekaran (1959) and Chandrasekhar (1960a, b). An alternative experimental procedure, in which the magnitudes of primary and secondary extinction are evaluated independently, has been described by Bragg and Azároff (1961).

There is still another way that imperfections in crystals can be studied with the aid of X-ray intensities. The presence of point defects, for example, interstitial atoms, can be studied by topographic methods when they form relatively large clusters in a crystal (Schwuttke, 1961) or by observing variations in the electron density distribution when they are dispersed but present in sufficient amounts to affect the intensities (Mohanty and Azároff, 1961). This procedure is similar to that used for studying the distribution of valence electrons (Brill *et al.*, 1938; Witte and Wölfel, 1958; Hosemann and Bagchi, 1953; Schoknecht, 1957; Black and Taylor, 1958) and, like the measurements of extinction, requires very accurate X-ray intensities. Some of the factors affecting accurate intensity measurement and the actual utilization of measured intensity values in crystal perfection studies are described below.

INTEGRATED REFLECTING POWER

The electron density variation in the unit cell volume V of a crystal can be related to the intensity or power of the X-ray beam reflected by a plane $H = (hkl)$ by means of the structure factor F_H. The power reflected by a coherent region (mosaic block)

$$Q = \left| \frac{e^2}{mc^2} \frac{F_H}{V} \right|^2 \lambda^3 \left(\frac{1 + \cos^2 2\theta}{2 \sin \theta} \right) \tag{1}$$

where the symbols used have their usual meaning. The expression for the integrated reflecting power R_H, formally defined as the ratio of the total power reflected to the total power incident on the crystal, depends on whether the transmission (Laue) arrangement or the reflection (Bragg) arrangement is employed. Because the transmission arrangement has boundary conditions more amenable to exact solution (Zachariasen, 1945), the formulas for this case are considered in detail below; analogous expressions obtain for the Bragg arrangement (cf. Chandrasekhar, 1960b). Neglecting temperature induced vibrations of atoms, for which allowance usually can be made, the integrated reflecting power for the Laue case can be written (Zachariasen, 1945)

$$R_H = \frac{Q'\,T}{\gamma} \exp[-(\mu+gQ')T/\gamma] \tag{2}$$

where T is the crystal thickness, γ is the direction cosine of the incident beam, μ is the linear absorption coefficient, $Q' = f(A)Q$, where $f(A)$ is the primary extinction coefficient, and g is the secondary extinction coefficient. The above equation (2) applies to the "ideally imperfect crystal" and, although many crystals examined to date do not appear to consist of discernible "mosaic blocks," this model has been used successfully to interpret the reflecting power of some of the most perfect silicon crystals grown.

When the structure of a crystal can be assumed to be known, all the terms in Eqs. (1) and (2) usually can be calculated except the extinction coefficients $f(A)$ and g. (They are considered separately in the next section.) It is thus possible to study the perfection of a crystal by comparing measured and calculated intensities. In calculating the structure factor F, however, it is necessary to know the scattering powers (atomic form factors) of the individual atoms comprising the crystal. Tabulated values of form factors usually refer to isolated atoms or ions but do not take into account the distortion of outer electron orbitals by the crystal field. Attempts have been made to determine the valence electron contributions to form factors in transition metals by subtracting the inert gas core contributions directly from the scattering powers of a few small-angle reflections (Weiss and De Marco, 1958). As already pointed out by Hume-Rothery et al. (1958), such procedures are not too satisfactory because they are predicated on spherically symmetric distributions and the validity of these measurements is not clearly established at present (cf. Batterman, 1959a; Weiss and De Marco, 1959; Freeman and Weiss, 1959).

It is also important to consider the actual measurement of integrated reflecting powers. In measuring the reflecting power of a set of planes H, it is necessary that all the coherent regions in a crystal get an equal opportunity to reflect the incident beam, a condition usually satisfied by rocking the crystal. The incident beam must be monochromatic and the total power intercepted by the crystal must be known. In the classical double-crystal arrangement, the incident beam is monochromatized by the first crystal and the second crystal is sufficiently large to intercept the entire beam, so that this arrangement is limited to studies for which sufficiently large crystals are available. In the more usual single-crystal arrangements, a small crystal is completely bathed in the incident beam. Even if this beam is rendered effectively monochromatic, for example, by the use of balanced filters, it is usually not possible to measure accurately the incident power, because it is not the same for all reflections due to the irregular cross-fire in the incident beam. An arrangement in which the incident beam divergence is controlled is shown in Fig. 1.

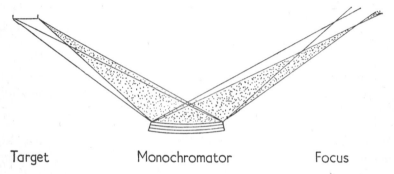

Target   Monochromator   Focus

FIG. 1. Focusing action of a bent-crystal monochromator.

Provided that the intensity distribution in the tube target is uniform and the monochromator's surface is properly treated, the beam incident on the crystal placed at the focus has very nearly uniform divergence. The reflected beam has a similar divergence so that the integrated reflecting power can be determined by forming the ratio of the reflected and incident powers (Azároff, 1957). Since the specimen crystal in this arrangement is wholly bathed in the incident beam, it is first necessary to estimate the portion of the incident beam actually intercepted by the crystal. By reducing the dimensions of the focal spot, however, the incident beam can be made smaller than the crystal (Azároff, 1961). Ideally, the focal spot should be reduced to a point so that the crystal can intercept the entire incident beam. In practice, it has not yet proved possible to construct a satisfactory doubly curved crystal, but work is currently in progress to determine the full extent to which bent-crystal monochromators can be utilized. In the absence of a suitable arrangement for measuring absolute integrated reflecting powers, it is necessary to resort to scaling procedures which are usually subject to errors, principally in determining the extinction coefficients in Eq. (2).

EXTINCTION EFFECTS

The early experimental verifications of Eq. (2) included several attempts to estimate the magnitude of the extinction effects in real crystals (James, 1948). These were mainly limited to cases where primary extinction was negligible (cf. Hirsch, 1956). Vand (1955) has described an analytical procedure for estimating the extinction effects when both kinds of extinction are present. In a recent study of crystal perfection, Chandrasekaran (1959) used the intensity ratio of reflected beams respectively polarized in a direction perpendicular and parallel to the reflecting planes to estimate the magnitude of extinction effects. As pointed out by Chandrasekhar (1960 *a*, *b*), polarization ratio measurements cannot distinguish between primary and secondary extinction, so that the crystal perfection determined by this means is somewhat ambiguous.

The difficulty in resolving primary from secondary extinction is due to the exponential dependence of the reflected power on both, as can be seen in Eq. (2). This difficulty can be overcome only if either kind of extinction is small enough to be negligible or by "guessing" correctly the magnitude of either extinction factor. The secondary extinction coefficient g expresses the relative tilts between Darwin's coherent blocks, while the primary extinction coefficient $f(A)$ takes into account the phase relations between X-rays scattered by successive planes within a block in a complicated function of

$$A = \frac{e^2 \, |F'_H| \, \lambda t_0}{mc^2 \, V_\gamma} \tag{3}$$

where t_0 is the effective block thickness and the other symbols have their usual meaning (Zachariasen, 1945). Note that for the transmission arrangement A in Eq. (3) is a function of the structure factor magnitude, the X-ray wavelength used, and t_0. Since the effective block thickness is not known in advance, an experimental evaluation of the primary extinction coefficient can proceed either by varying F_H or λ. (In the reflection arrangement A does not appear to depend on λ.)

A systematic procedure for determining the primary extinction coefficient by fitting the correct $f(A)$ curve to absolute intensities measured at several wavelengths has been described by Bragg and Azároff (1961). The sensitivity of this method is illustrated in Fig. 2, where the assumption of several values of t_0 in (3) is compared. When the primary extinction coefficient is correctly determined, the plot in Fig. 2 should be a straight line whose slope determines the secondary extinction coefficient

g according to (2). Such a straight line results for the silicon crystal used when the effective block size $t_0 = 1{\cdot}75 \times 10^{-3}$ cm, whereas deviations from linearity show up when t_0 differs from the correct value by as little as 14%. The slope of the straight line then determines the secondary extinction coefficient g which can be used, in turn, to deduce the average block tilts (Zachariasen, 1945). The values of tilt thus determined are in good agreement with those deduced from reflection breadth measurements on the same crystal. Thus it is possible to evaluate both extinction factors

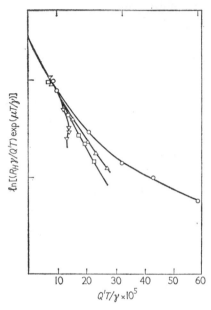

FIG. 2. Effect of extinction on the reflecting power of the (11$\bar{1}$) planes of a silicon crystal. ○ $t_0 = 10^{-3}$ cm, △ $t_0 = 1{\cdot}5 \times 10^{-3}$ cm, □ $t = 1{\cdot}75 \times 10^{-3}$ cm, ▽ $t_0 = 2{\cdot}0 \times 10^{-3}$ cm.

by this method and to determine the "perfection" of a crystal. It should be noted that meaningful results can be obtained only if absolute integrated reflecting powers are used to construct the curves in Fig. 2. Their interpretation is confined to the physical reality of the Darwin model in that the size of the blocks t_0 indicates the extent of the coherent regions in a crystal but does not directly disclose the nature of the imperfections that disrupt the crystal's coherency.

In view of the obvious relation between imperfections and the magnitude of the extinction effects it is of interest to consider briefly just how imperfections can influence X-ray intensities. The intensity contrasts observed when the Berg-Barrett topographic arrangement is used have been explained by Newkirk (1958) as arising from variations in the extinction effects due to dislocations lying in the reflecting planes. In fact he has shown how differences in the reflecting powers of crystallographically equivalent planes can be used to disclose the location and the Burgers vector of a dislocation.† This means that specific arrays of imperfections can influence the reflection intensities of different but symmetryequivalent planes in an unlike manner, even in the same crystal. (This should not be confused with the fact that extinction effects differ for crystallographically unrelated planes, because their F_H values differ, so that extinction effects are greater for reflections having larger reflecting powers.) Assuming then that the extinction effects in the silicon crystal described above, Fig. 2, are caused by parallel dislocations lying in the (111) planes, a relation derived by Gay *et al.* (1953) can be used to estimate the dislocation density in this crystal. The density of dislocations D can be expressed in terms of the Burgers vector of the dislocations b, the effective size of the blocks t_0, and their relative tilts α, by

$$D = \frac{\alpha}{t_0 b} \tag{4}$$

Using the results of Bragg and Azároff's measurements, the dislocation density in the silicon crystal that they examined was $1{\cdot}4 \times 10^6$ cm^{-2}. This density is in fair agreement with that deduced from etch pit counts carried out on the same crystal. Even if the above intensity analysis based on the Darwin model is not entirely justifiable, since other possible imperfection arrays also can affect the extinction, it does provide a "figure of merit" for a crystal which is not without practical value (cf. Azároff, 1963).

Any array (not necessarily regular) of parallel dislocations serves to disrupt the homogeneity of a crystal in a direction that is perpendicular to the array. Nevertheless, interpreting the block thickness t_0 in Eq. (3) to be an "average" spacing between dislocations more or less parallel to the reflecting planes, it is possible to estimate the dislocation densities for which X-ray diffraction methods are particularly effective. The dependence of the primary extinction coefficient on wavelength is shown in Fig. 3 for several values of t_0. The very small deviation of curve A from unity shows that dislocation densities in excess of 10^8 cm^{-2} ($t_0 = 10^{-4}$ cm) are sufficiently large to render the crystal "ideally imperfect" so that only secondary extinction is still a real factor; experimental measurements place this limit closer to 10^7 cm^{-2} (e.g. Robinson and Levinstein, 1961). Similarly, when the dislocation density has dropped to 10^4 cm^{-2},

---

† Bonse (1958, 1961) attributes the contrast to aperiodicities in the lattice rather than to extinction. It is not clear at present, however, whether this is a unique model or a special case of the more general Darwin model.

the crystal can be considered to be "ideally perfect" and although primary extinction is present, it doesn't vary appreciably in the wavelength regions commonly used (or for different F_H values at a constant λ). Note that the "constancy" of $f(A)$ in this case (curve E) may lead to the erroneous conclusion that the crystal is "ideally imperfect" unless absolute reflecting powers are measured. The intermediate range of dislocation densities, therefore, is the one best suited to X-ray analysis. Figure 3 also shows that different wavelength X-radiations should be used for various concentrations, namely, long wavelengths when the dislocation density is large and shorter wavelengths when it is small. When this relation between X-ray wavelengths and dislocation densities is recognized, it becomes clear why some investigators have reported the

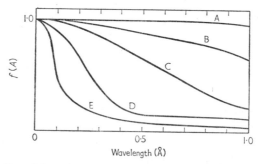

Fig. 3. Variation of the primary extinction factor $f(A)$ with X-ray wavelength, calculated for the $11\bar{1}$ reflection of silicon having negligible dispersion in the wavelength region shown. Curve A is calculated for $t_0 = 10^{-4}$ cm, B for 10^{-3} cm, C for 2×10^{-3} cm, D for 5×10^{-3} cm, and E for 10^{-2} cm.

presence of dislocations in crystals similar to those in which others failed to detect them. Although it has been assumed in the discussion in this paragraph that dislocations were solely responsible for extinction, other imperfections present in a crystal also have an effect. For example, Batterman (1959b) used Cu $K\alpha$ radiation to examine several orders of the 111 reflection in germanium and concluded that extinction was caused primarily by strains produced by point defects rather than by dislocations.

ELECTRON DENSITY SYNTHESES

The first to use electron density syntheses for the accurate mapping of valence electron distributions in crystals, Brill *et al.* (1938) showed that accurately measured absolute intensities could be used successfully for this purpose. Their measurements on sodium chloride were repeated by Krug *et al.* (1955), who also synthesized an electron density using structure factors calculated from tabulated values of the atomic form factors. The small differences observed in the syntheses using experimental and calculated structure factors were of the same order as the differences between calculated and measured values of the atomic form factors and fell within the standard deviations estimated for the experimental measurements. These results are cited primarily in order to demonstrate the validity of electron density syntheses in the study of detailed electron distributions in crystals.

It has also been suggested by Cochran (1958) that molecular densities differ by a comparatively small amount from the superposition of atomic densities so that it is possible to make use of "difference" syntheses in which the electron densities of certain atoms are subtracted from the total. In preparing such difference densities it is of course necessary that the experimentally determined and calculated densities be on the same scale. This is another case where intensities should be measured on an absolute basis. In the absence of absolute measurements, the intensities must be scaled by comparison to calculated values and here errors can creep in due to uncertainties in the atomic form factors and the extinction effects present. If such errors are suitably minimized, however, the synthesis of difference electron densities constitutes a very powerful tool for the study of small departures from the electron density of ideally perfect crystals, since any artifacts (ripples) and finite series termination errors, tend to subtract out. It is clear that the success of such an analysis depends entirely on how accurately the intensities are measured and corrected.

In a study of interstitial atoms present in zinc oxide (ZnO) crystals (Mohanty and Azároff, 1961) the intensities were measured with an average internal inconsistency and standard deviation less than $\pm 2\%$. After correcting the measured intensities for extinction, anomalous dispersion etc., the experimentally determined F's were used to prepare a difference synthesis by subtracting the electron density of a relatively pure ZnO crystal from that of a crystal that had been doped to saturation in zinc vapour. As can be seen in the difference synthesis in Fig. 4, the interstitial zinc atoms occupy normally empty octahedral sites at the corners of the unit cell shown. Since only experimental structure factor values were used in this difference synthesis, any errors present in tabulated form factors were excluded. The electron density in Fig. 4 is on an absolute scale so that the number of interstitial atoms present, approximately 10^{20} atoms/cm^3, can be determined by measuring the volume of the origin peak. The observed density agrees with the measured lattice constant changes and other experimental observations. It should be noted that the success of such an analysis depends on the presence of a sufficient density of point defects. For example, in a parallel study of cadmium sulphide (Mohanty and Azároff, 1960) no variations in the electron density greater than the estimated standard deviation were observed.†

As an indication of the extent to which electron density syntheses can be utilized, consider a recent examination of indium antimonide (InSb) by Attard (1962). Apart from its interest to semi-conductor theory, InSb is particularly well suited to an X-ray diffraction study. Both atoms have very nearly the same mass so that the Debye-Waller theory can be used to estimate their thermal vibrations. They also have similar inner-electron structures so that the same atomic core (palladium) can be subtracted from both kinds of atoms in an attempt to ascertain their

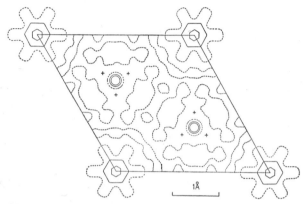

FIG. 4. Difference electron density of zinc oxide (ZnO) projected along c. This synthesis was prepared by subtracting the experimentally determined density of a pure crystal from that of a heavily doped one. The zero contour is shown dashed, the solid contours are in equal steps of $1e/Å^2$. The deepest negative depressions of $-1 \cdot 1e/Å^2$ are marked by crosses. (All the hk0 reflections detectable with Ag $K\alpha$ radiation were included.)

valence electron distributions. Attard measured over 300 individual reflections from a small spherical crystal using Mo $K\alpha$ radiation and balanced filters, although only 142 reflections lie in the asymmetric portion of the molybdenum limiting sphere. The average internal consistency of symmetry-equivalent reflections was about 2% and $R = (\Sigma \, ||F_{obs}| - |F_{calc}||)/\Sigma \, |F_{calc}| = 0\cdot02$. The Debye temperature calculated from the experimentally determined temperature factor was 180°K as compared to 200°K and 208°K reported by Potter (1956). The

† The importance of accurate intensity measurement in such studies cannot be over-stated. In an earlier study of a series of cadmium sulphide crystals, Shuvalov (1956, 1957) reported observing "electron bridges" between adjacent atoms in a low-resistivity (highly doped) crystal. Because he had used photographically recorded intensity values inadequately corrected for extinction effects, Shuvalov's results were subject to serious errors as his own re-examination of these syntheses showed (Rumsh et al., 1960).

intensities were corrected for absorption, extinction (only secondary extinction appeared to be present), temperature effects, Lorentz-polarization effects, and anomalous dispersion. Since InSb has the non-centrosymmetric zinc blende structure, phase angles and structure factors were computed using Thomas-Fermi-Dirac (T.F.D.) atomic scattering factors calculated for In and Sb by Thomas and Umeda (1957) and anomalous dispersion factors tabulated by Dauben and Templeton (1955).

In order to evaluate the number of valence electrons at the In and Sb sites, Attard calculated structure factors for a fictitious structure in which both atoms are replaced by palladium, again making use of T.F.D scattering curves. A difference synthesis was then prepared by subtracting the electron density of the Pd atom "structure" from that of InSb. This procedure is justified when the object of the investigation is the determination of the "excess" number of electrons at an atomic site. The structure factors of the fictitious palladium crystal are the Fourier transforms of its assumed electron density. The electron density function

$$\rho_{Pd}(xyz) = \frac{1}{V} \sum \sum \sum (F_{Pd})_{hkl} \exp\left[2\pi i(hx + ky + lz)\right] \qquad (5)$$

then reproduces the total electron density at the palladium atom sites (total of 46 electrons) regardless of the detailed distribution within the atoms assumed in calculating the structure factors. When the difference synthesis $\rho_{InSb} - \rho_{Pd}$ is formed, the peak volumes at the atomic sites correctly represents the total number of electrons in excess of 46 present at each site as long as the palladium electrons were initially assumed to lie within a volume not larger than that of the In and Sb atoms. Moreover, the difference synthesis has the important advantage that series-termination errors are virtually absent.

The difference synthesis calculated by Attard, along a line joining the In and Sb atoms, is shown in Fig. 5. Because the electronic distribution of the palladium "core" is essentially spherical, the calculated form factor values are less subject to error than those for atoms having outer electrons in less certain orbitals. Moreover, since both atoms have the same inner cores, their subtraction from the atomic densities produces similar errors in the electron density residues of each atom. By measuring the volumes of the two peaks shown in Fig. 5 it was found that they contain 3.51 ± 0.05 and 4.61 ± 0.05 electrons, respectively. Their sum of $8.12 \pm 0.09e$ differs from the expected eight electrons by about the estimated standard deviation. The average charge transfer of $0.45 \pm 0.05e$ deduced from this difference synthesis can be compared to $0.34e$ deduced from infrared absorption measurements of Spitzer and Fan (1955). It also can be converted to an "effective charge" of $0.17 \pm 0.02e$ having

5

significance in electrical conductivity studies (Ehrenreich, 1957, 1959). By comparison, Ehrenreich used experimental electron mobility values to calculate an effective charge in InSb of 0·18 electrons. The validity of such "effective" charge calculations, however, has been questioned recently by Cochran (1961).

The physical validity of Attard's results is difficult to evaluate.† Certainly the experimental accuracy of the intensity measurements is

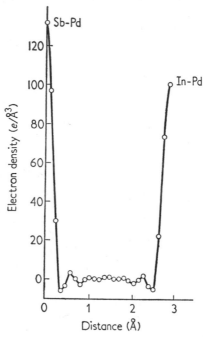

FIG. 5. Difference electron density of indium antimonide (InSb) along a line joining the centres of an indium and antimony atom. This synthesis was prepared by subtracting ρ_{Pd} from ρ_{InSb} calculated using all the reflections detectable with Mo $K\alpha$ radiation.

representative of the best attainable by modern counter methods. The magnitudes of the errors in the various theoretical correction factors cannot be estimated properly in the absence of a more rigorous theory. Note that the excess electrons in Fig. 5 lie within the ionic radii of both atoms although this undoubtedly is a consequence of subtracting struc-

† A calculation of the standard deviation of the electron density at the special positions occupied by In and Sb in this structure (Cruickshank and Rollett, 1953) gives $\sigma[\rho(000)]$ and $\sigma[\rho(\frac{111}{444})] = 0·202$. Although these values are larger than the standard deviations deduced by assuming a random accumulation of errors throughout the cell, they are nevertheless smaller than the peaks observed by Attard in the difference density.

ture factors calculated using atomic form factors rather than the scattering factors of the actual inner cores. Thus the agreement between the average charge transferred as deduced from the difference synthesis and comparable values inferred from infra-red absorption and from mobility measurements may be fortuitous. On the other hand, it may represent a kind of upper limit to the magnitudes of electron density variations that can be determined with X-ray diffraction methods.

Conclusion

It is clear from the above discussion that the so-called lattice defects affect X-ray intensities primarily by controlling the magnitudes of extinction effects. The extent to which reflections from different planes are thus affected depends on the relative disposition of the dislocations, their density, and the structure-factor magnitudes of specific reflections. It is also conceivable that extinction effects can also be produced by other kinds of imperfections so that it is usually not possible to determine unambiguously the nature of the imperfections present by X-ray intensity analyses alone.

Point imperfections such as interstitial atoms also may affect the extinction of an X-ray reflection. Their main effect, however, is to alter the electron density distribution from that of an ideal crystal so that the resulting changes in the structure factors produce changes in the reflecting powers of different planes. By preparing appropriate difference syntheses, variations in the electron density can be observed provided that the point defect density is sufficiently large. In the preparation of such syntheses, extremely accurate intensities are needed and great care must be exercised in converting the measured intensity values to structure factors. Specifically, the magnitudes of the extinction effects, thermal vibrations of the atoms, form factor values, anomalous dispersion, and other corrections must be known with an accuracy no less than that allowed by the magnitude of the variations sought in the electron density. On the other hand, difference syntheses show much more clearly the detailed variations and can be evaluated quantitatively, when properly prepared, because series-termination errors are virtually absent.

Acknowledgement

The author wishes to acknowledge that this analysis was supported by a grant from the Air Force Office of Scientific Research, U.S.A.

References

Attard, A. E. (1962). Ph.D. Thesis, I.I.T.
Azároff, L. V. (1957). *Acta cryst.* **10**, 413.

Azároff, L. V. (1961). *Z. Kristallogr.* **115**, 256.
Azároff, L. V. (1963). *Progress in Chemistry of the Solid State,* Vol. 1. Pergamon Press, New York.
Barrett, C. S. (1945). *Trans. Amer. Inst. min. (metall.) Engrs* **161**, 15.
Batterman, B. (1959a). *Phys. Rev. Letters,* **2**, 47.
Batterman, B. (1959b). *J. appl. Phys.* **30**, 508.
Berg, W. (1931). *Naturwissenschaften* **19**, 391.
Berg, W. (1934). *Z. Kristallogr.* **89**, 286.
Black, P. J. and Taylor, W. H. (1958). *Rev. mod. Phys.* **30**, 55.
Bonse, U. (1958). *Z. Phys.* **153**, 278.
Bonse, U. (1961). In: *Direct Observation of Imperfections in Crystals,* p. 431 (J. B. Newkirk and J. H. Wernick, eds.). Interscience, New York.
Borrmann, N. G., Hartwig, W. and Irmler, H. (1958). *Z. Naturf.* **13a**, 423.
Bragg, R. H. and Azároff, L. V. (1961). In: *Direct Observation of Imperfections in Crystals,* p. 415 (J. B. Newkirk and J. H. Wernick, eds.). Interscience, New York.
Brill, R., Grimm, H. G., Hermann, C. and Peters, C. L. (1938). *Ann. Phys. Lpz.* **34**, 393.
Chandrasekaran, K. S. (1959). *Acta cryst.* **12**, 916.
Chandrasekhar, S. (1960a). *Acta cryst.* **13**, 588.
Chandrasekhar, S. (1960b). *Advanc. Phys.* **9**, 363.
Cochran, W. (1958). *Rev. mod. Phys.* **30**, 47.
Cochran, W. (1961). *Nature, Lond.* **191**, 60.
Cruickshank, D. W. J. and Rollett, J. S. (1953). *Acta cryst.* **6**, 705.
Darwin, C. G. (1914). *Phil. Mag.* **27**, 315, 675.
Darwin, C. G. (1922). *Phil. Mag.* **43**, 800.
Dauben, C. H. and Templeton, D. H. (1955). *Acta cryst.* **8**, 841.
Ehrenreich, H. (1957). *J. Phys. Chem. Solids,* **2**, 132.
Ehrenreich, H. (1959). *J. Phys. Chem. Solids,* **9**, 129.
Ewald, P. P. (1916). *Ann. Phys. Lpz.* **49**, 1, 117.
Ewald, P. P. (1917). *Ann. Phys. Lpz.* **54**, 519.
Freeman, A. J. and Weiss, R. J. (1959). *Phil. Mag.* **4**, 1086.
Gay, P., Hirsch, P. B. and Kelly, A. (1953). *Acta met.* **2**, 315.
Guinier, A. and Tennevin, J. (1949). *Acta cryst.* **2**, 133.
Hirsch, P. B. (1956). *Progr. Metal Phys.* **6**, 236.
Hosemann, R. and Bagchi, S. N. (1953). *Nature, Lond.* **171**, 785.
Hume-Rothery, W., Brown, P. J., Forsyth, J. B. and Taylor, W. H. (1958). *Phil. Mag.* **3**, 1466.
James, R. W. (1948). *The Optical Principles of the Diffraction of X-Rays.* G. Bell and Sons Ltd., London.
Krug, H., Witte, H. and Wölfel, E. (1955). *Z. phys. Chem.* **3**, 296.
Lang, A. R. (1958). *J. appl. Phys.* **29**, 597.
Lang, A. R. (1959). *Acta cryst.* **12**, 249; *J. appl. Phys.* **30**, 1748.
Mohanty, G. P. and Azároff, L. V. (1960). *Phys. Rev.* **120**, 1224.
Mohanty, G. P. and Azároff, L. V. (1961). *J. chem. Phys.* **35**, 1268.
Newkirk, J. B. (1958). *J. appl. Phys.* **29**, 995; *Phys. Rev.* **110**, 1465.
Potter, R. F. (1956). *Phys. Rev.* **103**, 47.
Ramachandran, G. N. (1944). *Proc. Indian Acad. Sci.* **A19**, 280.
Ramaseshan, S. and Ramachandran, G. N. (1953). *Acta cryst.* **6**, 364.
Ramaseshan, S. and Ramachandran, G. N. (1954). *Proc. Indian Acad. Sci.* **A39**, 20.

Robinson, W. H. and Levinstein, H. J. (1961). In *Direct Observation of Imperfections in Crystals*, p. 561 (J. B. Newkirk and J. H. Wernick, eds.). Interscience, New York.

Rumsh, M. A., Shuvalov, Yu. N. and Smirnov, L. A. (1960). *Fiz. tverdovo Tela*, **2**, 369.

Schoknecht, G. (1957). *Z. Naturf.* **12a**, 932; 938.

Schwuttke, G. H. (1961). In *Direct Observations of Imperfections in Crystals*, p. 497 (J. B. Newkirk and J. H. Wernick, eds.). Interscience, New York.

Shulz, L. G. (1954). *J. Metals*, **200**, 1082.

Shuvalov, Yu. N. (1956). *C. R. Acad. Sci. U.R.S.S.* **109**, 753.

Shuvalov, Yu. N. (1957). *J. tech. Phys., Moscow*, **26**, 1870.

Spitzer, W. G. and Fan, Y. (1955). *Phys. Rev.* **99**, 1893.

Thomas, L. H. and Umeda, K. (1957). *J. chem. Phys.* **26**, 293.

Vand, V. (1955). *J. appl. Phys.* **26**, 1191.

Webb, W. W. (1961). In *Direct Observations of Imperfections in Crystals*, p. 29 (J. B. Newkirk and J. H. Wernick, eds.). Interscience, New York.

Weiss, R. J. and De Marco, J. J. (1958). *Rev. mod. Phys.* **30**, 59.

Weiss, R. J. and De Marco, J. J. (1959). *Phys. Rev. Letters* **2**, 148.

Witte, H. and Wölfel, E. (1958). *Rev. Mod. Phys.* **30**, 51.

Zachariasen, W. H. (1945). *Theory of X-Ray Diffraction in Crystals*. Wiley, New York.

Discussion

S. CHANDRASEKHAR: I was interested to note that in the plot of $(F_{obs}/F_{calc})^2$ versus $(F_{calc})^2$ for InSb shown by Prof. Azaroff, $(F_{obs}/F_{calc})^2$ is consistently less than unity for the stronger reflections. If the object of the investigation is the precise determination of electron density and charge transfer, it would appear that estimating the extinction by a comparison of F_{obs} and F_{calc} is wholly unjustified, because the calculated values are based on a spherical distribution of electron density for each atom. The difference between F_{obs} and F_{calc} could, of course, be due to extinction but, on the other hand, it may represent a genuine difference between the Thomas-Fermi distribution for a free atom and the electron density distribution as it actually exists in the crystal.

L. V. AZAROFF: The plot you refer to appears in the original paper describing the electron distribution in InSb (*J. Appl. Phys.* **34**, No. 4 (1963)) and was used for determining the extinction correction. It is true that the reflections affected by extinction lie on a straight line that cuts the ordinate at 0·84 rather than the theoretically expected value of 1·0. We attributed this to primary extinction which was assumed to be constant for this range of F_{hkl} values.

It is quite possible, as you suggest, that this alternatively may be caused by over-estimating F_{cal} in this range since, if the valence electrons are distributed non-spherically, their contributions to these reflections should be smaller than that assumed in the Thomas-Fermi model. This is not likely to affect the final conclusions drawn, however, since these reflections contribute equally to the electron density at 000 and $\frac{1}{4}\frac{1}{4}\frac{1}{4}$ so that, in the difference electron density finally calculated, they would affect the absolute magnitudes of the peak volumes in Fig. 5 but not the difference between them. It should be noted that, if the above contention is correct, it means that the total volume of the two maxima should be smaller than the 8·12 electrons actually observed, which would improve the agreement with the expected value of 8 electrons.

G. N. RAMACHANDRAN: I would like to know how the scaling of the intensities was done to such an extent as to be able to measure the difference significantly.

L. V. AZAROFF: The scale factor was determined using reflections at large θ values which are relatively independent of valence electron contributions. As long as the same scattering factors (Thomas-Fermi) are used to calculate the "cores" of both atoms, the difference in the volumes of the two difference-map peaks should be significant.

H. JAGODZINSKI: Did you ever observe some anisotropic behaviour of extinction?

L. V. AZAROFF: No, but we have not looked for any.

Correction for Extinction Errors in Crystal Structure Analysis

S. Chandrasekhar

Department of Physics, University of Mysore,
Mysore, India

ABSTRACT

The paper describes an apparatus for correcting for extinction errors in crystal structure analysis by the use of plane polarized X-rays. The application of the technique to a study of reflections from hexamethylene tetramine is discussed in detail.

1. INTRODUCTION

It has been shown that it is possible to correct for primary and secondary extinction errors in the analysis of crystals by the use of plane polarized X-rays (Chandrasekhar, 1956, 1960a). Consider a small mosaic crystal of arbitrary shape and of volume V, completely bathed in the incident X-ray beam. If the beam is polarized with the electric vector normal to the plane of incidence, the integrated reflection

$$\rho_\perp = AQV \tag{1}$$

where

$$Q = \left(\frac{Ne^2}{mc^2}\right)^2 \frac{\lambda^3}{\sin 2\theta} |F|^2$$

F is the structure factor corrected for thermal vibration and A the absorption factor. If the crystal suffers from primary or secondary extinction, or a combination of the two, the true integrated reflection for normal polarization

$$\rho_\perp = \frac{\rho'_\parallel - \rho'_\perp \cos^4 2\theta}{\cos^2 2\theta - \cos^4 2\theta} \tag{2}$$

may be determined from measurements of $\rho'_\perp$ and $\rho'_\parallel$, the integrated reflections in the presence of extinction for normal and parallel polarizations respectively. This expression is valid to a good approximation when the proportional reduction of intensity due to extinction ϵ $[= (\rho_\perp - \rho'_\perp)/\rho_\perp]$ is not greater than about 25%. The chief limitation of the technique is that the equation becomes ill-conditioned for values of θ approaching 0°, 45° and 90° (Chandrasekhar and Phillips, 1961), but this difficulty may be overcome in principle by employing different wavelengths. The sensitivity of the method and its dependence on various factors have been discussed in detail by Szabó (1961) for extinction in X-ray as well as in neutron magnetic scattering (Chandrasekhar and Weiss, 1957).

The theory was verified experimentally in the determination of extinction in small crystals of rock-salt (Chandrasekhar, 1960a, b). The structure factors corrected for extinction by this method were found to agree very well with those due to Renninger (1952) and Witte and Wölfel (1958).

2. EXPERIMENTAL METHOD

The experimental technique has recently been improved by Dr. Phillips and the writer (Chandrasekhar and Phillips, 1960, 1961) at the Davy Faraday Research Laboratory. We have devised a simple apparatus for rotating the plane of polarization of the incident X-ray beam

TABLE I. Barkla's polarization experiment
$\rho_\phi/\rho_\perp$ for 311 reflection of diamond

	Experimental		
ϕ	Observed mean for four quadrants	Corrected for depolarization of incident beam	Theoretical $\sin^2\phi$
90°	1·000	1·000	1·0000
75°	0·937	0·937	0·9329
60°	0·749	0·747	0·7500
50°	0·594	0·591	0·5868
45°	0·505	0·502	0·5000
40°	0·415	0·411	0·4132
30°	0·254	0·249	0·2500
20°	0·123	0·117	0·1170
10°	$0·037_8$	$0·031_6$	0·0302
0°	$0·007_3$	$0·000_9$	0·0000

which can be used conveniently in crystal structure analysis. The 311 reflection of diamond with $2\theta = 91°\ 34'$ for Cu $K\alpha$ is utilized to produce polarized X-rays. The X-ray tube and diamond crystal are mounted on a graduated disc which can be rotated about a horizontal axis collinear with the collimator of a single crystal diffractometer in such a way that the reflected beam passes along the axis for every setting of the disc. The diamond is in the form of a plate† (approximately $8 \times 7 \times 2·5$ mm)

† The diamond plate was lent by Dr. H. J. Milledge.

with (111) faces and the asymmetry of the 311 reflection produces a broad beam convenient for use with small crystals completely bathed in X-rays. This beam is sufficiently strong for measurements of reflections from a crystal mounted on the diffractometer to be made in the usual way by means of a proportional counter and crystal oscillation mechanism (Arndt et al., 1960).

The apparatus was tested by performing Barkla's polarization experiment, using the 311 reflection from small diamond crystals mounted on the diffractometer. The variation of the integrated intensity with polarization angle ϕ was measured for a range of angles in each of the four quadrants and from observations on several specimens the maximum value of the ratio of the intensities of the two perpendicularly polarized components of the incident beam was estimated to be 0·0064. The observed data for one specimen and the corresponding values corrected for the small depolarization of the incident beam are given in Table I. It will be seen that there is a close agreement between experiment and theory.

A similar method was adopted by Chandrasekaran (1956), who used the 311 reflection of copper ($2\theta = 90°$ 12′ for Cu $K\alpha$) and was able to show that the depolarization of the beam was only 0·0018.

3. RESULTS WITH HEXAMETHYLENE TETRAMINE

The elimination of extinction errors by means of this technique was tested in a study of reflections from hexamethylene tetramine, $C_6H_{12}N_4$ (space group I $\overline{4}$3m, $a = 7·02$ Å; Andresen, 1957). These crystals were chosen because some reflections are known to suffer heavily from extinction (Brill et al., 1939), and because it seemed likely that liquid air shock treatment would change the state of perfection of the crystals (Lonsdale, 1948) and enable a comparison to be made of corrected intensities from the *same* crystal with different amounts of extinction.

The striking change in the reflection curve from a small crystal brought about by liquid air treatment is shown in Fig. 1. The measurements were made with the crystal bathed in the diamond-reflected polarized beam. The freshly grown crystal is perfect enough to resolve the α_1 and α_2, but the thermal shock destroys the perfection almost completely. Indeed, the integrated intensity of the 110 reflection from the fresh crystal was less than 20% of that from the same crystal after it was dipped a few times in liquid air.

Figure 2 illustrates the application of the method to one crystal with diameter about 0·05 cm. The ratio $\rho'_{\parallel}/\rho'_{\perp}$ for a range of reflections is plotted against 2θ. The upper curve is the theoretical curve for a perfect crystal with small absorption, the lower that for an ideal mosaic. The measured values are those for a fresh crystal (circles), and for the same crystal after one liquid air treatment (crosses) and after a second treatment (triangles). Clearly strong reflections from the fresh crystal have values appropriate to a perfect crystal, but the double liquid air treatment has reduced all reflections to values near those for an ideal mosaic.

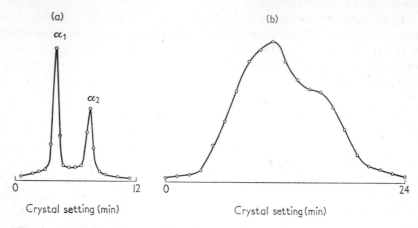

Fig. 1. 110 Reflection curve from small crystal of hexamethylene tetramine (a) freshly grown crystal; (b) after liquid air treatment.

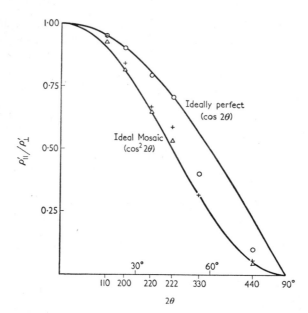

Fig. 2. $\rho'_{\parallel}/\rho'_{\perp}$ for reflections from hexamethylene tetramine: ○ freshly grown crystal; + after one liquid air treatment; △ after two liquid air treatments.

It must be remarked, however, that the strongest two reflections 110 and 222 were found to be extinguished even after repeated liquid air treatment. Seven other crystals of different sizes were examined and in none of them was it possible to eliminate the extinction completely for these two reflections. Nor was there any systematic relationship between crystal size and the amount of residual extinction, indicating that primary extinction was probably taking place in these crystals (Chandrasekhar, 1960b). These results again bring out the well-known fact that a crystal may behave as an ideal mosaic for a weak reflection and yet show a high degree of perfection (extinction) for a very strong one. This is in fact to be expected from theory. Consider, for instance, primary extinction in a perfect crystal. As shown by Zachariasen (1945, p. 134) the dynamical theory of diffraction for a perfect "thick" crystal applies when $A \gg 1$, whereas the kinematical "thin" crystal approximation holds good when $A \ll 1$, where

$$A = \frac{e^2 \lambda}{mc^2 V} \frac{|F| K t_0}{\sqrt{(|\gamma_0 \gamma_H|)}}$$

The quantity $t_0/\sqrt{(|\gamma_0 \gamma_H|)}$ could be regarded as the effective linear dimension of the perfect block. Thus, under certain circumstances, the thin crystal formula may hold for the weakest reflections, but may not be valid for the strong ones. A similar reasoning may be put forward when a crystal suffers from secondary extinction. Chandrasekaran (1959) has argued that it is to be assumed that if the degree of perfection is zero or 100% for one reflection it will be so for all orders of reflection from the same set of planes. Moreover, he has concluded from his measurements that the degree of perfection of a crystal is approximately the same for different orders of reflection from the surface. His argument as well as his experimental conclusions are at variance with our observations and, in the general case, contrary to the predictions of theory.

The measurements for this crystal of hexamethylene tetramine are shown in Table II, together with the integrated intensities corrected for extinction by the use of Eq. (2). These corrected values agree well for the different states of perfection of the crystal when the extinction is not greater than 25%. It may be pointed out that the normal crystal absorption factor is unaltered by the liquid air treatment.

The complete set of measurements on this crystal (carried out jointly by Dr. Phillips and the writer) took 8 hours, with no breaks. There was evidence of a slight decrease in the intensities of reflections from hexamethylene tetramine on prolonged exposure to air—approximately 6% in 24 hr. No allowance has been made for this effect in the results presented here. Furthermore, the measurements have not been corrected for normal crystal absorption and they are on an arbitrary scale. The data have been corrected, however, for the small depolarization of the incident beam. The results for the seven other crystals, appropriately scaled, are in very good agreement. It is estimated that the values of $\rho_\perp$ in Table II are

TABLE II. Measurements on hexamethylene tetramine

	hkl	$\rho'_\perp$ (obs)	$\rho'_\parallel$ (obs)	$\rho'_\parallel/\rho'_\perp$	ϵ (expt)	$\rho_\perp$	Theoretical $\rho'_\parallel/\rho'_\perp$	
							Ideally perfect $\cos 2\theta$	Ideal mosaic $\cos^2 2\theta$
Freshly grown crystal	110 $\theta = 8° 56'$	5 294	5 047	0·953	Highly perfect	—	0·9517	0·9057
	200 $\theta = 12° 42'$	2 056	1 860	0·905	Highly perfect	—	0·9033	0·8159
	220 $\theta = 18° 6'$	993	788	0·794	Highly perfect	—	0·8070	0·6512
	222 $\theta = 22° 22'$	3 374	2 397	0·710	Highly perfect	—	0·7104	0·5047
	330 $\theta = 27° 46'$	603	245	0·406	28%	841	0·5660	0·3203
	440 $\theta = 38° 24'$	1 529	162	0·106	> 30%	—	0·2286	0·0523
After liquid air treatment	110	22 148	20 947	0·946	> 30%	—		
	200	3 654	3 057	0·837	12%	4 160		
	220	1 898	1 264	0·666	6%	2 020		
	222	10 290	6 010	0·584	24%	13 556		
	330	805	255	0·317	0%	805		
	440	2 664	149	0·056	7%	2 862		
After further liquid air treatment	110	28 400	26 355	0·928	20%	35 800		
	200	4 000	3 260	0·815	0%	4 000		
	220	1 953	1 270	0·650	0%	1 953		
	222	12 220	6 535	0·535	11%	13 692		
	330	817	—	—	—	817		
	440	2 792	147	0·053	0%	2 792		

accurate to $\pm 2·5\%$ for the unextinguished reflections (e.g. 200, 220, 330 and 440 "after further liquid air treatment") and $\pm 5\%$ for the extinguished ones.

It is of interest to compare these results with those of Becka and Cruickshank (private communication) who have recently undertaken a detailed X-ray study of hexamethylene tetramine. They have concluded from their refinement that the 110 and 222 reflections are heavily extinguished in all their crystals even after repeated liquid air treatment; this is in accordance with our own experience. Their room temperature F's (from photographs) along with our extinction corrected values (derived from

TABLE III. $C_6H_{12}N_4$ structure factors at room temperature

hkl	F_{obs} (Becka and Cruickshank)	F_{obs} (from $\rho_\perp$ in in Table II)
110	—	44·53
200	18·18	17·61
220	14·44	14·44
222‡	35·39†	41·74
330	10·81	11·03
440	21·81	22·16

† Value extrapolated from variation of F with crystal size.
‡ Value of $F_{calc} = 40·13$.

$\rho_\perp$ "after further liquid air treatment") are shown in Table III for comparison.§ The scaling factor was chosen to give the same ΣF for the two sets of reflections (excluding 110 and 222). There is a tolerable agreement for 200, 220, 330 and 440, but the main point of interest is that their F_{calc} (222) compares favourably with our experimental value. (F (110) was throughout excluded in the calculations.)

REFERENCES

Andresen, A. F. (1957). *Acta cryst.* **10**, 107.
Arndt, U. W., Faulkner, T. H. and Phillips, D. C. (1960). *J. sci. Instrum.* **37**, 68.
Brill, R., Grimm, H. G., Hermann, C. and Peters, C. (1939). *Ann. Phys., Lpz.* **34**, 393.
Chandrasekaran, K. S. (1956). *Proc. Indian Acad. Sci.* **A44**, 387.
Chandrasekaran, K. S. (1959). *Acta cryst.* **12**, 916.
Chandrasekhar, S. (1956). *Acta cryst.* **9**, 954.
Chandrasekhar, S. (1960a). *Acta cryst.* **13**, 588.
Chandrasekhar, S. (1960b). *Advanc. Phys.* **9**, 363.
Chandrasekhar, S. and Phillips, D. C. (1960). *Abstracts of 5th International Congress*, International Union of Crystallography held at Cambridge.
Chandrasekhar, S. and Phillips, D. C. (1961). *Nature, Lond.* **190**, 1164.
Chandrasekhar, S. and Weiss, R. J. (1957). *Acta cryst.* **10**, 598.

§ The writer is indebted to Professor D. W. J. Cruickshank for these results prior to publication.

Lonsdale, K. (1948). *Acta cryst.* **1**, 12.

Renninger, M. (1952). *Acta cryst.* **5**, 711.

Szabó, P. (1961). *Acta cryst.* **14**, 1206.

Witte, H. and Wölfel, E. (1958). *Rev. mod. Phys.* **30**, 51.

Zachariasen, W. H. (1945). *The Theory of X-ray Diffraction in Crystals*. Wiley, New York.

DISCUSSION

V. M. PADMANABHAN: I would like to know whether the instrument was used in conjunction with the Weissenberg mechanism or whether only a few reflections were tried.

S. CHANDRASEKHAR: No. We did it only for a few reflections.

V. M. PADMANABHAN: I would like to know the order of the time of exposure one has to give.

S. CHANDRASEKHAR: About 10 to 25 times the exposure one would give normally.

M. J. BUERGER: I would like to make a comment which pertains mainly to the question of nomenclature. I think the time has come when we should stop using the word "extinction" in this particular instance, because it is impossible to speak of a reflection as being 20% extinct. It would be better to speak of it as attenuated by 20%.

S. CHANDRASEKHAR: I suppose there is a historical reason for this because the word "extinction" was introduced by Darwin in his classical paper.

W. A. WOOSTER: By how much is the time of a structural investigation increased when you use the apparatus described here as compared with a usual diffractometer?

S. CHANDRASEKHAR: In a typical case of hexamethylene tetramine which we tried, it took about one hour per extinguished reflection.

G. N. RAMACHANDRAN: I would like to supplement what Dr. Chandrasekhar has described. In the instrument described by him, the X-ray source and the polarizer are together made to rotate about the axis of the spectrometer. We have actually designed an instrument—whose construction is practically complete—which is simpler compared to this. The X-ray tube and polarizer are kept stationary and the crystal holder and counter in the spectrometer can be made to rotate together about the axis of the collimator at any setting.

Intensity of X-Ray Reflections from Perfect and Mosaic Crystals

R. Parthasarathy, G. N. Ramachandran and
M. Mallikarjunan

*Department of Physics, University of Madras,
Madras, India*

ABSTRACT

The paper reports the results of an investigation based on the dynamical theory of X-ray interference which has revealed an interesting result, namely that, for internal reflections (Laue case), the integrated intensity of a perfect crystal can, under certain circumstances, be *greater* than that of a mosaic crystal of the same thickness. This strange result has been verified experimentally, using thin plates of perfect and mosaic calcite crystals of different thicknesses. The consequence of this result on the extinction effects in crystals is discussed.

The theory also indicates that the polarization ratio for a perfect crystal can be very small for an internal reflection provided the thickness is large enough, and that it can be definitely less than the mosiac value, namely $\cos^2 2\theta$, unlike that for surface reflections. Hence, it is possible to have a perfect crystal polarizer using a reflection of Bragg angle not necessarily close at 45°.

In addition, these studies have suggested various possible methods for measuring the angular dependence of the imaginary part $\Delta f''$ of the dispersion correction.

1. Introduction

It is well known that the integrated intensity of an X-ray reflection from a crystal depends on its state of perfection. Thus, in measuring the intensities of various reflections for structure analysis, it is usual to use a mosaic crystal, but the observed intensity for very strong reflections often suffers from extinction or a reduction, from the mosaic value because the crystal is not ideally mosaic. If we consider the reflection from the surface of the crystal, then it can be theoretically shown that a perfect crystal always gives an integrated intensity which is less than that of a mosaic crystal (Hirsch and Ramachandran, 1950).

In view of this and of the fact that extinction effects are very commonly observed, it has been generally supposed that a perfect crystal always gives an integrated intensity less than that of a mosaic crystal. Recent theoretical and experimental studies by the authors, however, indicate that, for an internal reflection, i.e. a reflection in which the reflected beam emerges from the surface opposite to that on which X-rays are

133

incident, it is sometimes possible to have the opposite result, namely the perfect crystal having a larger integrated reflection. Consequently, the general problem of the intensity of an internal reflection under various conditions of incidence and polarization was carefully examined and the main results of this investigation are given in this paper, with particular emphasis on their practical applications. The detailed derivation of the various formulae are expected to be published elsewhere and only an outline of these are given here wherever necessary. In particular, it may be mentioned that the polarization ratio α (Ramaseshan and Ramachandran, 1954) is not necessarily confined to the limits $|\cos 2\theta|$ and $\cos^2 2\theta$ as in the case of a surface reflection, but may take values far lower than the mosaic limit. This result leads to the possibility of designing a polarizer for X-rays using a perfect crystal and a reflection whose Bragg angle is not necessarily close to $45°$. The theoretical results also indicate various new methods of determining the angular dependence of the imaginary part $\Delta f''$ of the dispersion correction.

2. THEORETICAL RESULTS FOR AN INTERNAL REFLECTION

The dynamical theory of X-ray interference for an internal reflection (Laue case) in a perfect crystal has been discussed by a number of authors, chiefly by von Laue (1952), Zachariasen (1945, 1952), Ramachandran and Kartha (1952), Hirsch (1952), Ramachandran (1954) and Kato (1955). In particular, Ramachandran (1954) and Kato (1955) have worked out the theory in detail and have given analytical expressions for integrated reflection and transmission. For the present purpose, the results of Ramachandran (1954) are used and his equations are recast in a convenient form for discussion. The notation is mainly that of Zachariasen (1945) and Ramachandran (1954).

We shall use the y-scale of Zachariasen in the theoretical formulae for the integrated intensity. The relation of this to the integrated intensity in the glancing angle scale, or the θ-scale is given by the formula

$$\rho = (\mathrm{d}\theta/\mathrm{d}y)\, R^y$$

$$= [K|\psi'_H|/(|b|)^{1/2} \sin 2\theta]\, R^y \tag{1}$$

Here, ρ and R^y are the integrated intensities in the θ- and y-scales respectively, $\psi'_H = -(\mathrm{e}^2/\pi m\nu^2)\, F'_H$, where F'_H is the real (dispersion) part in the structure amplitude of the reflection $H(hkl)$, $b = (\gamma_0/\gamma_H)$, where γ_0, γ_H are the direction cosines of the angles made by the incident and diffracted beams with the normal to the surface of the crystal, K is the polarization factor ($= |\cos 2\theta|$ and 1 respectively, for the electric vector parallel and perpendicular to the plane of incidence) and θ is the Bragg angle.

The integrated intensity of an internal reflection in the y-scale can be put in the form (Ramachandran, 1954; a few minor corrections have been made in the formulae of Ramachandran)

$$R^y_{\text{perf}} = \frac{\pi}{2}(\exp - P)\left[I_0(|j|\,P) - 1 + \int_0^{P/|G|} J_0(x)\,dx\right] \qquad (2)$$

Here

$$j^2 = a^2 + (k^2/G^2) \qquad (3)$$

$$a = (1-b)/(1+b) \qquad (4)$$

$$k = F''_H/F'_H \qquad (5)$$

$$G = -F''_0(1+b)/2K\sqrt{(|b|)}\,|F'_H| \qquad (6)$$

and

$$P = \frac{\mu t}{2}\left(\frac{1}{\gamma_0} + \frac{1}{\gamma_H}\right) \qquad (7)$$

where t is the crystal thickness and μ is the linear absorption coefficient of the crystal. Equation (2) has been derived under the condition that the reflection concerned is not weak, i.e. $|F'_H| \gg |F''_H|$ or $|F''_0|$.

Similarly, for a reflection which is appreciably asymmetric, i.e. b is very different from unity or $|G|^2 \gg 1$, the integrated intensity (in the y-scale) is given by

$$R^y_{\text{perf}} = \frac{\pi}{2|G|}(1+k^2)\exp(-P)\frac{\sinh aP}{a} \qquad (8)$$

The same expression is obtained for a mosaic crystal also, so that under these conditions a perfect and a mosaic crystal give the same integrated reflection, very similar to the case of a surface reflection.

Consider now Eq. (2). When $P/|G|(= 2A$ of Zachariasen$) \gg 1$, we have

$$\int_0^{P/|G|} J_0(x)\,dx \to 1$$

Under these conditions, Eq. (2) simplifies to

$$R^y_{\text{perf}} = (\pi/2)\exp\left[-\frac{\mu t}{2}\left(\frac{1}{\gamma_0} + \frac{1}{\gamma_H}\right)\right]I_0(|j|\,P) \qquad (9)$$

When the reflection is symmetric, i.e. the Bragg planes are perpendicular to the surface, Eq. (9) is further simplified and becomes

$$R^y_{\text{perf}} = (\pi/2)\exp(-\mu t/\gamma_0)\,I_0(kP/|G|) \qquad (10)$$

$$= (\pi/2)\exp(-\mu t/\gamma_0)\,I_0(K\epsilon\mu t/\gamma_0) \qquad (11)$$

where

$$\epsilon = F''_H/F''_0 \qquad (12)$$

The corresponding expression for the integrated intensity of a symmetric internal reflection given by a mosaic crystal is (putting $1 + k^2 \approx 1$)

$$R^y_{\text{mos}} = (\pi P/2|G|) \exp(-P) \tag{13}$$

$$= (\pi/2)(K\epsilon\mu t/\gamma_0 k) \exp(-\mu t/\gamma_0) \tag{14}$$

The above equations are strictly true only if the atoms are at rest. For an actual crystal having thermal oscillations, it can be shown (Parthasarathy, 1960) that exactly similar formulae are obtained, provided we replace F_H by $F_H \exp(-M)$, y by $y \exp(-M)$, ϵ by $\epsilon \exp(-M)$ and so on, where $\exp(-M)$ is the Debye-Waller temperature factor.

3. PRACTICAL RESULTS

A. *General discussion*

For simplicity, we shall consider in what follows only symmetrical reflections ($b = 1$) and assume also that X-rays are plane polarized. Then Eqs. (11) and (14), which are valid for a perfect and mosaic crystal respectively, can be recast as follows by putting

$$\epsilon K = m \tag{15}$$

and re-introducing $P = \mu t/\gamma_0$:

$$R^y_{\text{perf}} = (\pi/2) \exp(-P) I_0(mP) \tag{16}$$

$$R^y_{\text{mos}} = (\pi/2) \exp(-P)(mP/k) \tag{17}$$

Hence

$$\frac{\rho_{\text{perf}}}{\rho_{\text{mos}}} = \frac{R^y_{\text{perf}}}{R^y_{\text{mos}}} = \left(\frac{1}{k}\right)\frac{mP}{I_0(mP)} \tag{18}$$

It should be remembered that Eq. (16) for a perfect crystal is not valid for small thicknesses, i.e. for small P. Simple considerations, as well as exact theory, indicate that $\rho_{\text{mos}} \simeq \rho_{\text{perf}}$ under these conditions. We shall discuss in particular the range for which $P > 1$, noting that $m = \epsilon K$ is of the order of unity. In Eq. (18), the numerator increases directly as P while the denominator increases exponentially with P. Hence, when P is large enough (or when the thickness t is large enough), the denominator will be larger than the numerator and ρ_{perf} will be greater than ρ_{mos}. The actual value of P or t at which the reversal occurs will depend on the value of k and ϵ for the crystal. The variation of R^y_{perf} and R^y_{mos} for a typical crystal is illustrated in Fig. 1, which shows that the reversal occurs in the region of $P(= \mu t/\gamma_0) = 6$, i.e. for a thickness $t \sim 0 \cdot 3$ mm for crystals of moderate absorption like calcite (with $\mu \sim 200$ cm^{-1}). This result has actually been verified from experiment and is described below (Section 3, B).

The physical explanation of these surprising results may be readily given in terms of the Borrmann effect. Thus, it is well-known that the effective absorption coefficient μ_E for a perfect crystal when it is set for a Bragg reflection is

$$\mu_E = \mu(1 - K\epsilon) \tag{19}$$

Since ϵ is usually only slightly less than unity, and $K = 1$ for perpendicular polarization, $\mu_E \ll \mu$ for this case and even for parallel polarization, $\mu_E < \mu$. Hence, the effective absorption coefficient when the

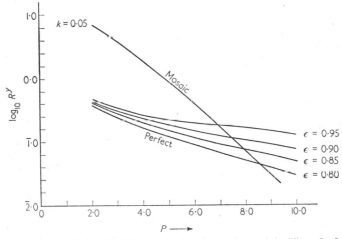

FIG. 1. Variation of R^y with P for perfect and mosaic crystals. The calculations were made for $G = 0.05$, which roughly corresponds to the value for the (211) reflection of calcite.

reflection occurs is much smaller than μ, the normal absorption coefficient. Consequently the integrated reflection of a perfect crystal becomes greater than that of a mosaic crystal.

In fact, the form of Eq. (19) for the effective absorption coefficient can be obtained from Eq. (16) by taking the asymptotic value $[e^x/\sqrt{(2\pi x)}]$ for $I_0(x)$. We then have

$$R^y_{\text{perf}} = (\pi/2)(2\pi m P)^{-1/2} \exp[(1 - m) P] \tag{20}$$

Since $m = K\epsilon$, the exponential term has the form $\exp[-\mu(1 - K\epsilon)t/\gamma_0]$ which agrees with Eq. (19).

B. *Experimental results*

The strange fact that the integrated intensity of a perfect crystal can be greater than that of a corresponding mosaic crystal has actually been verified in this laboratory, using perfect and mosaic crystals of thickness varying from 0·2 mm to 1·0 mm. The 211 reflections from thin cleavage plates of calcite were studied using a Geiger-counter spectrometer. The near-perfect specimens were obtained by cleaving a clear transparent block of calcite. For the mosaic specimens, a block of milky calcite was cleaved and the plates thus obtained were ground to the required thickness. Since the cleavage of the calcite is parallel to one of the (211) planes, the 211 reflections could be obtained both as a surface reflection and as an internal reflection at another setting of the crystal. Since the reflecting planes (211) are not at right angles to the surface of the plate,

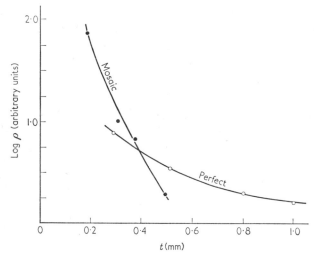

Fig. 2. Experimental data on the variation of the integrated intensity with crystal thickness for the 211 internal reflection of calcite. Note the crossing of the curves for perfect and mosaic crystals.

the internal reflection is not symmetric, but the asymmetry is quite small. To allow for the effects due to the asymmetry, the integrated intensity for the internal reflection was measured on either side of the incident beam, i.e. with $b(= \gamma_0/\gamma_H)$ less than and greater than unity, and the average was taken. The integrated intensity for the surface reflection was also measured for the various plates and these values were used to test the perfection of the crystal plates. It was found from these measurements that the plates cleaved from the clear transparent block of calcite exhibited a good degree of perfection whereas the plates obtained from the milky white calcite were nearly mosaic.

The experimental results are summarized in Fig. 2. A comparison of Figs. 1 and 2 shows that the experimental variation of ρ_{perf} and ρ_{mos} with crystal thickness is in accord with the calculations. From Fig. 2, it may be seen that ρ_{perf} is smaller than ρ_{mos} when the thickness t is small and that it becomes greater than ρ_{mos} when t is large. The cross-over occurs at a thickness $t \simeq 0.4$ mm.

Thus, it has been possible to show by experiment that, provided the thickness is large enough, a perfect crystal can give an integrated intensity *larger* than that of a mosaic crystal of the same thickness. This actually occurs for quite small thicknesses, less than 0.5 mm, for a reflection of moderate intensity like the 211 of calcite.

4. Variation of Polarization Ratio α with Absorption

The polarization ratio α is defined by

$$\alpha = \frac{\rho_{\parallel}}{\rho_{\perp}} = K \frac{(R^y)_{\parallel}}{(R^y)_{\perp}} \tag{21}$$

where $\rho_{\parallel}$ and $\rho_{\perp}$ are the intensities of the parallel and perpendicular components and the factor $K = |\cos 2\theta|$ occurs because of the scale factor involved in the conversion from the glancing angle scale to the y-scale. Since the integrated intensity R^y for an actual crystal depends on a number of factors such as crystal perfection, absorption and crystal thickness, the polarization ratio α is also in general dependent on these factors. Ramaseshan and Ramachandran (1954) first showed experimentally that the polarization ratio α is different for perfect and mosaic crystals. They used this as a criterion for finding the degree of perfection of a crystal. This has subsequently been developed to correct for extinction effects in crystals (Chandrasekaran, 1956; Chandrasekhar, 1956, 1960). The basis of this method is to study the variation of α with crystal perfection. In the case of a surface reflection, the quantity α takes the value $\cos^2 2\theta$ for a mosaic crystal and $|\cos 2\theta|$ for a perfect non-absorbing crystal, with intermediate values for an absorbing perfect crystal, depending on the absorption coefficient, asymmetry, etc. A discussion of the variation of α with these factors has been made by Ramaseshan and Ramachandran (1954). A similar attempt has now been made for an internal reflection and the results obtained are summarized here.

For simplicity, consider a symmetric internal reflection. Then, using Eq. (16) and (21), it can be shown that α_{perf}, the polarization ratio for a perfect crystal, takes the form

$$\alpha_{\text{perf}} = (|\cos 2\theta|)[I_0(\epsilon P |\cos 2\theta|)/I_0(\epsilon P)] \tag{22}$$

Thus, α_{perf} is a function of $P(= \mu t/\gamma_0)$, ϵ and $|\cos 2\theta|$. On the other hand, the polarization ratio α_{mos} for a mosaic crystal is independent of absorption, crystal thickness and other effects, but is simply equal to $\cos^2 2\theta$.

Hence, for any particular reflection (i.e. for a particular Bragg angle θ) α_{mos} is a constant but it appears that under suitable conditions, the polarization ratio of an internal reflection of a perfect crystal can take values even lower than the mosaic limit, namely $\cos^2 2\theta$. This may also be seen from Fig. 3, which illustrates the variation of α_{perf} and α_{mos} with μt and the Bragg angle for a typical reflection. It is seen from the figure that α_{perf} may be much smaller than α_{mos} even at values of the Bragg angle not anywhere near $45°$. This large reduction in α_{perf} is essentially

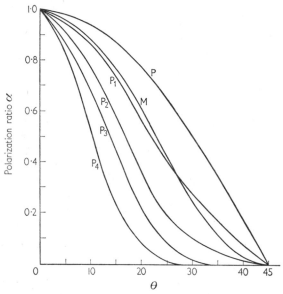

FIG. 3. Variation of the polarization ratio α with absorption, crystal thickness and Bragg angle for perfect and mosaic crystals: P = perfect, non-absorbing; P_1, P_2, P_3, P_4 = perfect, with $\mu\epsilon t = 2$, 4, 6, 10 respectively; M = mosaic crystal.

due to the *preferential absorption* of the component with parallel polarization, as may be seen from the values of the effective absorption coefficient for the two states, which are $\mu(1-\epsilon)$ and $\mu(1-K\epsilon)$ for the perpendicular and parallel polarization respectively. Since the former will be much less than the latter, for sufficiently large thicknesses, the parallel component can be eliminated. However, the actual intensity of the polarized component would also be reduced considerably. Hence, the perfect crystal polarizer is to be used when the emphasis is not on the intensity but on the purity of plane polarization. Recently, Cole *et al.* (1961) have used a perfect crystal polarizer employing this method.

5. Extinction Effects in Crystals

It is usually understood that the presence of perfect blocks in a mosaic crystal causes an extinction of X-ray intensity and that the perfect crystal always gives an integrated intensity which is smaller than the mosaic crystal. This, however, is strictly true only for a surface reflection. On

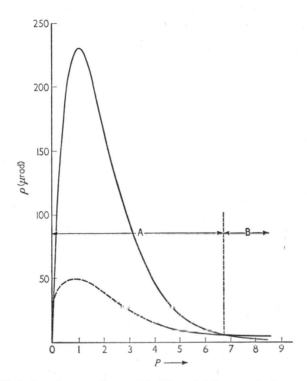

Fig. 4. Variation of ρ_{perf} and ρ_{mos} with $P(= \mu t/\gamma_0)$ for a typical crystal. In the region A, $\rho_{\text{perf}} < \rho_{\text{mos}}$ and in the region B, the converse is true.

the other hand, as has been shown above, the perfect crystal may give an integrated intensity which is *greater* than the corresponding value for a mosaic crystal for an internal reflection.

Consider Fig. 4 which illustrates the variation of the integrated intensity ρ with $P (= \mu t/\gamma_0)$ for a perfect and a mosaic crystal. This relates to a symmetrical internal reflection from a typical crystal having $\mu = 200$, $F''_H = 50$, giving $G = 0.05$, the same value as for Fig. 2. The value of ρ_{mos} was calculated from Eq. (13). The integrated intensity of a perfect crystal was calculated from Eq. (16) for large P (i.e. $P > 4$). For small P

(in particular when $P/|G|$ is small), the expression for R^y_{perf} takes the form

$$R^y_{\text{perf}} = \frac{\pi P}{2|G|}\,(\exp - P)\left[1 - \frac{P^2}{12|G|^2}\right] \tag{23}$$

This follows from Eq. (2), since

$$I_0(|j|\,P) = I_0(kP/|G|), \quad \text{since } b = 1 \quad \text{and} \quad a = 0$$

$$\approx 1, \quad \text{since } k \ll 1$$

and

$$\int_0^{P/|G|} J_0(x)\,\mathrm{d}x = 2\sum_0^\infty J_{2n+1}(P/|G|) \tag{24}$$

$$\approx \frac{P}{|G|}\left[1 - \frac{P^2}{12|G|^2}\right] \tag{25}$$

Comparing Eqs (13) and (23), it will be seen that for thin crystals, the integrated intensity of a perfect specimen is less than that of a mosaic specimen. On the other hand, when P is large, there is a cross-over, and $\rho_{\text{perf}} > \rho_{\text{mos}}$. The full lines in Fig. 4 indicate the data actually calculated, while the dashed line is extrapolated.

Thus, if a crystal is thin enough (P lying in the region A of Fig. 4), then any deviation from an ideally mosaic state would decrease the integrated reflection. On the other hand, if it is thick enough (P in region B), the opposite effect occurs and any deviation from the ideally *perfect* state would lead to a decrease in intensity. However, since the block size in mosaic crystals (like those used for structure analysis) is usually quite small, this result is not of importance to the correction for lack of ideal mosaicity in such cases, which would only lead to a reduction in the integrated intensity with respect to the ideally mosaic case.

6. Methods for Determining the Angular Dependence of $\Delta f''$

The above studies suggest three possible methods for determining the angular variation of the imaginary part $\Delta f''$ of the scattering factor, namely by measuring

(a) the ratio $\rho_{\text{perf}}/\rho_{\text{mos}}$;

(b) the effective absorption coefficient μ_E for a sufficiently thick perfect crystal, and

(c) the polarization ratio α_{perf}.

The formulae for these quantities are:

(a) $\dfrac{\rho_{\text{perf}}}{\rho_{\text{mos}}} = \dfrac{I_0(K\epsilon P)}{K\epsilon P/k}$ for a single state of polarization (26)

$= \dfrac{KI_0(K\epsilon P) + I_0(\epsilon P)}{(1 + K^2)(\epsilon P/k)}$ for unpolarized X-rays (27)

(b) $\mu_E = (1 - \epsilon\,|\cos 2\theta|)$ for parallel polarization (28a)

$= (1 - \epsilon)$ for perpendicular polarization (28b)

(c) $\alpha_{\text{perf}} = |\cos 2\theta|\,[I_0(\epsilon P\,|\cos 2\theta|)/I_0(\epsilon P)]$ (29)

In all these formulae, all the quantities other than ϵ are known, and hence $\epsilon = F_H''/F_0''$ can be determined, as a function of Bragg angle.

In the case of method (b), it is not essential to use plane polarized X-rays, for by using a sufficiently thick crystal, the component with parallel polarization can be suppressed, as mentioned above. Then, the measured value of μ_E would refer to the perpendicularly polarized component. In fact, such a method has been used by Hunter (1958, 1959a, b) and more recently by Battermann (1962) for measuring the angular dependence of $\Delta f''$ of germanium.

REFERENCES

Battermann, B. W. (1962). *Phys. Rev.* **126**, 1461.
Chandrasekhar, S. (1956). *Acta cryst.* **9**, 954.
Chandrasekaran, K. S. (1956). Ph.D. Thesis, University of Madras.
Chandrasekhar, S. (1960). *Acta cryst.* **13**, 588.
Cole, H., Chambers, F. W. and Wood, G. (1961). *J. appl. Phys.* **32**, 1942.
Hirsch, P. B. (1952). *Acta cryst.* **5**, 176.
Hirsch, P. B. and Ramachandran, G. N. (1950). *Acta cryst.* **3**, 187.
Hunter, L. P. (1958). *Proc. Acad. Sci. Amst.* **B61**, 214.
Hunter, L. P. (1959a). *J. appl. Phys.* **30**, 874.
Hunter, L. P. (1959b). *I.B.M.J. Research Develop.* **3**, 106.
Kato, N. (1955). *J. phys. Soc. Japan* **9**, 690.
Laue, M. von (1952). *Acta cryst.* **5**, 619.
Parthasarathy, R. (1960). *Acta cryst.* **13**, 803.
Ramachandran, G. N. (1954). *Proc. Indian Acad. Sci.* **A39**, 65.
Ramachandran, G. N. and Kartha, G. (1952). *Proc. Indian Acad. Sci.* **A35**, 145.
Ramaseshan, S. and Ramachandran, G. N. (1954). *Proc. Indian Acad. Sci.* **A39**, 20.
Zachariasen, W. H. (1945). *Theory of X-Ray Diffraction in Crystals.* Wiley, New York.
Zachariasen, W. H. (1952). *Proc. nat. Acad. Sci., Wash.* **38**, 378.

DISCUSSION

G. N. RAMACHANDRAN: I would like to add that a good account of the theory of propagation of X-rays in perfect crystals is available in the book by M. von Laue, *Röntgenstrahl-Interferenzen*, 3rd Ed., 1960. Akademische Verlagsgesellschaft, Frankfurt am Main.

Net Plane "Interferometry" and Applications

M. RENNINGER

Kristallographisches Institut der Universität, Marburg, West Germany

ABSTRACT

A technique is described whereby lattice deformations of the order of less than a tenth a second of arc can be made visible by a double spectrometer device. A modification of this enables one to obtain a picture, the so-called "Zebra Pattern", in which niveau lines of the deformations are obtained. Some of the results obtained by these techniques are reported. (1) "Frozen in" lattice deformations remaining from the process of growth. (2) "Reversible" elastic deformations resulting from surface treatment, which are wholly removable by etching. (3) Example of a remarkable arrangement of screw dislocations crossing a whole crystal disc. (4) A paradox concerning the mosaic distortion caused by grinding.

1. TECHNIQUE OF NET PLANE INTERFEROMETRY

Bonse and Kappler (1958) and Bonse (1958, 1961) have shown that a topographic picturing of crystal faces is possible by means of their own X-ray interferences, obtained with very high angular resolution by using double diffractometric methods, which allow the measurement of lattice deformations down to the order of fractions of a second of arc. Bonse and Kappler used these methods for investigating the smallest distortions observed directly till now, namely the dislocations. This paper deals with some results which can be obtained about fields of deformation in larger areas using similar methods, with decreased microscopic, but further on increased angular, resolution by a factor of 8 achieved by combining the method of Bonse with another (Renninger, 1961), viz. the application of asymmetrical reflection.

The studies have been made on the (111) faces of discs of silicon. Figure 1 gives a sketch of the device. A crystal A of silicon, known to be highly perfect, is set for an asymmetric reflection from the (511) planes from its (111) surface. This gives a primary beam for the second crystal B, much wider in cross-section, but on the other hand much "sharper" in its angular co-ordination to the wavelength. The crystal to be tested, B, is set for a symmetrical 333 reflection. 333 and 511 have the same spacing, and so the double-diffractometric $(n, -n)$ position is realized. However, the angular sharpening caused by the asymmetric reflection of the first crystal results in the 333 rocking curve of crystal B, if it is reflecting like a perfect crystal, to have the characteristic asymmetric form of its intrinsic diffraction pattern (Renninger, 1961). Its width at half maximum is a little more than 2″, in agreement with theory. It is shown in Fig. 2 (the curve is recorded twice in order to demonstrate the good reproducibility of its form and width). Five ϑ-positions of the crystal are indicated by arrows as (a), (b), (c), (d), (e). They are separated by about 1″ from each other. A series of five single exposures was taken at these ϑ-positions and the resulting photographs are shown in Fig. 3 (a) to (e). These were made at: (c) full maximum, (b) and (d) half maximum, (a) and (e) ~ 1/10 maximum on both sides. These pictures were taken from one of the best crystals available to the author, nearly free of dislocations, after the surface layer disturbed by the process of cutting and grinding had been etched away. The same features are shown by nearly all crystals of average, up to best

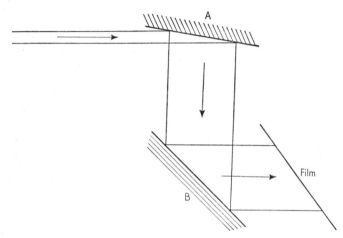

FIG. 1. Arrangement for obtaining the surface topographs.

quality. The pictures show that even the smallest lattice deformations give strong contrasts of blackening in the exposures (b) and (d) because of the steep slopes on both sides of the rocking curve, even though such deformations are not at all observable in the exposure (c), i.e. whose angular deviation does not extend beyond the top plateau of the rocking curve, which has a width of only a few tenths of a second.

To get pictures of the kind shown in Fig. 3, where the whole crystal is reflecting all at once, the net planes of both crystals must be exactly parallel, to within less than a minute of arc. Now it is possible to depart intentionally from this condition, i.e. to tilt the second crystal by some minutes of arc out of the exact parallel position, with its normal away from the plane of incidence. Then, instead of the *whole* crystal face, only a horizontal strip will be reflecting at a time. This strip moves across the face in the vertical direction when the crystal is turned by the ϑ-axis. It is straight if both crystals are undistorted. But if one of them, suppose the test-crystal, contains lattice deformations, then the strip is curved and may even be considered as a kind of niveau line, a niveau line not of the net plane itself but of its fluctuations in orientation and lattice parameter, just as optical wedge interference fringes are niveau lines of a mirror surface. This resemblance is even more evident if one takes a series of pictures superposed on one another at ϑ-positions of the crystal changed stepwise. This results in a kind of "zebra"-pattern. In Fig. 4 are shown (a) a single strip, and (b) a "zebra" pattern produced in this manner. The deviation from parallelism was here 5′, and between neigh-

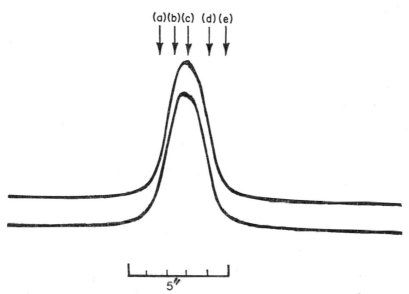

(a)(b)(c) (d)(e)

5″

FIG. 2. Two records of the ($(511)^{V}, -(333)^{S}$) rocking curve with marks of the ϑ-positions at which photographs are taken.

bouring strips the ϑ-interval was 5″. A further example is given in Fig. 5, namely, the "zebra" pattern of a crystal "kinked" in the middle by an angle of 3″. The "kinking" shows itself in the same way as does a step of a test object with optical interferences. In the same way, a small angle grain boundary also will show itself, but the kink in that picture has another cause to be discussed later.

2. Some Interesting Results

We shall now discuss some of the most interesting results.

(i) As already mentioned, lattice deformations of the type shown in Fig. 3 are contained in all crystals up to the most perfect ones and these deformations become greater as the thickness of the crystal disc decreases. Thus, Fig. 6 is a series of pictures taken with a crystal of quality no worse than that of Fig. 3, but of a thickness of only 0·3 mm (the thickness of the first one was 1·5 mm). The single pictures in this series have a greater ϑ-distance (2″). The "zebra" pattern of the same crystal is shown in Fig. 7. The crystal was tilted by 5′ and the ϑ-steps were 10″. From this, it appears that the tensions remaining from the process of growth are causing larger deformations as the thickness decreases. These "frozen in" deformations are not at all influenced by any kind of surface treatment such as grinding, scratching and etching. Recent preliminary experiments seem to show that they sometimes get weaker by annealing near the melting point.

(ii) Any kind of surface violation produces additional fields of deformation which extend to distances of several millimetres from the place of the violation, for example they pass through to the back side of the disc. Figures 8 and 9 show the results of scratches both on the faces opposite to the reflecting ones at discs of thickness 1·5 mm, Fig. 8 that of a small circle scratched in and Fig. 9 A that of a straight scratch crossing the diameter of the disc. It will be seen that the result of the latter is a "kinking" of the whole disc by an angle of 3″. The corresponding rocking curve is shown in Fig. 10 A. Figure 5 is in fact the "zebra" pattern of this face. The height of the steps in the strips also indicates a kink angle of 3″.

A further example is shown in Figs. 9 B and 10 B. Here a very weak scratch made with a diamond glass cutter has caused a "kink" of 15″. Both halves of the scratched disc give nearly "intrinsic" rocking curves and between the two there is a long ϑ-range in which the reflected intensity is zero. In the X-ray pictures of Fig. 9 B the ϑ-difference between (a), (b), (c) and between (d), (e), (f), is $\sim 1″$, but between (c) and (d) it is 13″.

Grinding of a crystal disc on one side produces a spherical bending of the whole disc like a "saucer", convex on the ground side. The bending radius is in the region of 30m for discs of 1 mm thickness. The X-ray pictures of such a crystal taken by reflection at the face opposite to the ground one show only a small *vertical strip* reflecting at each ϑ-position. This strip migrates in a horizontal direction if the crystal is turned by the ϑ-axis. So likewise a kind of "zebra" pattern can be obtained, but quite different from those which are obtained from an unviolated but tilted crystal. Here a *vertical* strip is migrating *horizontally*, as in Fig. 11. In this figure, the ϑ-distance between two neighbouring "zebra" strips is 10″, and the deformed crystal therefore is reflecting over a region of more than 100″ (width of the rocking curve).

(iii) It is surprising to note that all deformation produced by surface violations (scratching, grinding, etc.) are of a purely elastic and reversible nature. They are wholly removed by etching the crystal for quite a short time (removing a depth of less than 10 μ). The crystal then returns to its initial state and is showing no more deformations than those "frozen in" as mentioned before.

Interpretation of all the facts reported before may be attempted on the basis of the assumption suggested by experiments of Smekal and collaborators (Smekal, 1942, Marx *et al.*, 1943) and by calculations of

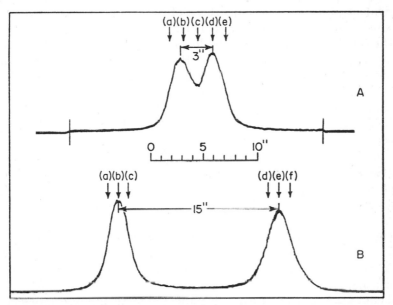

FIG. 10. Rocking curves of the crystals of Fig. 9—A that of 9 A; B that of 9 B.

Madelung (1942): In the trace of scratching, plastic deformation takes place on account of local melting of the material and the strain caused by such a deformation tends to bend the disc backward.

3. AN INSTRUCTIVE EXAMPLE OF DISLOCATION ARRANGEMENT

Figure 12 shows the topographic double diffractometric X-ray reflection pictures from both sides of a silicon disc (thickness 2 mm) cut from a crystal drawn in crucible and containing very few dislocations in the other parts. The arrangement is the same as for the pictures discussed earlier, but with improved microscopic resolution. The pictures were taken on photographic material of medium granularity and sensitivity.

The points (looking like "pits" or "hills") visible on them are believed to be emerging points of screw dislocations, most of them going right through the thickness of the crystal disc. The pattern of their arrangement is closely congruent (but inversely) on the two pictures: almost every one of the "pits" on one of them may be co-ordinated uniquely to a corresponding one on the other picture. So we can say that most of the dislocations get through the disc in groups parallel to one another, with the exception of occasional steps which they may undergo in the interior. Certainly they may have mainly three different, crystallographically equivalent, directions, perhaps those of the section wedges of the three octahedral faces $(11\bar{1})$, $(1\bar{1}1)$ and $(\bar{1}11)$.

The conclusion that we have to do with screw dislocations seems to be quite evident on account of the fact that each of the "pits" has a dark-bright contrast, which is "vertical", i.e. normal to the plane of X-ray reflection. This leads to their "plastic" impression, and the contrast arises from the tilting of the reflecting net planes, which decreases the glancing angle on *one* side, and increases on the *other* exactly what is expected of a net plane screwed like a winding stair. By observing which side of a "pit" is the bright one, we can distinguish the sense of screwing, i.e. the sign of the Burgers vector. It will be noticed that this sign is opposite for the upper and the lower rows of dislocations in the pictures and so causes a tilting of the sector between them by an angle of about a second.

The concentric halos in the pictures are due to the "frozen in" lattice deformations mentioned earlier. Evidently they have nothing directly to do with dislocations. It may be supposed that they mark different concentrations of "point defects". They result from variation of the spacing and not of the net plane tilting, as indicated by their uniform blackening roundabout.

4. A PARADOX CONCERNING THE DEPTH OF LATTICE DISTORTIONS PRODUCED BY ABRASIVE TREATMENT OF CRYSTALS

As is well known, the lattice of all crystals, including those of very hard and brittle ones like Si and Ge, is heavily distorted at surfaces that have been ground. In the course of attempts at clarifying the nature of those distortions, some quantitative data were obtained by a study of the (111) faces of silicon, which seem to be worth discussing.

Chemically polished faces of good Ge and Si crystals reflect X-rays quantitatively like perfect crystals. Using the (111) face of such a silicon crystal and the device described before, a two-crystal $((511)^{\mathrm{V}}, -(333)^{\mathrm{S}})$ rocking curve having a width of $2''$ is obtained (the one shown in Fig. 2).

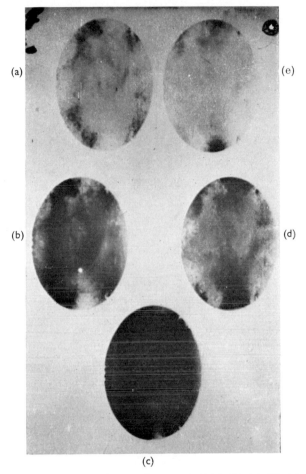

FIG. 3. The patterns obtained at settings marked (a), (b), (c), (d), (e), in Fig. 2 from a crystal of thickness $1\frac{1}{2}$ mm.

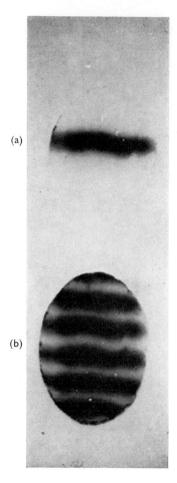

FIG. 4. Patterns of the same crystal as in Fig. 3, but crystal tilted by 5′. (a) A single strip, and (b) a "zebra" pattern obtained with multiple exposure at ϑ-intervals of 5″.

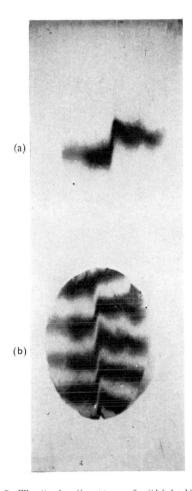

(a)

(b)

Fig. 5. The "zebra" pattern of a "kinked" crystal.

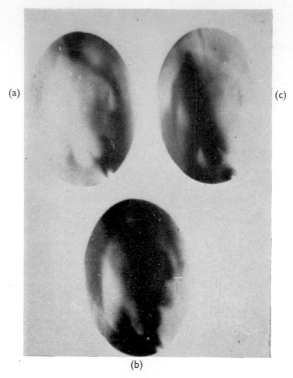

FIG. 6. Topographs obtained with a thin crystal (thickness 0·3 mm).

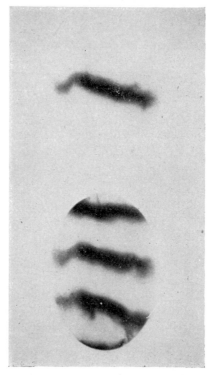

FIG. 7. "Zebra" pattern of the crystal used for Fig. 6.

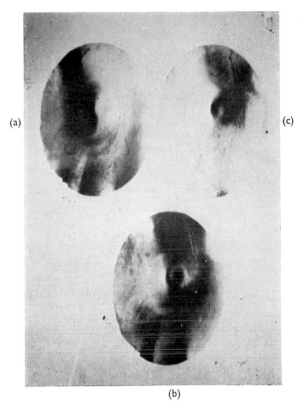

(a)

(c)

(b)

FIG. 8. A small circle scratched into the back side.

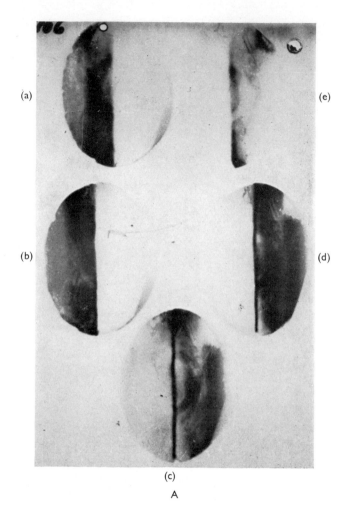

(a)

(e)

(b)

(d)

(c)

A

FIG. 9. Patterns illustrating that the deformation produced by a scratch passes right through the thickness of a disc. Two examples of straight scratches on the back crossing the diameter of the disc (thickness 1·5 mm). A—Scratched by a corundum needle ("zebra" pattern is given by Fig. 5).

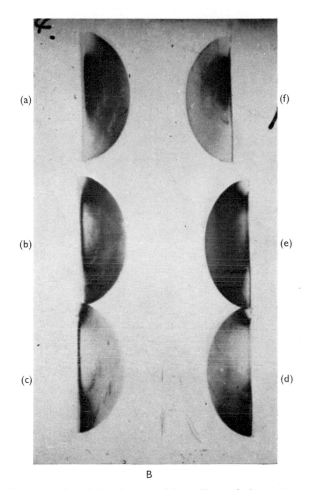

(a)

(f)

(b)

(e)

(c)

(d)

B

FIG. 9 continued. B—Scratched by a diamond glass cutter.

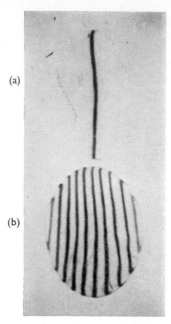

(a)

(b)

FIG. 11. Pattern of a crystal disc ground at the back side. (a) Single exposure.
(b) Superposed exposures at ϑ-intervals of $10''$ ("zebra" pattern of another
kind).

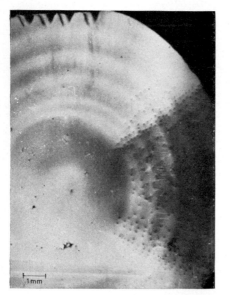

FIG. 12. Topographic patterns of the opposite sides of a silicon disc (thickness
2 mm). The shaded points are due to screw dislocations. Note the correspondence in the two pictures. The millimetre graduation gives the scale.

The form and width of the curve, as well as the integrated reflection $(10\cdot2 \times 10^{-6})$, are in full agreement with the dynamical theory.

After grinding the test crystal with boron carbide of grain size $5\,\mu$, the width of the rocking curve becomes $10''$ at half maximum and nearly $1'$ at one-tenth of maximum.

If now the crystal is etched quite a little, so that a surface layer of not more than $2\,\mu$ is removed (measured by an interferometric method), the face immediately reflects again just as it did before the abrasive treat-

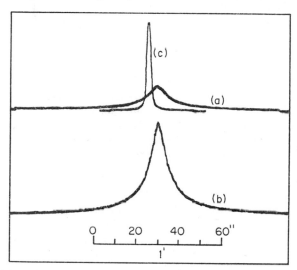

Fig. 13. Rocking curves (angular scale much smaller than in Figs. 2 and 10): (a) and (b) of a crystal ground by $5\,\mu$ grain abrasive; (b) with fourfold ordinate scale; (c) of the same crystal after chemical removal of a layer of thickness $2\,\mu$ (same ordinate scale as (a)).

ment. All the quantities like the width and form of the rocking curve, the integrated reflection, etc., attain the values for the perfect crystal. This is shown by Fig. 13 (a) and (c), which are respectively the rocking curves of the crystal in the ground state and in the etched state, both on the same ordinate scale (but an angular scale much smaller than in Fig. 2).

Such a behaviour obviously manifests a strange paradox. It is easy to calculate that the depth of the crystal layer, which must contribute to the reflection in order to give the integrated reflection measured for the ground crystal (19×10^{-6}), must be at least $12\,\mu$ (still more, if absorption and extinction are taken into account). Further, the reflected radiation coming out of such a depth is spread over an angle of nearly $1'$, proving that the crystal material must be disoriented down to that depth over the same angular range ("mosaic texture"). However, after the chemical removal of only $2\,\mu$, all this disorientation has disappeared!

6

We must conclude that the acid has *not removed* the damaged layer, but has "*healed*" it, i.e. has *turned back* the disorientated crystal grains. What may be the mechanism of such a behaviour, and what is the nature of the distorted layer, 10 μ thick at least, before and after the etching? It is quite impossible to think that the layer in the ground state consists of crystal grains broken up, for the face is quite compact after the grinding process. Again, the question of how the crystallites find the place to be tilted, and later to be re-oriented only by removal of a very thin surface layer, has to be explained.

REFERENCES

Bonse, U. (1958). *Z. Phys.* **153**, 278.
Bonse, U. (1961). Proc. Techn. Conf. St. Louis, Miss., p. 431.
Bonse, U. and Kappler, M. (1958). *Z. Naturforsch.* **13a**, 348.
Madelung, E. (1942). *Naturwissenschaften* **30**, 223.
Marx, Th., Klemm, W. and Smekal, A. (1943). *Naturwissenschaften* **31**, 143.
Renninger, M. (1961). *Z. Naturforsch.* **16a**, 1110.
Smekal, A. (1942). *Naturwissenschaften*, **30**, 224.

DISCUSSION

L. V. AZAROFF: Are the planes examined (111) planes? If so, do you think that the annular rings are formed by thermal stresses during growth?

M. RENNINGER: Yes, all observations have been made with (111) planes. The annular rings are the effect of variations in the lattice spacings, since lattice tilts would not form continuous circles. They are supposed to be formed by variation of point defect concentration.

Wave-optical Theory of Diffraction in Single Crystals

N. KATO

Department of Applied Physics, Faculty of Engineering,
Nagoya University, Nagoya, Japan

ABSTRACT

The dynamical theory of wave diffraction in ideally perfect and in distorted single crystals is described in terms of wave-optical principles that are well known in light optics. Emphasis is put on differences between the electron and X-ray cases. A plane-wave solution in the Fresnel region is adequate for the former, whereas a spherical-wave solution in the Fraunhofer region must be used for the latter. In perfect and slightly distorted crystals the stationary phase principle is extensively used as a guiding principle. In distorted crystals it is shown that a lamellar crystal approach is useful. Some new results are included, particularly on the ray optics of slightly distorted crystals.

1. INTRODUCTION

In this article it is intended to present some of the fundamental principles of wave optics in single crystals where Bragg reflection takes place. Here the single crystal includes not only ideally perfect crystals but also distorted ones. In principle, the phenomena concerned should be understandable through the so-called dynamical theories of diffraction. As is well known, these theories have been developed for perfect crystals from the time immediately after the discovery of crystal diffraction (Darwin, 1914a, b; Ewald, 1917, 1920, 1924; Bethe, 1928; von Laue 1931). Most of the essentials are already included in these classics either explicitly or in implicit forms. The theory, however, is still in progress of development both in its fundamental aspects and in its applications. One of the particularly urgent problems is to understand diffraction images of lattice defects in terms of diffraction theory.

The article is divided into three parts. In Section 2 some optical principles for a homogeneous medium are summarized. The stationary phase principle of Kelvin (for example, Jeffreys and Jeffreys, 1950) is also described. Perfect crystals are dealt with in Section 3. The contents are a summary of the papers by Ewald (1958) and by the author (1952a, b; 1953; 1958; 1960a, b; 1961a, b; 1962). Section 4 is devoted to distorted crystals. Ray optics is placed on a sound foundation. Lamellar crystal approaches are also described briefly.

2. SUMMARY OF WAVE-OPTICAL PRINCIPLES IN A HOMOGENEOUS MEDIUM

We take the Maxwell and Schrödinger equations as the master equations for X-rays and electrons. Description, however, is given mainly for a plane-polarized field of X-rays since, if necessary, it can easily be translated to material waves.

A. *A plane wave and a spherical wave*

A plane wave is specified by a constant amplitude ψ and a constant wave vector $\mathbf{K}$, namely

$$\Phi_p = \psi \exp i(\mathbf{K} \cdot \mathbf{r}) \tag{1}$$

On the other hand a spherical wave is specified by an amplitude $A/4\pi$ at unit distance from the source and a constant wave number K. Thus it has the form

$$\Phi_s = \frac{A}{4\pi r} \exp iKr \tag{2}$$

Here Φ_p and Φ_s mean either an electric or a magnetic field vector. As is well known, Φ_s may be considered as a superposition of plane waves. Mathematically,

$$\Phi_s = \frac{Ai}{8\pi^2} \int\limits_{-\infty}^{+\infty}\!\!\int \frac{1}{K_z} \exp i(\mathbf{K} \cdot \mathbf{r})\, \mathrm{d}K_x\, \mathrm{d}K_y \tag{3}$$

where $K_{x,y,z}$ are components of $\mathbf{K}$. K_z is given by

$$K_z = (K^2 - K_x^2 - K_y^2)^{1/2} \tag{4}$$

for a wave propagating in the z-direction.† Maxwell's equations relate the frequency ν to $|\mathbf{K}| \equiv K$, and in a vacuum

$$\mathbf{K}^2 = (2\pi\nu/c)^2 \equiv E \tag{5}$$

c being the velocity of light. In a medium of refractive index n or of mean polarizability proportional to Q_0, the square of the wave vector becomes

$$\mathbf{k}^2 = (2\pi\nu n/c)^2 = E - Q_0 \tag{5'}$$

E being defined by Eq. (5). Equations such as (5) and (5′) are called the dispersion relations. The surface of Eq. (5) or (5′) in reciprocal space is called the dispersion surface.

---

† For discussions on the meaning of imaginary values for large $K_{x,y}$ reference should be made to a good article by Ratcliffe (1956) on wave propagation.

B. *Refraction*

(1) *Plane-wave cases.* Refraction and reflection of a plane wave at an infinite boundary between two media can be illustrated conventionally by Fig. 1 (a) and 1 (b) in real and reciprocal space respectively. The wave vectors **K** and **k** are related by

$$\mathbf{K} = \mathbf{k} + \Delta\mathbf{n} \tag{6}$$

because of tangential continuity of **K** and **k** at the boundary. Here **n** is the unit vector of the normal.

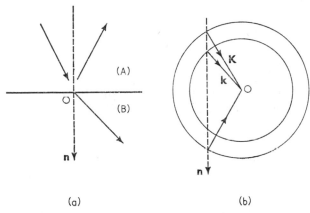

(a)   (b)

Fig. 1. Refraction and reflection: (a) in real space; (b) in reciprocal space.

Neglecting the surface reflection,† the refracted wave is given by

$$\Phi_p^h = \psi \exp i\{(\mathbf{K}\cdot\mathbf{r}_s) + (\mathbf{k}\cdot\mathbf{r} - \mathbf{r}_s)\} \tag{7}$$

where $\mathbf{r}_s$ is the vector indicating the boundary. When Eq. (6) is satisfied only the length $L = (\mathbf{n}\cdot\mathbf{r}_s)$ needs to be specified concerning $\mathbf{r}_s$.

(2) *Spherical-wave cases.* The refracted wave of a spherical wave is easily derived from the case of a plane wave. Since a spherical wave has the form of Eq. (3), the refracted wave is

$$\Phi_s^h = \frac{Ai}{8\pi^2} \int\limits_{-\infty}^{+\infty}\!\!\int \frac{1}{K_z} \Phi_p^h(\mathbf{K})\, dK_x\, dK_y$$

$$= \frac{Ai}{8\pi^2} \int\limits_{-\infty}^{+\infty}\!\!\int \frac{1}{K_z} \exp i\{(\mathbf{K}\cdot\mathbf{r}_s) + (\mathbf{k}\cdot\mathbf{r} - \mathbf{r}_s)\}\, dK_x\, dK_y \tag{8}$$

---

† Since the amplitude ratio (refl./refr.) $= \Delta/2K_z$ for $K_z \gg \Delta$, this is always justified in usual cases of X-rays and electrons.

The integration can be carried out by the stationary phase method which is explained later on. Neglecting a small quantity in the expression of the amplitude we will find

$$\Phi_s^h \cong \frac{A}{4\pi r} \exp i\{Kr_a + kr_b\} \tag{9}$$

where r_a and r_b are the path lengths in the medium of (A) and (B) respectively. The path is given by geometrical optics.

C. *Optical diffraction*

If we limit the wavefront of a plane wave by putting a slit at the boundary between (A) and (B) we have a diffracted wave in the medium (B). The general form of such a diffracted wave is

$$\Phi_d = \int\int \psi(\mathbf{k}) \exp i(\mathbf{k}\cdot\mathbf{r}) \, dK_x \, dK_y \tag{10}$$

where $\psi(\mathbf{k})$ is given by conditions at the slit. Generally, ψ only takes appreciable values for an angular spread of $\mathbf{k}$ confined within the angle

$$\Delta\phi \sim S/\lambda$$

where S is the dimension of the slit, λ being the wavelength.

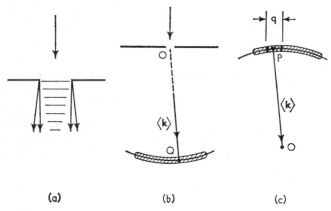

Fig. 2. Diffraction: (a) Fresnel region (real space); (b) Fraunhofer region (real space); (c) distribution of component waves (reciprocal space).

(1) *Fresnel diffraction.* In the region of (B) very close to the slit we need only consider a mean wave vector $\langle\mathbf{k}\rangle$ which satisfies Eq. (6). Let a plane be drawn tangential to the dispersion surface at a point corresponding to $\langle\mathbf{k}\rangle$. Then the wave very close to the slit propagates in a direction perpendicular to this plane with a wavefront of width S (cf. Fig. 2 (a)).

The wave function is the same as that given in the case of an infinite boundary except at the peripheries of the wavefront. The region having the above properties is called the *Fresnel region*.

(2) *Fraunhofer diffraction*. If we take a position in (B) a long distance from the slit, then calling this position **R**, we can show that Eq. (10) tends to

$$\Phi_d(\mathbf{R}) = \frac{k_z \exp ikR}{iR} \psi(\mathbf{k}) \tag{11}$$

provided that $\psi(\mathbf{k})$ is slowly varying. Under these conditions

$$\mathbf{k} = \mathbf{R}(k/R) \tag{12}$$

This implies that the spatial distribution of $\Phi_d(\mathbf{R})$ in real space is proportional to the distribution of the component waves $\psi(\mathbf{k})$ in reciprocal space. This is illustrated in Fig. 2(b) and (c). $\overrightarrow{OQ}$ in real space must be parallel to $\overrightarrow{OP}$ in reciprocal space.

D. *Stationary phase method*

Equations (9) and (11) are derived from Eqs. (8) and (10) by using the stationary phase method. This is not only a powerful method for obtaining a particular type of Fourier transform but also is very instructive for understanding the physical meaning of wave propagation. Here, for simplicity, one-dimensional cases are explained.

We take a particular type of Fourier transform given by

$$\Phi(x,z) = \int \{\psi(k) \exp ig(k).z\} \exp ikx \, dk \tag{13}$$

in which, as indicated, g is a function of k. With changing k, the phase term $\exp i(gz + kx)$ oscillates very rapidly for large z so that no net contribution to Φ results, except from such parts of the integral in which the phase $(gz + kx)$ takes a nearly stationary value. Expanding the phase in a power series at the stationary points $[k]$,† we obtain

$$\Phi(x,z) \cong \sum_{[k]} \psi([k]) \exp i[gz + kx] \int_{-\infty}^{+\infty} \exp i\left(\frac{k-[k]}{q}\right)^2 dk$$

$$= \sum_{[k]} \sqrt{\left(\frac{2\pi}{|q|}\right)} \psi([k]) \exp i[gz + kx] \tag{14}$$

where $\qquad \left[\frac{\partial g}{\partial k}\right] z + x = 0, \quad \text{and} \quad \frac{1}{q^2} = \frac{1}{2}\left[\frac{\partial^2 g}{\partial k^2}\right] z \tag{15}$

† Generally plural. Hereafter [ ] is used to denote a quantity at the stationary points.

We may regard $|q|$ as the width of the region in k-space which contributes to the integral. Upon increasing z and the curvature of $g(k)$, the width $|q|$ decreases.

Now we return to the problems of Eqs. (9) and (11). In these formulae the phase has the form

$$T = (\mathbf{K} \cdot \mathbf{r}_s) + (\mathbf{k} \cdot \mathbf{r} - \mathbf{r}_s) \tag{16}$$

Eqs. (10) and (11) representing a special case with $\mathbf{K} = \mathbf{k}$, so that $R = r_a + r_b$. In two-dimensional cases (see, for example, Born and Wolf, 1959) the stationary points of T are given by

$$\left[\frac{\partial T}{\partial \xi} \right] = 0 \tag{17}$$

where ξ stands for K_x and K_y. If we set $\mathbf{r}_s$ always parallel to $[\mathbf{K}]$, so that

$$\left[\frac{\partial (\mathbf{K} \cdot \mathbf{r}_s)}{\partial \xi} \right] = 0$$

we have

$$\left[\left(\frac{\partial \mathbf{k}}{\partial \xi} \cdot \mathbf{r} - \mathbf{r}_s \right) \right] = 0 \tag{18}$$

Thus it is concluded that the direction of $\mathbf{r} - \mathbf{r}_s$ must be normal to the dispersion surface. Under this condition

$$[T] = (K r_a) + (k r_b) \tag{19}$$

where r_a and r_b are the path lengths in the media (A) and (B) respectively. The amplitude must be proportional to the amplitude of the component waves at the stationary point $[\mathbf{k}]$. The proportionality factor depends on the contribution of the component waves in the vicinity of $[\mathbf{k}]$. This is $1/R$ approximately in the case of Eq. (9) and exactly in the case of Eq. (11).

3. Wave Fields in Ideally Perfect Crystals

Everything can be followed along the same lines as described for a homogeneous medium, except that one takes a Bloch wave in the medium (B) in place of a plane wave. Although a Bloch wave is a superposition of plane waves it can be specified by a single wave vector $\mathbf{k}_0$ and amplitude ψ_0 in a given crystal. Here, for simplicity, only the two-wave case is considered. Therefore the Bloch wave has the form

$$\Phi_b = \psi_0 \{ \exp i(\mathbf{k}_0 \cdot \mathbf{r}) + c \exp i(\mathbf{k}_g \cdot \mathbf{r}) \} \tag{20}$$

where $\mathbf{g}$ is a reciprocal lattice vector and c is the amplitude ratio of the $\mathbf{k}_g$- to the $\mathbf{k}_0$-wave. In diffraction theories the $\mathbf{k}_0$- and $\mathbf{k}_g$-waves are called the direct and the diffracted waves, respectively. The dispersion relation for the Bloch wave is

$$(E - Q_0 - \mathbf{k}_0^2)(E - Q_0 - \mathbf{k}_g^2) = Q_g Q_{-g} \tag{21}$$

where Q_g is proportional to the gth Fourier coefficient of the polarizability. The amplitude ratio c is also given by

$$c = \frac{E - Q_0 - \mathbf{k}_0^2}{Q_{-g}} = \frac{Q_g}{E - Q_0 - \mathbf{k}_g^2} \tag{22}$$

A. *Plane wave solution*

Let us consider refraction of a plane wave by a crystalline medium. This is the problem of crystal diffraction of a plane wave. The wave vector $\mathbf{k}_0$ is given similarly to Eq. (6) by

$$\mathbf{k}_0 = \mathbf{K} + \delta \mathbf{n} \tag{23}$$

Since the dispersion surface has two branches we have two δ values corresponding to a single value of $\mathbf{K}$. This situation is similar to double

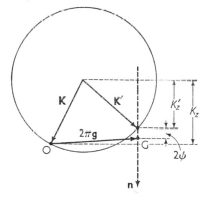

FIG. 3. Geometrical meaning of parameter ϕ in reciprocal space.

refraction of visible light, even though the physical meaning is not exactly the same. Thus the waves excited by a plane wave in the crystal are

$$\Phi_p^c = \psi_0 \exp i(\mathbf{K} \cdot \mathbf{r}_s) \sum_{i=1,2} S^{(i)} \{ \exp i(\mathbf{k}_0^{(i)} \cdot \mathbf{r} - \mathbf{r}_s) + c^{(i)} \exp i(\mathbf{k}_g^{(i)} \cdot \mathbf{r} - \mathbf{r}_s) \} \tag{24}$$

The coefficients $S^{(i)}$ are determined by the boundary conditions

$$\sum S^{(i)} = 1 \quad \text{and} \quad \sum c^{(i)} S^{(i)} = 0$$

6*

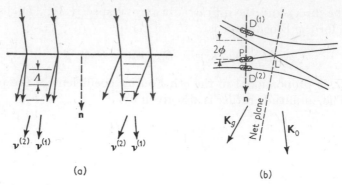

Fig. 4. Plane wave solution: (a) in real space with $\phi \sim 0$ (left) and $\phi > 0$ (right);
(b) in reciprocal space.

TABLE I. Amplitudes and phases of waves in a perfect crystal

Branch		Amplitude	Phase	
			Real part	Imaginary part
Direct (0)	(1)	$\dfrac{\phi + \sqrt{(\phi^2 + B^2)}}{2\sqrt{(\phi^2 + B^2)}}$	$(-\phi + \sqrt{\{\phi^2 + B^2\}})\,t$	$\dfrac{B'}{2\sqrt{(\phi^2 + B^2)}}\,t$
	(2)	$\dfrac{-\phi + \sqrt{(\phi^2 + B^2)}}{2\sqrt{(\phi^2 + B^2)}}$	$(-\phi - \sqrt{\{\phi^2 + B^2\}})\,t$	$-\dfrac{B'}{2\sqrt{(\phi^2 + B^2)}}\,t$
Diffracted (g)	(1)	$\dfrac{Q_g/\cos\theta_g}{2\sqrt{(\phi^2 + B^2)}}$	$(-\phi + \sqrt{\{\phi^2 + B^2\}})\,t$	$\dfrac{B'}{2\sqrt{(\phi^2 + B^2)}}\,t$
	(2)	$-\dfrac{Q_g^{\cdot}/\cos\theta_g}{2\sqrt{(\phi^2 + B^2)}}$	$(-\phi - \sqrt{\{\phi^2 + B^2\}})\,t$	$-\dfrac{B'}{2\sqrt{(\phi^2 + B^2)}}\,t$

$B^2 = |Q_g|^2/\cos\theta_0\cos\theta_g$; $\quad\theta_0$ = angle between $\mathbf{K}_0$ and $\mathbf{n}$;

$B' = Q_g'/\cos\theta_0\cos\theta_g$; $\quad\theta_g$ = angle between $\mathbf{K}_0 + 2\pi\mathbf{g}$ and $\mathbf{n}$;

t = thickness of the crystal; $\quad Q_g'$ = imaginary part of $Q_g Q_{-g}$.

Note: The phases here are $(\mathbf{k}_0^{(i)} - \mathbf{K}\cdot\mathbf{r} - \mathbf{r}_s)$. The corresponding form of Eq. (24) is then

$$\Phi_p^c = \psi_0 \exp i(\mathbf{K}\cdot\mathbf{r}) \sum_{i=1,2} S^{(i)} \exp i(\mathbf{k}_0^{(i)} - \mathbf{K}\cdot\mathbf{r} - \mathbf{r}_s)$$

$$+ \psi_0 \exp i\{(\mathbf{K}\cdot\mathbf{r}) + 2\pi(\mathbf{g}\cdot\mathbf{r} - \mathbf{r}_s)\} \sum_{i=1,2} S^{(i)} c^{(i)} \exp i(\mathbf{k}_0^{(i)} - \mathbf{K}\cdot\mathbf{r} - \mathbf{r}_s).$$

The common factors $\psi_0 \exp i(\mathbf{K}\cdot\mathbf{r})$ and $\psi_0 \exp i\{(\mathbf{K}\cdot\mathbf{r}) + 2\pi(\mathbf{g}\cdot\mathbf{r} - \mathbf{r}_s)\}$ are omitted.

This result can be called the plane wave solution and it is described in the standard texts.

From a practical point of view it is most convenient to introduce a single parameter ϕ given by

$$\phi = \tfrac{1}{2}(K_z - K_z' - 2\pi g_z) \tag{25}$$

The geometrical meanings of ϕ, K_z', etc. are shown in Figs. 3 and 4 (b). The parameter ϕ specifies the degree of deviation from the exact Bragg condition. Using this parameter the amplitudes and the wave vectors of the four component waves of Φ_p^c are listed in Table I.

B. *Spherical-wave solution*

Next we consider refraction of a spherical wave. Here again the situation is very similar to the case described for Φ_s^h (cf. Eq. 8). We can construct the refracted wave by the superposition of plane waves, thus

$$\Phi_s^c = \frac{Ai}{8\pi^2} \int\limits_{-\infty}^{+\infty}\!\!\int \frac{1}{K_z} \Phi_p^c(\mathbf{K})\, dK_x\, dK_y \tag{26}$$

where Φ_p^c is given by Eq. (24). Now we see a similarity between each of the component waves in Eq. (26) and the waves in Eq. (8) or Eq. (10).

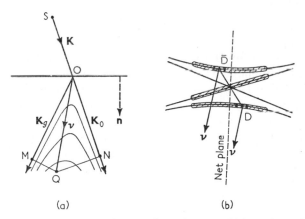

FIG. 5. Spherical wave solution: (a) in real space; (b) in reciprocal space.

Given the source and an observation point, the path of each component wave and its amplitude are determined by the same rules as described for the Φ_s^h or Φ_d waves.

In the present case, however, it is very important to realize that the direction of wave propagation is normal to the dispersion surface, and it is not parallel to either $\mathbf{k}_0$ or $\mathbf{k}_g$. Taking $\mathbf{\nu}$ to be a unit vector along the normal of the dispersion surface, we can write

$$[T^{(i)}] = (Kr_a) + (\mathbf{k}^{(i)} \cdot \mathbf{\nu}) \, r_b \qquad (27)$$

Here again r_a and r_b are the path lengths in each medium. The path is shown schematically in Fig. 5 (a). The difference in the direction of $\mathbf{k}$ and $\mathbf{\nu}$ is also familiar in double refraction of visible light. This difference in direction can be derived from various approaches, for example, by calculating the Poynting vector (von Laue, 1952, 1953) or the group velocity (Wagner, 1959). It seems, however, worth while to derive it in the present way since we need to consider the wave functions themselves when interference phenomena are our main concern.

C. *Pendellösung fringes*

The most fundamental aspect of the crystal wave is that two kinds of waves are excited and interfere with each other. Each wave corresponds to a different branch, (1) or (2). This dynamic picture of crystal waves was first explicity described by Ewald and called by him Pendelösung of the wave equation.

The Pendellösung interference is observable both in X-ray and electron waves (Kato and Lang, 1959; Heidenreich, 1942; Kinder, 1943). Here we are concerned with X-ray diffraction topographs such as "section topographs" (Lang, 1957) and "projection topographs" (Lang, 1959), and with electron micrographs. We find, however, that the fringes in the two cases appear rather different in several respects. In order to understand this we must examine the physical quantities involved in the diffraction phenomena. Typical figures for the relevant quantities are listed in Table II. The meaning of the notation used there and also in the following account is given in the legend to the table.

With electrons we have lens systems, so that any type of incident wave can be produced in principle. In high-resolution electron microscopes, however, we use a highly collimated beam with a fairly large width H of the wavefront. Thus the incident wave is characterized by the following conditions:

> (i) $H > tW(w)$ in real space
> (ii) $\Delta\theta > w$ in reciprocal space† $\qquad\qquad$ (28)

In the condition (i), W is the angular width of wave propagation in real space corresponding to the width w in reciprocal space. The angle W cannot be greater than $2\theta_B$. If (i) is satisfied the effects of Fresnel diffraction

---

† In Table II w is estimated from the conditions in real space. Since, however, the specimen is located in the Fraunhofer region of the incident wave, w also gives the angular width in reciprocal space (see Section 2, C(2)).

TABLE II. Comparison between X-ray and electron waves

	Incident wave				Crystal			Diffracted wave	Resolving power
	w	$\dfrac{\Delta\lambda}{\lambda}$	λ	H	ϑ_B	$\Delta\theta$	t	H_1	d
X-Rays	10^{-3}–10^{-4}	10^{-3}	~ 1 Å	5μ	$\sim 10°$	10^{-5}	~ 1 mm	0·4 mm	$\sim 1\,\mu$
Electrons	10^{-4}	10^{-4}	5×10^{-2} Å	$50\,\mu$–10 Å	$\sim 1°$	10^{-2}	$\sim 10^2$ Å	$50\,\mu$–10 Å	10 Å

w = Angular width;

$\Delta\lambda$ = spread in wavelength;

H = effective width of wavefront on the entrance surface;

H_1 = effective width of wavefront on the exit surface
(lower limit in the electron case is determined by specimen dimensions);

θ_B = Bragg angle;

$\Delta\theta$ = angular width of Bragg reflection.

are negligible. Moreover, if $H > 2\theta_B t$, the (1) and (2) waves overlap each other in any case as shown in Fig. 4 (a). In this sense Pendellösung fringes are observed in the *Fresnel region* defined in Section 2, C. The condition (ii) simply shows that the incident wave excites two wave points $D^{(1)}$ and $D^{(2)}$ which are connected to the wave point P on the incident wave by Eq. (23). Thus the Pendellösung fringes must be parallel to the crystal surface and the fringe distance

$$\Lambda = \frac{2\pi}{(\mathbf{k}^{(1)} - \mathbf{k}^{(2)} . \mathbf{n})} \qquad (29)$$

If the Bragg condition is satisfied exactly the fringe distance must be a maximum since in this case the distance between $D^{(1)}$ and $D^{(2)}$ is a minimum. This is clearly shown in the electron micrograph of a bent wedge-crystal (Fig. 6 (b)). A plane wave solution is fairly adequate for electron cases.

In X-ray cases, on the contrary, the incident wave may be characterized by

   (i) $H < tW(w)$ in real space

   (ii) $\Delta\theta < w$ in reciprocal space$\Big\}$ (30)

Here the effective width H is estimated to be $r_a \Delta\theta$ since the Bragg reflection takes place only within this region. The condition (ii) implies that the whole of the important region of the dispersion surface is, in practice, excited (Fig. 5 (b)). The waves propagate in every direction between $\mathbf{K}_0$ and $\mathbf{K}_g = \mathbf{K}_0 + 2\pi\mathbf{g}$, where $\mathbf{K}_0$ satisfies the Bragg condition exactly. If we take an observation point Q we can trace the path SOQ as explained in Section 3, B. For Q the effective region of the dispersion surface is confined to a region in the vicinity of D and $\overline{\text{D}}$† at which the normals $\boldsymbol{\nu}$ are both parallel to QO in real space. In this sense, the Pendellösung fringes are observed in the Fraunhofer region as defined in Section 2, C (2). The interesting feature is that the Fraunhofer region appears at a very short distance from the place where the wavefront is disturbed. The reason is that the curvature of the dispersion surface of the crystal where the Bragg condition is satisfied is 10^4 times larger than in vacuum.

The fringes are no longer parallel to the crystal surface and fringe distances are determined by

$$\Lambda = \frac{2\pi}{(\mathbf{k}(\boldsymbol{\nu}) - \overline{\mathbf{k}}(\boldsymbol{\nu}) \cdot \boldsymbol{\nu})} \qquad (31)$$

Upon changing the direction OQ, the fringe distances are changed. Along the net plane, Λ must be a minimum, since in this case the difference between $\mathbf{k}$ and $\overline{\mathbf{k}}$ along the $\boldsymbol{\nu}$ direction becomes a maximum. This is

---

† Here D and $\overline{\text{D}}$ are used instead of $D^{(1)}$ and $D^{(2)}$ for the wave points on different branches in order to show that they are conjugate with each other.

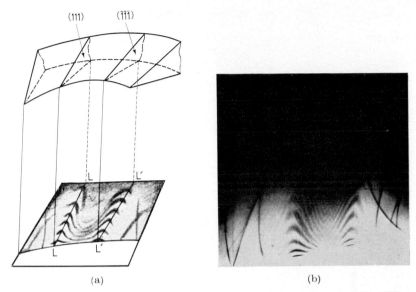

(a)   (b)

FIG. 6. (a) Geometrical conditions of (b): (111) extinction locus LL, ($\overline{1}\overline{1}\overline{1}$) extinction locus L'L'. (b) Electron microscope image of bent wedge-shaped crystal, aluminium. (After Kamiya and Uyeda, 1962.)

FIG. 7. X-Ray section topograph of wedge-crystal, silicon 440. (After Kuriyama et al., unpublished.)

Fig. 10. Electron micrograph of molybdenite, dislocation images horizontal.
(After Stowell, unpublished.)

Fig. 11. X-Ray section topograph of silicon, dislocation images horizontal. (After
Authier and Lang, unpublished.)

shown in the X-ray diffraction section topograph for a wedge-shaped crystal (Fig. 7).

In real cases, to be exact, the path SOQ is slightly different for the (1)- and (2)-waves. Moreover, the stationary phase method which enables us to trace the path is only applicable to the region more than about 10^{-1} mm from the entrance surface.† In the more exact calculation, still

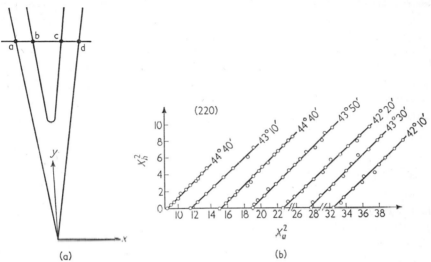

(a)   (b)

FIG. 8. Measurements on Pendellösung fringes. (After Kuriyama *et al.*, 1962.) (a) Construction for finding X_a and X_h on section topographs such as Fig. 7. (b) Plot of X_h^2 versus X_a^2.

neglecting the curvature of the **K** vector, we have the intensity distribution for the diffracted waves

$$I = \sqrt{\left(\frac{\cos\theta_0}{\cos\theta_g}\right)} \frac{|\beta|}{32\pi Kr} J_0^2(\zeta) \tag{32}$$

Here β is a constant proportional to $|Q_g|$,‡ θ_0 and θ_g are the angles between $\mathbf{K}_0$ and $\mathbf{n}$, and $\mathbf{K}_g$ and $\mathbf{n}$, respectively. Moreover,

$$\zeta = |\beta|\, \mathrm{QM.QN} \tag{33}$$

where QM and QN are the perpendicular distances from Q to $\mathbf{K}_0$ and $\mathbf{K}_g$ respectively. Thus the fringes must be hyperbolae with asymptotes $\mathbf{K}_0$ and $\mathbf{K}_g$. If this is so then the observed fringes in the section topograph of a wedge-crystal must also be hyperbolae whose asymptotes are the edges of the diffraction pattern.

† The third term in the expansion of $[T]$ must be neglected (see Eq. (14) in one-dimensional case).

‡ Equation (13) of Kato (1961*b*) defines β.

If we take $X_a = d - a$ and $X_h = c - b$ in Fig. 8 (a), we have

$$X_a^2 = X_h^2 + \text{const.} \qquad (34)$$

for any direction of $abcd$, from an elementary geometrical calculation. Fig. 8 (b) is an example of a plot of X_h^2 against X_a^2. The observed points lie on a straight line for a particular fringe, and the straight lines make almost 45 degrees with the co-ordinate axis as expected from the theory. This constitutes the most direct verification of the hyperbolic form of the dispersion surface (Kuriyama $et\ al.$, 1962).

Finally, one remark should be added. Direct observations of the (1)- and (2)-waves which come out from the exit surface have been carried out for both electrons (Cowley and Rees, 1946, 1947) and X-rays (Authier, 1960). These observations are complementary to the observations of interference.

4. DISTORTED CRYSTALS

Studies of optical principles in distorted crystals are still going ahead actively, although several new approaches have been proposed over the last few years (Cowley and Moodie, 1957a, b, 1958, 1959; Sturkey, 1957, 1962; Howie and Whelan, 1960, 1961; Kato, 1960a, in press). All of these may be called "lamellar crystal methods", the idea of which is, perhaps, traceable back to Darwin's work (1914a, b). Here we follow the theory of Howie and Whelan and a more general one of Kato.

First the theories are developed for a crystal which has no "lateral distortion", which means that the lattice distortion does not produce any change in the x- and y- components of the local $\mathbf{g}$-vector. Under this condition it is sufficient to consider only one transmitted and one diffracted wave. Next the theories are combined with "diaphragm procedures" or "column approximations" (Hirsch $et\ al.$, 1960) which are explained later. This enables us to treat more general cases. In fact, if the distortion is small enough we can show that even the lateral distortion can be taken into account within a column (Kato, in preparation).

A. *Lamellar crystal theories in cases of no lateral distortions*

We divide a crystal into many slices of thickness Δz which are parallel to the crystal surface. If the slices are thin enough the Fourier components of the wave function $\begin{pmatrix} F_0 \\ F_g \end{pmatrix}_i$ on the exit surfaces of the ith and those on the $i+1$th slice are connected by

$$\begin{pmatrix} F_0 \\ F_g \end{pmatrix}_{i+1} = \begin{pmatrix} e^{i\phi\Delta z} & Q_{-g}\Delta z \\ Q_g\Delta z & e^{-i\phi\Delta z} \end{pmatrix}_i \begin{pmatrix} F_0 \\ F_g \end{pmatrix}_i \qquad (35)$$

omitting a scalar factor to the matrix. The notations ϕ and Q_g have the same meaning as in the case of the perfect crystal but now take into account the changes in ϕ with changing i. Denoting the matrices by $\mathbf{R}_i$ we shall obtain the Fourier component $\begin{pmatrix} T \\ R \end{pmatrix}$ of the wave function at the exit surface as follows,

$$\begin{pmatrix} T \\ R \end{pmatrix} = \mathbf{R}_N \mathbf{R}_{N-1} \ldots \mathbf{R}_1 \begin{pmatrix} 1 \\ 0 \end{pmatrix} \tag{36}$$

The initial condition $\begin{pmatrix} 1 \\ 0 \end{pmatrix}$ comes from assuming a plane wave as the incident wave. Therefore a plane wave solution is given by

$$\Phi_p^{dc} = \exp i\left\{ (\mathbf{K}\cdot\mathbf{r}) - \int_0^t \phi\,dz \right\} \begin{pmatrix} T \\ R \exp 2\pi i \int_{\mathbf{r}_s}^{\mathbf{r}} (\mathbf{g}\cdot d\mathbf{r}) \end{pmatrix} \tag{37}$$

The exponential term comes from the scalar term omitted previously. The integration must be taken over the crystal thickness t because ϕ is a function of z.

A spherical wave solution is easily obtained by the same rule as in the case of the perfect crystal, as follows:

$$\Phi_s^{dc} = \frac{Ai}{8\pi^2} \iint \frac{1}{K_z} \Phi_p^{dc}\,dK_x\,dK_y \tag{38}$$

B. *"Diaphragm procedure"* or *"column approximation"*

In the general case where lateral distortions are included it is convenient to combine the above theory with the "diaphragm procedure". If we require the wave function at P, we cover the crystal with a diaphragm as shown in Fig. 9. Then the wave fields in the crystal may be confined within a small region. If we can take the crystal in this region

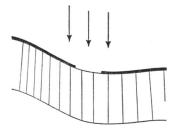

FIG. 9. The diaphragm procedure.

to be perfect in the lateral directions, we may replace the crystal by a hypothetical one which has no lateral distortions but the same vertical distortions as the real crystal. Then we can take off the diaphragm and can apply the previous theory. The results must be correct at P if we can neglect the optical diffraction effects due to the hole in the diaphragm. If the crystal is not heavily distorted in the lateral directions, the hole can be taken large enough to make such diffraction effects negligible.

In the case of electrons where the Fresnel region is important the wave fields behind the hypothetical diaphragm will be a straight column in the direction of wave propagation. On the other hand, in X-ray cases, the wave field becomes broader as one goes into the crystal. Still, if the crystal is not heavily distorted, we may follow a trajectory of the rays which correspond to a particular region on the dispersion surface. The parameter ϕ should be reckoned along this trajectory. If the crystal is heavily distorted we cannot select a suitable size of hole: the procedure is then not applicable and a more general theory is required.

C. *Pendellösung fringes: ray trajectories*

The matrix multiplication which appears in Eq. (36) can be obtained by a kind of perturbation approach. The first approximation of the perturbation series is listed in Table III which corresponds to Table I. Comparing Table III with Table I we can see a reasonable correspondence between the crystal waves in perfect and distorted crystals. At this stage of approximation the crystal can be considered as perfect in a local region.

As an example of these results, we consider the behaviour of Pendellösung fringes. In electron cases the crystal waves (1) and (2) excited by a plane wave can again be specified by a single parameter ϕ_0, which is the ϕ-value at the incident surface. The value of ϕ at any point may be written as

$$\phi = \phi_0(x, y) + \Delta\phi(x, y, z)$$

The phase difference between the (1) and (2) waves is, therefore,

$$P = 2 \int_0^t \{(\phi_0 + \Delta\phi)^2 + B^2\}^{1/2} \, dz \tag{39}$$

If the crystal distortion has a centre of symmetry at $(x_0 y_0)$, $\phi(x, y)$ has also the same symmetry. Thus the Pendellösung fringes too will have the same symmetry. This is seen in the case of the extinction contours which lie almost perpendicular to a screw dislocation as shown in Fig. 10.

In X-ray cases, the (1) and (2) waves which arrive at a given point on the exit surface do not, in general, correspond to the same values of ϕ_0. In the perfect crystal these values of ϕ_0 are of equal magnitude but of

TABLE III. Amplitudes and phases in distorted crystals.

The phases and amplitudes in $\binom{T}{R}\exp - i\int_0^t \phi\, dz$ are listed (cf. Eq. 37). The common factors there are omitted

Branch		Amplitudes	Phases	
			Real part	Imaginary part
Direct (0)	(1)	$\dfrac{1}{2}\dfrac{\beta_1 \beta_N}{\alpha_1 \alpha_N}$	$\displaystyle\int_0^t (-\phi + \sqrt{\{\phi^2 + B^2\}})\,dz$	$\dfrac{1}{2}\displaystyle\int_0^t \dfrac{B'}{\sqrt{(\phi^2 + B^2)}}\,dz$
	(2)	$-\dfrac{1}{2}\dfrac{\gamma_1 \gamma_N}{\alpha_1 \alpha_N}$	$\displaystyle\int_0^t \{-\phi - \sqrt{\{\phi^2 + B^2\}}\}\,dz$	$-\dfrac{1}{2}\displaystyle\int_0^t \dfrac{B'}{\sqrt{(\phi^2 + B^2)}}\,dz$
Diffracted (g)	(1)	$\dfrac{Q_g}{2\alpha_1 \alpha_N}(\beta_1/\beta_N)$	$\displaystyle\int_0^t (-\phi + \sqrt{\{\phi^2 + B^2\}})\,dz$	$\dfrac{1}{2}\displaystyle\int_0^t \dfrac{B'}{\sqrt{(\phi^2 + B^2)}}\,dz$
	(2)	$-\dfrac{Q_g}{2\alpha_1 \alpha_N}(\gamma_1/\gamma_N)$	$\displaystyle\int_0^t (-\phi - \sqrt{\{\phi^2 + B^2\}})\,dz$	$-\dfrac{1}{2}\displaystyle\int_0^t \dfrac{B'}{\sqrt{(\phi^2 + B^2)}}\,dz$

$\alpha = (\phi^2 + B^2)^{1/4}$; $\beta = \{\phi + \sqrt{(\phi^2 + B^2)}\}^{1/2}$; $\gamma = \{\phi - \sqrt{(\phi^2 + B^2)}\}^{1/2}$.

Subscripts 1 and N refer to the incident surface and the exit surface respectively.

opposite sign. Applying again the stationary phase method to Eq. (38) we can determine the parameters $\phi_0^{(1)}$ and $\phi_0^{(2)}$ for the (1) and (2) waves. The phase changes due to lattice distortion give rise to a distortion of the fringes. Similar arguments on symmetry, as were considered in the electron case, tell us that the fringe deviations must have mirror symmetry with respect to screw dislocation images. This is beautifully shown in Fig. 11, which is an X-ray section topograph.

Another interesting point is that the ray trajectories are bent continuously when passing through slightly bent crystals. Penning and Polder (1961) worked out this problem postulating that a variation $d\mathbf{k}_0$ along the trajectory will be in the direction of the gradient of the inhomogeneity. The results could be obtained by the stationariness of the phase change along the rays between two fixed points (Fermat's principle in optics.) Mathematically

$$\delta \int_{r_1}^{r_2} (\mathbf{k}_0 \cdot \mathbf{v})\, dl = 0 \qquad (40\text{a})$$

$$\delta \int_{r_1}^{r_2} (\mathbf{k}_g \cdot \mathbf{v})\, dl = 0 \qquad (40\text{b})$$

In order to be consistent in these equations it should be postulated that

$$\delta \int_{r_1}^{r_2} (\mathbf{g} \cdot \mathbf{v})\, dl = 0 \qquad (40\text{c})$$

These variational principles give us the change of the wave vector and $\mathbf{g}$ vector which must be satisfied along the rays. Here $\mathbf{k}_0$ and $\mathbf{k}_g$ are conceived as functions of position through $\mathbf{g}$ and also as functions of $\mathbf{v}$ as given for the perfect crystal. Euler's differential equations corresponding to these variational equations show that

$$\frac{d\mathbf{k}_0}{dl} = \nabla_r(\overset{\downarrow}{\mathbf{k}_0} \cdot \mathbf{v}) \qquad (41\text{a})$$

$$\frac{d\mathbf{k}_g}{dl} = \nabla_r(\overset{\downarrow}{\mathbf{k}_g} \cdot \mathbf{v}) \qquad (41\text{b})$$

$$\frac{d\mathbf{g}}{dl} = \nabla_r(\overset{\downarrow}{\mathbf{g}} \cdot \mathbf{v}) \qquad (41\text{c})$$

where ∇_r means the gradient in real space and operates on the quantity indicated by the arrow. According to the geometrical relation

$$\frac{d}{dl}\mathbf{g} = \left(\frac{d\mathbf{r}}{dl} \cdot \nabla_r\right)\overset{\downarrow}{\mathbf{g}} \qquad (42)$$

we can show that Eq. (41c) is always satisfied if rot $\mathbf{g} = 0$ as Penning and Polder (1961) also have noticed. Remembering that $E = h\nu$ remains constant, so that along the ray path

$$\frac{\mathrm{d}}{\mathrm{d}l}E(\mathbf{k}_0, \mathbf{g}) = 0 \tag{43}$$

we can write for $\mathbf{k}_0$

$$\frac{\mathrm{d}\mathbf{k}_0}{\mathrm{d}l} = -\nabla_r\left(\overset{\downarrow}{\mathbf{g}} \cdot \frac{\nabla_g E}{|\nabla_k E|}\right) + \nabla_r(L) \tag{44}$$

where L is a constant along a given ray and is determined by the initial conditions at the point r_1. As far as the component $\mathrm{d}\mathbf{k}_0$ along the ray direction is concerned, the result coincides with Penning and Polder's Eq. (18), if the operation ∇_r is taken as in Eq. (44) above.

D. *Large distortions*

If the distortion is large the perturbation approach is not practical. The theory, however, suggests that the wave point does not remain on a particular branch of the dispersion surface but jumps to the other branch. In electron cases all these waves overlap each other in the crystal and hence all of them must be considered as coherent components in the total disturbance at a point on the exit surface. In X-ray cases, if the wave point jumps to the other branch the direction of wave propagation also changes abruptly and the wave is spatially separated from the one which remains on the first branch. This situation looks more like a scattering process. It may be anticipated that the waves behave more or less as incoherent waves under such conditions.

In electron cases, the matrix calculation can be done either using electronic computers or analogue methods of calculation. Howie and Whelan (1960, 1961) showed that the results of calculation can explain dislocation images beautifully.

Kato (1960a; in preparation) proposed an analogue method of calculating the matrix multiplication. Since the matrix $\mathbf{R}_i$ (Eqs. 35, 36) is a two-by-two unitary matrix in non-absorbing cases, it corresponds to the rotation of a rigid body. Multiplication by all $\mathbf{R}_i$ corresponds to successive operations of rotation. Therefore it is possible to find the final results of the calculation by considering the geometrical analogue of rotation of a sphere. By this method it was shown that white-and-black images of dislocations can be explained by the dynamical theory. The method is instructive and convenient in non-absorbing cases since the behaviour of the crystal waves is readily visualized.

Acknowledgements

It is the author's great pleasure to express his thanks to Dr. Lang who gave him much help in preparing this article. Also it is perhaps a most appropriate time to express the author's thanks to Professor Ewald and Dr. Lang who stimulated him to carry out his works reviewed here. The author wishes also to thank Professor Uyeda, Dr. Kamiya, Dr. Authier, Dr. Lang and Dr. Stowell who kindly permitted him to reprint their figures herein. Finally, it should be mentioned that this article was prepared during a stay at Bristol University, England, in the Summer of 1962.

REFERENCES

Authier, A. (1960). *C. R. Acad. Sci., Paris* **251**, 2003.

Bethe, H. A. (1928). *Ann. Phys., Lpz.* **87**, 55.

Born, M. and Wolf, E. (1959). *Principles of Optics*, p. 750. Pergamon Press, London.

Cowley, J. M. and Moodie, A. F. (1957a). *Proc. phys. Soc. Lond.* **B70**, 486.

Cowley, J. M. and Moodie, A. F. (1957b). *Acta cryst.* **10**, 609.

Cowley, J. M. and Moodie, A. F. (1958). *Proc. phys. Soc. Lond.* **71**, 533.

Cowley, J. M. and Moodie, A. F. (1959). *Acta cryst.* **12**, 360.

Cowley, J. M. and Rees, L. G. (1946). *Nature, Lond.* **158**, 550.

Cowley, J. M. and Rees, L. G. (1947). *Proc. phys. Soc. Lond.* **59**, 287.

Darwin, C. G. (1914a). *Phil. Mag.* **27**, 315.

Darwin, C. G. (1914b). *Phil. Mag.* **27**, 675.

Ewald, P. P. (1917). *Ann. Phys., Lpz.* **54**, 519.

Ewald, P. P. (1920). *Z. Phys.* **2**, 332.

Ewald, P. P. (1924). *Z. Phys.* **30**, 1.

Ewald, P. P. (1958). *Acta cryst.* **11**, 888.

Heidenreich, R. D. (1942). *Phys. Rev.* **62**, 291.

Hirsch, P. B., Howie, A. and Whelan, M. J. (1960). *Phil. Trans.* **A252**, 499.

Howie, A. and Whelan, M. J. (1960). *Proc. of the European Regional Conference on Electron Microscopy, Delft*, **1**, 181, 194.

Howie, A. and Whelan, M. J. (1961). *Proc. roy. Soc.* **A263**, 217.

Howie, A. and Whelan, M. J. (1962). *Proc. roy. Soc.* **A267**, 206.

Jeffreys, H. and Jeffreys, B. S. (1950). *Methods of Mathematical Physics*. University Press, Cambridge.

Kamiya, Y. and Uyeda, R. (1962). *J. phys. Soc. Japan* **17**, Supplement B-II, 191.

Kato, N. (1952a). *J. phys. Soc., Japan* **7**, 397.

Kato, N. (1952b). *J. phys. Soc., Japan* **7**, 406.

Kato, N. (1953). *J. phys. Soc., Japan* **8**, 350.

Kato, N. (1958). *Acta cryst.* **11**, 885.

Kato, N. (1960a). Congress of International Union of Crystallography, Cambridge. *Acta cryst.* **13**, 1091 (Abstract).

Kato, N. (1960b). *Acta cryst.* **13**, 349.

Kato, N. (1960c). *Z. Naturf.* **15a**, 369.

Kato, N. (1961a). *Acta cryst.* **14**, 526.

Kato, N. (1961b). *Acta cryst.* **14**, 627.

Kato, N. (1962). *J. phys. Soc. Japan* **17**, Supplement B-II, 53.

Kato, N. and Lang, A. R. (1959). *Acta cryst.* **12**, 787.

Kinder, E. (1943). *Naturwissenschaften* **31**, 149.

Kuriyama, H., Hattori, H. and Kato, N. (1962). Read to Japanese Physical Society.

Lang, A. R. (1957). *Acta Met.* **5**, 358.

Lang, A. R. (1959). *Acta cryst.* **12**, 249.

Laue, M. von (1931). *Ergeb. exact. Naturw.* **10**, 133.

Laue, M. von (1952). *Acta cryst.* **5**, 619.

Laue, M. von (1953) *Acta cryst.* **6**, 217.

Penning, P. and Polder, D. (1961). *Philips Res. Rep.* **16**, 419.

Ratcliffe, J. A. (1956). *Rep. Progr. Phys.* **19**, 188.

Sturkey, L. (1957). Congress of International Union of Crystallography, Montreal. *Acta cryst.* **10**, 858 (Abstract).

Sturkey, L. (1962). *Proc. phys. Soc. Lond.* **80**, 321.

Wagner, E. H. (1959). *Acta cryst.* **12**, 345.

SECTION III
Crystal Disorder

On Disorder Phenomena in Crystals

H. JAGODZINSKI

*Mineralogisches Institut der Technischen Hochschule, Karlsruhe, West Germany
and Max-Planck-Institut für Silikatforschung, Würzburg, West Germany*

ABSTRACT

The general solution of disorder problems may be given, applying the semi-classical approximation, the validity of which seems to be doubtful for the one-dimensional case. The mathematical treatment of two- or three- dimensional problems remains difficult even for this approximation, because of the existence of critical points. General laws for X-ray diffraction photographs, showing sharp reflection besides diffuse ones may be given. In cases where diffuse maxima only are at the sites of a reciprocal lattice, the theory of satellites may be applied to get a qualitative or even a quantitative estimate of the disorder problem in question.

Normally all crystals are disordered and it is well known from theoretical considerations that disorder produces a diffuseness of X-ray reflections, the intensity of which is proportional to the degree of disorder. As the diffuse scattering is distributed over the reciprocal space and not concentrated into spots, these diffuse intensities are only detectable in cases of a relatively high degree of disorder. Therefore the experimental technique, using strictly monochromatized X-rays is important, if only low degrees of disorder are expected. In spite of these experimental difficulties, many problems have been solved so far, and it seems to be clear that the solution of any disorder problem may be found, provided the correct model for the type of disorder can be suggested. Therefore the situation for disordered crystals is quite similar to that of pure structure determination at a time when trial and error methods were mainly applied.

As has been pointed out by Cowley (1950), Fourier transformation of the diffuse intensities is possible. The result is a Patterson function, which is no longer periodic. In addition to the statistical structure of small regions of the crystal (created by short-range order), the fading of short-range order as a function of the distance from a given atom may also be evaluated. The general solution of the disorder problem is very simple if only one or two kinds of atoms and lattice sites have to be considered, but the problem becomes increasingly difficult for more complex structures.

177

The statistical theory of disorder problems normally applies to the so-called "semi-classical approximation". This theory holds for cases where the kinetic part of energy is independent of the configurational part, so that both may be separated. Obviously this assumption is not correct, but it may well be used in cases where the work done to create a fault is high compared with its influence on the vibrational spectrum of the crystal. This theory gives a simple expression for the probability p of mistakes, namely,

$$p = A \exp(-Q/kT) \tag{1}$$

where Q is the so-called activation energy of the fault (A is a constant). Equation (1) is valid only if the concentration of faults is low enough, so that their interaction energies may be neglected. In all other cases, the energy of a fault is strongly dependent on the number and arrangement of faults in its neighbourhood.

A theory including the interactions of faults needs a very complicated mathematical background; problems of this kind could only be solved for some simple two-dimensional cases, where the atoms are distributed over a given number of lattice sites. Typical of two- and three-dimensional problems is the occurrence of critical temperatures for long-range order. A general theoretical treatment is possible for one-dimensional problems, where no critical temperature occurs between ordered and disordered states.

The simplicity of the semi-classical treatment of one-dimensional problems and the fact that the X-ray effects may easily be detected on account of the relatively intense diffuse scattering—concentrated on rods in reciprocal space—are the reasons why this kind of disorder is so often described in the literature. But, as we shall see below, its thermodynamic interpretation leads to considerable difficulties. As mentioned above, only one Laue condition fails to be valid; therefore the intensity is distributed along lines in reciprocal space. The structure consists of nets with the same unit-cell dimensions within the plane of a net, but their arrangement in the third (disordered) dimension shows disorder with respect to the types or positions (or both) of the nets. Figure 1 (a) and (b) shows the effect of this disorder for $RhSn_2$ (Jagodzinski and Hellner, 1956), in which the disorder is with respect to the different kinds of layers and maucherite (Jagodzinski and Laves, 1948) in which the disorder is with respect to the different positions of equivalent layers. Disorders of this type were first mentioned in a paper by Mauguin (1928). The first theoretical treatments were given by Landau (1937), Lifschitz (1937), Wilson (1942) and Hendricks and Teller (1942). From a thermodynamic point of view, one-dimensional disorder should not occur in crystals that are infinite in all three dimensions, if a non-vanishing difference in energy for the plane unit cell of the nets has to be introduced for a fault in the stacking or the arrangement of different kinds of layers. In this case, the degree of disorder is dependent on the size of the layers and should tend to zero for crystals of infinite size. It follows from thermodynamic considerations that the degree of disorder should vanish during growth into the ordered directions. The large abundance of one-dimensional disordered crystals reveals that the existence of disorder cannot be a question of thermodynamic equilibrium alone, at least for the major part of disordered crystals (exceptions may be the layer structures such as graphite and some clay-minerals, where the energy differences are extremely small). Two possibilities have therefore to be discussed.

(1) The disorder has been created during a stage of growth, when its degree was in a thermodynamical equilibrium. This means that the extensions into the ordered directions must have been small for the first nuclei. Further growth cannot remove the faults, which become increasingly unstable.

(2) The mechanism of growth itself introduces faults into small regions of the growing parts, which too cannot recover during growth.

In both cases, a uniform degree of disorder should be expected for all crystals grown under the same conditions. It is assumed here that a large number of faults are present, so that statistical laws are applicable. This is only true for some cases, e.g. graphite, dodecahydrotriphenylene. On the other hand, SiC shows disordered and ordered types of crystals grown under the same conditions. In the case of a stacking disorder (disorder of positions of layers), ordered polytypes are typical for the ordering process. This was shown for synthetic ZnS crystals with a slightly disordered Wurtzite structure by heat treatment at lower temperatures. It was in fact demonstrated by Müller (1952) that a large variety of polytypes occurs in a temperature region, where the hexagonal and the cubic arrangement have nearly the same free energy. This ordering process is essentially effected by edge dislocations, the formation of new screw dislocations being very improbable in this case.

Recently, some very important investigations on screw dislocations have been carried out especially for SiC and CdI_2 crystals. They lead to an explanation of the polytypes put forward by Frank (1951). According to this theory, the period of the crystals is created by the spiral growth as shown in Fig. 2. Recently this assumption has been worked out in more detail by Mitchell (1957), Bhide and Verma (1959) and others.

Even this explanation fails to explain all experimental facts. The degree of disorder, defined as the number of disordered layers with respect to the state of order approached by the crystal, is not uniformly distributed. The distribution curve of the degree of disorder has two distinct maxima for the abundance of disordered crystals (Fig. 3), which may not be explained by growth spirals for the whole crystal (Jagodzinski, 1954). We have therefore advanced an explanation in a qualitative

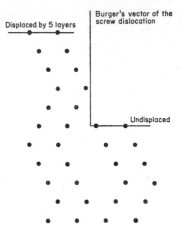

FIG. 2. The generation of polytypes by screw dislocations (after Frank); original structure SiC II (6 layers), generated structure SiC I (15 layers).

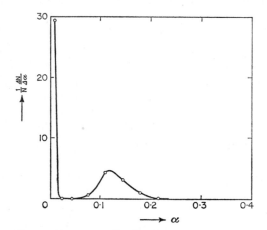

FIG. 3. Frequency distribution of faults in SiC.

way by introducing the vibration entropy. It is quite obvious that the vibration entropy favours ordered states, because every fault in the stacking sequence gives rise to a series of low frequency terms in the vibration spectrum of the crystal, thus producing a smaller number of frequency distributions within a given energy interval (smaller vibration entropy). On the other hand, the probability (configuration entropy) of disordered states increases with the number of faults. In this way the two maxima of the distribution of disorder may be qualitatively explained. It is evident that only a quantitative interpretation can give full information about the frequency spectrum of the different polytypes. Clearly the abundance of different polytypes may be markedly influenced by screw dislocations, but screw dislocations alone are not the only factors necessary for their explanation. It should be mentioned here that this behaviour is typical for one-dimensional cases at high temperatures. Here we have, according to definition, only a small energy difference for a fault, a small contribution to configuration entropy (only a one-dimensional distribution function), but a comparatively high contribution to vibration entropy (a large number of atoms belong to a single fault). Therefore it is not astonishing that one-dimensional disorder in three-dimensional crystals shows the anomaly described above.

Figure 4 shows a cubic crystal, which has a marked tendency towards an arrangement of a six-layered SiC (Type II). The important features of this disordered crystal, which occurs very frequently in low temperature syntheses of SiC (below 2000°C), are the sharp reflections on the diffuse rods $10l$ in reciprocal space. Reflections $11l$ or, more generally, hkl with $h - k \equiv 0$ (mod 3) are also sharp. This is the general law for a stacking disorder of positions

$$A = 0, 0 \qquad B = \tfrac{1}{3}, \tfrac{\bar{1}}{3} \qquad C = \tfrac{\bar{1}}{3}, \tfrac{1}{3}$$

But the sharp maxima $10l$, which must be due to a certain long-range order, have to be explained.

These sharp maxima do not coincide with any diffuse maxima which should occur when a cubic crystal gradually transforms into a hexagonal SiC crystal II. In this case, the sharp reflections might be explained in terms of the long-range order of the originally cubic crystals. But an additional diffuse reflection should be expected at the same position, as may easily be shown theoretically.

The interpretation of this photograph may be given as follows. Consider two kinds of layers F and F', which consist of a set of equal nets of SiC, differing only in the way they are put together. If these layers are stacked without any displacement, we have a disorder problem of different kinds of layers (different structure factors) which gives sharp reflections for $l = \tfrac{1}{3}$, $l = \tfrac{2}{3}$, if it consists of three layers of SiC in the positions ABC and ACB. The diffuse maxima, indicating a superstructure of six SiC layers, reveal that a regular arrangement of alternating F and F' is approached. Thus this crystal is characterized by a sequence with some disorder with respect to the F's but no displacements between them. All calculations with a possible displacement of the F's gives a diffuseness for all reflections on the lattice rows $(10l)$ or, more general, $h - k \not\equiv 0 \pmod 3$. There must be a disorder in the case of the cubic crystals with the arrangement

$$\text{A} \boxed{\text{B C}} \quad \text{A} \boxed{\text{B C}} \quad \text{A} \boxed{\text{B C}}$$

showing displacement of layers only at the places indicated in the sequence. We have tried to give an explanation by introducing screw dislocations in a cubic crystal, but no possibility has been found to explain the diffuse reflections and the sharp ones, which cannot be attributed to different parts of the crystals. But it may be easily explained in terms of vibration entropy. In the temperature region where the cubic SiC becomes unstable, the crystal prefers the partially ordered states with some long-range order rather than the completely disordered states.

Besides this special case of layer disorder, there are many others which may be explained in terms of thermodynamical equilibrium. As an example, $RhSn_2$ may be mentioned here, where a problem connected with types and positions of layers exists (Jagodzinski and Hellner, 1956).

Two dimensionally disordered crystals are comparatively rare. Only two cases are known. Artinite has a periodic arrangement of CO_3 groups in the b-direction but has a statistical arrangement of the CO_3 chains with respect to a displacement parallel to b. Figure 5 shows a [010] Weissenberg photograph of the first diffuse layer line.

The second case has been dealt with by Gryder, Donnay and Ondik (1958) for sodium metaphosphate, which shows a very similar behaviour.

Let us now discuss the most complicated case of crystals showing three-dimensional disorder, where the diffuse intensity is distributed over the reciprocal space. It has proved to be convenient to consider three typical cases for studying the behaviour of X-ray intensities.

(1) The X-ray photographs show sharp reflections and a diffuse background scattering.
(2) All reflections are diffuse but the position of at least one part of the diffuse maxima has the translational symmetry.
(3) Cases showing diffuse maxima only, but without any translational symmetry.

The last type of disorder will not be discussed in this paper; here we have no crystalline order at all; only some short-range order parameters may be determined by Fourier transformation. Some general theoretical relations for disorder problems of this kind have been developed by Hosemann (1950, 1951), Kratky (1933) and other authors. The structural solution of a special problem involves considerable difficulties.

Sharp reflections besides diffuse ones are observed in cases where a geometrical translation exists for the positions of at least one part of the atoms. The most effective procedure for the interpretation begins with a normal structure determination with the aid of the integrated intensities of the sharp reflections. The Fourier synthesis yields a statistically occupied unit cell, where each peak is due to the mean value of electron density and displacements of the atoms occupying the position in question in all unit cells. For the second step, the diffuse intensities have to be interpreted.

Let us consider a crystal having a geometrical unit cell as defined above, with lattice sites ν (or μ) and kinds i (or k) and let the atomic scattering factor of the atom i be f_i. We define:

$w_{i|\nu}$ = *a priori* probability that the site ν be occupied by an atom of the kind i;

$F_{i|\nu} = f_i \exp\left(2\pi i \mathbf{r}_{i|\nu} \cdot \mathbf{h}\right)$;

$\mathbf{r}_{i|\nu}$ = displacement vector of atom i on site ν;

$\mathbf{h}$ = vector in reciprocal space.

If no relations exist for the occupation of neighbouring lattice sites, the intensities of sharp (I_s) and diffuse (I_d) reflections are given by:

$$I_s = \left|\sum_i \sum_\nu w_{i|\nu} F_{i|\nu} \exp -2\pi i(hx_\nu + ky_\nu + lz_\nu)\right|^2 \qquad (2)$$

$$I_d = N\left\{\sum_i \sum_\nu w_{i|\nu} f_i^2 - \sum_\nu \sum_{i,k} w_{i|\nu} w_{k|\nu} F_{i|\nu} F'_{k|\nu}\right\} \qquad (3)$$

The intensity of sharp reflections is governed by an averaged structure factor, but the diffuse scattering in equation (3) is proportional to the difference of two terms. There are no maxima or minima. If a large number of displacement vectors $\mathbf{r}_{i|\nu}$ occurs, $F_{i|\nu}$ has to be replaced by the sum or an integral over all displacement vectors. In this case, $F_{i|\nu}$ approaches zero with increasing diffraction angle and the intensity of sharp reflections gives a continuous background scattering vanishing with $\overline{f_i^2}$.

In the case of short-range order, the behaviour of sharp reflections remains the same, but the intensities of diffuse scattering will no longer be uniformly distributed in reciprocal space. Introducing short-range order probabilities

$W^{\mathbf{m}}_{ik|\nu\mu}$ = probability that the μth lattice site—in the unit-cell at a distance $\mathbf{m} = m_1\mathbf{a}_1 + m_2\mathbf{a}_2 + m_3\mathbf{a}_3$ from the original cell—be occupied by an atom of kind k, if the νth site in the original cell is occupied by an atom of kind i;

we have

$$W_{ik|\nu\mu}^{m} = w_{k|\mu} + M_{ik|\nu\mu}^{m}$$

with

$$\lim_{m\to\infty} M_{ik|\nu\mu}^{m} = 0, \quad M_{ii|\nu\nu}^{0} = 1 - w_{i|\nu}, \quad M_{ik|\nu\nu}^{0} = -w_{i|\nu}$$

The diffuse intensity for N (N = number of unit cells, $N\to\infty$) is now described by the equation

$$I_d = N \left\{ \sum_{\mathbf{m}} \sum_{i,k} \sum_{\nu\mu} w_{i|\nu} f_i f_k M_{ik|\nu\mu}^{m} \exp\left[2\pi i \mathbf{m} \cdot \mathbf{h}\right] \exp\left[-2\pi i(\mathbf{r}_\nu - \mathbf{r}_\mu) \cdot \mathbf{h}\right] \right\}$$

$$(4)$$

$\mathbf{r}_\nu$, $\mathbf{r}_\mu$ = position of the νth, μth atom in the unit cell. Equation (4) is a generalized formula, already used by McGillavry and Strijk (1946), Warren, Averbach and Roberts (1951) and, including displacements, by Borie (1961) and Münster and Sagel (1957) in a more or less specialized form. In Eq. (4) displacements from the exact positions are neglected. The $M_{ik|\nu\mu}^{m}$ describe the deviations, induced by short-range order effects, from the averaged distribution of atoms. They are almost periodical functions, with periodicities generated by the interactions of atoms.

In the case of vanishing long-range order, Eq. (3) gives diffuse maxima only; their position and diffuseness are regulated by the different functions $M_{ik|\nu\mu}^{m}$, which normally are monotonically decreasing periodic functions, but different in their character with respect to periodicity and decrease with $\mathbf{m}$. In cases where only one set of symmetrically equivalent functions $M_{ik|\nu\mu}^{m}$ occurs, sharp reflections besides diffuse maxima may exist for superstructure formation. Generally, all diffuse reflections may show a different shape.

Let us discuss the relations mentioned above for a particular example, which illustrates the situation. MgAl spinels, synthesized at high temperatures according to Verneuil's method, may have a considerable excess of Al_2O_3. As shown by Hägg and Söderholm (1935), there must be a deficiency of cations (voids). Jagodzinski and Saalfeld (1958) have shown with the aid of electron density projections on (110) that the voids occur at the Al sites, which have an octahedral oxygen co-ordination. Table I shows the experimental results for one natural and three synthetic spinels of different chemical compositions.

Consequently, the following crystal-chemical reaction with increasing Al_2O_3 content must be considered: $3Mg^{2+}$ on tetrahedrally co-ordinated sites are replaced by Al^{3+}; and a void on octahedrally co-ordinated sites is created, or

$$3Mg_T^{2+} \to 3Al_T^{3+} + \square_O^{3-}$$

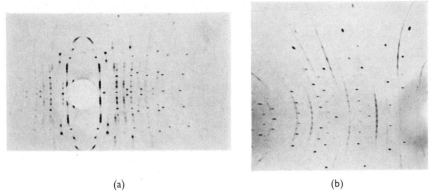

(a)   (b)

Fig. 1. One-dimensionally disordered crystals. (a) RhSn$_2$, showing disorder of different kinds of layers. (b) Ni$_3$As$_2$ (Maucherite), showing disorder of positions of the same layer type.

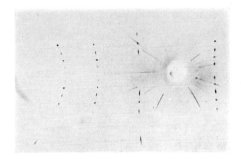

Fig. 4. SiC crystal, intermediate state between cubic β-SiC and SiC I.

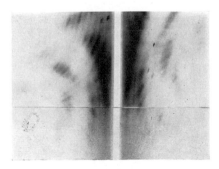

Fig. 5. Weissenberg photograph of the first diffuse layer line of Artinite (Mg$_2$[(CO$_3$)(OH)$_2$].3H$_2$O).

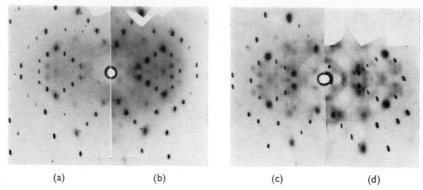

(a)   (b)   (c)   (d)

FIG. 6. Diffuse scattering of one natural and three synthetic samples of $MgO–Al_2O_3$ with different molar ratios of $MgO:Al_2O_3$: (a) 1:1 (natural), (b) 1:1 (synthetic), (c) 1:1·5 (synthetic), (d) 1:3·5 (synthetic).

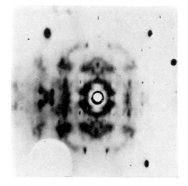

FIG. 7. Synthetic spinel 1:3·5 with X-rays parallel [110].

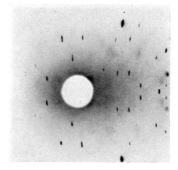

FIG. 8. As in Fig. 7, but back-reflection photograph.

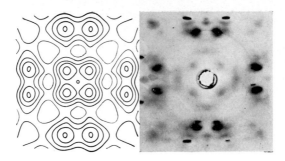

FIG. 9. Calculated intensity of a single void on the octahedral site including distortions of nearest neighbours, compared with the corresponding X-ray photograph.

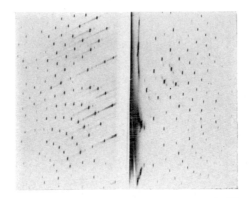

FIG. 10. Salicaldehyde methylimine-Cu complex. Weissenberg photograph [001] for zero (*left*) and first layer (*right*).

FIG. 11. Cu (II)–Salicaldehyde methylimine complex. Weissenberg photograph [100], showing increasing intensity of satellites with increasing *l*.

X-Rays can hardly distinguish between Mg^{2+} and Al^{3+}; consequently, the voids $\square_0^{3-}$ on octahedrally co-ordinated Al positions only may be detected applying X-ray methods. Neglecting displacements of neighbouring ions, a continuous diffuse background only should be expected, if no correlations between different voids are present, even if the 3Al ions replacing Mg^{2+} are in close contact with the void.

Figure 6(a)–(d) shows the diffuse scattering of one natural and three synthetic spinels $MgO.xAl_2O_3$ with different compositions x. It is clearly seen that the synthetic 1:1 spinel shows a diffuse background scattering, being considerably higher than that of a corresponding natural sample. Consequently, a markedly higher degree of disorder must be present. With increasing Al_2O_3 content, the relatively continuous background scattering begins to concentrate into maxima (see Fig. 6). There is no possibility of explaining this behaviour of diffuse intensity in terms of thermal lattice vibrations.

TABLE I. Integrated electron density (relative values) of the different atomic positions on (110) projections of spinels with different molar ratios $MgO:Al_2O_3$

	Al I	Al II	Mg	O I	O II	$\sum$ Cations	$\sum$ Anions
Nat. spinel	3·56	2·02	2·21	2·13	2·21	7·79	4·34
1:1	3·35	2·00	2·27	2·09	2·24	7·62	4·33
1:2	3·15	1·99	2·22	2·10	2·38	7·36	4·48
1:3·5	3·01	1·74	2·36	2·28	2·24	7·11	4·52

Typical of the disorder of the spinels supersaturated in Al_2O_3 is the behaviour of intensity at large diffraction angles. Figures 7 and 8 show clearly that the diffuse maxima, which are very pronounced for low diffraction angles (not extremely low) (Fig. 7) vanish for large diffraction angles. Figure 8 shows a continuous background without maxima. It follows from these experimental results that the diffuse maxima are mainly due to the displacements of oxygens and other ions around the void, which has a formal 3^- charge, and therefore has a considerable influence on the positions of the neighbouring ions.

A calculation of the diffuse intensity for a single void and six displaced oxygens, gives a diffuse intensity as shown in Fig. 9. There are diffuse maxima and minima in positions where the corresponding X-ray photographs also show maxima and minima. However, the experimental maxima are sharper and some maxima remain unexplained. The simple model used for the calculation cannot account for the more complex experimental results. The interaction of the voids must also be considered in order to get a better theoretical approximation.

Let us now consider the second type of disorder, where all reflections are diffuse, but which may be attributed to reciprocal lattice points, at least for a large number of reflections at lower diffraction angles. It is assumed here that the diffuse reflections have a fine structure, which may not be explained by broadening due to particle size or strains in a simple manner. In this case, it is often useful to apply the theory of satellites for a qualitative or even a quantitative solution. This theory has been developed for special cases by different authors (Daniel and Lipson, 1943; Dehlinger, 1927; Kochendörfer, 1939 and Hargreaves, 1951); it has recently been generalized by Korekawa (in preparation).

It may easily be shown that a pair of satellites in reciprocal space corresponds to a periodic fluctuation of electron density in crystal space. Let $g(\mathbf{h})$ represent a point lattice function in reciprocal space, $g(\mathbf{h} - \mathbf{h}_0)$ and $g(\mathbf{h} + \mathbf{h}_0)$ are the corresponding displaced functions for the pair of satellites. Let $r(\mathbf{h})$ and $i(\mathbf{h})$ describe amplitudes and phases of the satellites (real and imaginary parts). In reciprocal space, we have

$$g(\mathbf{h}) + r(\mathbf{h})\,[g(\mathbf{h} - \mathbf{h}_0) + g(\mathbf{h} + \mathbf{h}_0)] + i(\mathbf{h})[g(\mathbf{h} - \mathbf{h}_0) - g(\mathbf{h} + \mathbf{h}_0)]$$

Fourier transformation of this gives

$$G(\mathbf{r}) + \widehat{R(\mathbf{r})\,G}(\mathbf{r}) \cos 2\pi \mathbf{h}_0 \cdot \mathbf{r} + \widehat{I(\mathbf{r})\,G}(\mathbf{r}) \sin 2\pi \mathbf{h}_0 \cdot \mathbf{r} \qquad (5)$$

The functions represented by capital letters are the Fourier transforms of the corresponding functions in reciprocal space, and $\widehat{RG}$ and $\widehat{IG}$ represent the "faltung" of the two functions concerned. Equation (5) describes a periodic fluctuation of electron density only if $r(\mathbf{h}) = c_1$ and $i(\mathbf{h}) = c_2$, where c_1, c_2 are constants.

A longitudinal periodic displacement of atoms gives satellites increasing in intensity with diffraction angle. A transverse periodic displacement shows a similar behaviour, but the direction in which the intensity increases is altered because of the transverse character of the perturbation. The influence of a general distortional wave may be constructed by vectorial addition in crystal space. In reciprocal space, a similar vector addition leads to an anisotropic increase of intensities of satellites in all directions (and a decrease of the main reflections!).

However, there is a marked difference. A harmonic wave in electron density gives rise to one pair of satellites only. A general distortional wave generates an infinity of equidistant satellites, with amplitudes proportional to $J_\nu (2\pi \mathbf{a} \cdot \mathbf{h})$, i.e. Bessel functions of order ν for the νth satellites. Only for very small amplitudes $\mathbf{a}$ of the distortional wave in crystal space will the first satellite have the greatest intensity, compared with all other satellites. With respect to the distortional waves, this theory bears a close resemblance to the theory of thermal diffuse scattering of crystals, where very similar arguments are used for the longitudinal and transverse lattice waves. General displacements of atoms with nearest neighbour interactions will not be strictly periodic or harmonic. Thus a continuous superposition of harmonic waves has to be studied in order to get a general solution for distortions with interactions. One marked difference with respect to thermal diffuse scattering should be mentioned here. While considering lattice defects, fluctuations of electron density have to be considered as well. Furthermore, the phases between different harmonic terms are very important for a disorder problem. Consequently, the diffuse intensity in the neighbourhood of Bragg reflections may show considerable fluctuations as a consequence of interference between different waves.

As an example we may choose the precipitation of atoms B in a crystal of atoms A supersaturated in B. If the atoms precipitate on the lattice sites of A-atoms only (primitive lattice is assumed here), a density wave is produced having positive Fourier coefficients on both sides of the Bragg reflection ($f_B > f_A$). If precipitation is accompanied by a contraction of the lattice, the Fourier coefficients of the distortional waves are essentially positive on the high angle side and negative on the low angle side of the Bragg reflection. Therefore an asymmetrical intensity distribution is produced. This is well known for Al–Cu alloys, interpreted in a similar way by Preston (1940), Guinier (1942) and others. If a dilatation of the lattice accompanies precipitation, the signs of the distortional wave are reversed, and the opposite behaviour results.

As an example of an almost harmonic distortion, caused by sub-microscopical twinning, the [001] Weissenberg photograph of a complex organic compound is given. Figure 10 shows the $hk0$ and $hk1$ reflections of the crystal, demonstrating clearly that the disorder effect is due to translational waves ((1) no satellites in the zero-layer-line; (2) the same ratio of intensities of main reflections and first satellite in the first layer line). The distortion must be almost periodic, as the satellites are very sharp reflections.

Fig. 11 (Weissenberg photograph $(0kl)$) shows the decrease of intensities of main reflection and the increase of intensities of satellites with increasing index l. Evaluating the intensity ratio of main reflection to the first satellite, the amplitude of the lattice distortion may be determined.

In this paper, only some general viewpoints on disorder could be given. The examples chosen were investigated in our own laboratory. No attempt has been made here to deal with all the important work on disorder problems by various other authors, especially the large number of investigations on precipitation and superstructure formation in metals and alloys, such as AuCu, $AuCu_3$ or Al supersaturated in Cu, Mg or other metals.

REFERENCES

Bhide, V. G. and Verma, A. R. (1959). *Z. Kristallogr.* **111**, 142.
Borie, B. (1961). *Acta cryst.* **14**, 472.
Cowley, J. M. (1950). *J. appl. Phys.* **21**, 24.
Daniel, V. and Lipson, H. (1943). *Proc. roy. Soc.* **A181**, 368.
Dehlinger, U. (1927). *Z. Kristallogr.* **65**, 615.
Frank, F. C. (1951). *Phil. Mag.* **42**, 1014.
Gryder, J. W., Donnay, G. and Ondik, H. M. (1958). *Acta cryst.* **11**, 38.
Guinier, A. (1942). *J. Phys.* 124.
Hägg, G. and Söderholm, G. (1935). *Z. phys. Chem.* **B29**, 88.
Hargreaves, M. E. (1951). *Acta cryst.* **4**, 301
Hendricks, S. B. and Teller, E. (1942). *J. chem. Phys.* **10**, 147.
Hosemann, R. (1950). *Z. Phys.* **128**, 1.
Hosemann, R. (1951). *Acta cryst.* **4**, 520.
Jagodzinski, H. (1954). *Neues Jb. Min. Mh.* 49.
Jagodzinski, H. and Hellner, E. (1956). *Z. Kristallogr.* **107**, 124
Jagodzinski, H. and Laves, F. (1948). *Schweiz. Min. petrogr. Mitt.* **28**, 456.
Jagodzinski, H. and Saalfeld, H. (1958). *Z. Kristallogr.* **110**, 3.
Kochendörfer, A. (1939). *Z. Kristallogr.* **101**, 149.
Kratky, O. (1933). *Z. Phys.* **34**, 482.
Landau, L. (1937). *Phys. Z. Sowjet* **12**, 579.
Lifschitz, J. M. (1937), *Phys. Z. Sowjet* **12**, 623.
McGillavry, G. H. and Strijk, B. (1946). *Physica* **11**, 369.
Mauguin, Ch. (1928). *C. R. Acad. Sci., Paris* **187**, 303.
Mitchell, R. S. (1957). *Z. Kristallogr.* **109**, 1.
Müller, H. (1952). *Neues Jb. Min. Abh.* 43.
Münster, A. and Sagel, K. (1957). *Z. phys. Chem.* NF **12**, 145.
Preston, G. D. (1940). *Proc. phys. Soc.* **52**, 77.
Warren, B. E., Averbach, B. L. and Roberts, B. W. (1951). *J. appl. Phys.* **22**, 1493.
Wilson, A. J. C. (1942). *Proc. roy. Soc.* **A180**, 277.

DISCUSSION

R. SRINIVASAN: When the disorder phenomenon is of the pseudo-translational type, as for instance along a particular direction in a crystal, we have alternate layers which differ slightly in atomic co-ordinates—which gives rise to the alternate layers in the reciprocal lattice being strong and weak—and it appears possible to obtain an idea of the amount of disorder by a simple statistical method making use of a slightly modified form of the probability distribution curve. We have tried it at Cambridge on one of the members of the felspar series and the results are yet to be published.

H. JOGODZINSKI: What kind of felspar are you discussing here?

R. SRINIVASAN: It is the sodium-calcium series (albite–anorthite series). We tried it on the body centred member, namely bytownite where you have only two types of reflections.

H. JAGODZINSKI: I think the occurrence of satellites in felspars, which depends on sodium content, can also be explained on the satellite theory. On the other hand, the diffuseness of the body centred reflection may be explained by "antiphase domains".

On the Effect of the Impurities on Neutron Scattering by Crystals

IVAR WALLER

*Institute for Theoretical Physics, University of Uppsala,
Uppsala, Sweden*

ABSTRACT

It is shown how, by using Green's functions, the effect of isolated impurities can be calculated for harmonic lattice vibrations. Explicit formulae are given for the one-phonon scattering by local vibrations.

The theory of the scattering of neutrons by crystals containing static inhomogeneities has been treated by Krivoglaz (1961), assuming that the perturbations of the lattice vibrations are small. He has also considered briefly the local modes caused by strong perturbations. The aim of our paper is to investigate the neutron scattering by more exact methods when the lattice vibrations are strongly perturbed by isolated impurities. The method is the same as that used by the author (Waller, 1963) for the problem of the γ-radiation, including the Mössbauer effect, from an impurity nucleus.

Consider a Bravais lattice and let the vectors R denote the positions of the nuclei. R can then be considered as the cell index. Assume an impurity atom to be substituted for the original atom at $R = R_0$. We shall show how the change in the differential scattering cross-section caused by the impurity can be calculated by using Green's functions, assuming the forces caused by displacements of the atoms to be harmonic. We shall in particular consider the case where the forces in the lattice with the impurity (lattice L) are the same as those in the original lattice (lattice $\bar{L}$), and when there is cubic symmetry with respect to the impurity site. In this case the Green's functions for lattice L can be very simply expressed in those of the lattice $\bar{L}$. An explicit calculation is made for the one-phonon scattering caused by the localized vibrational modes that occur for the impurity atom and its environment if the mass M of the impurity atom is sufficiently smaller than the masses $\bar{M}$ of the atoms in the original lattice. We make in this calculation the assumption that the ordinary temperature factors are the same for all nuclei with the exception of the impurity. For sufficiently high temperatures, i.e. when classical statistics are valid for the lattice vibrations, all temperature

189

factors, including that of the impurity, are in effect the same. For lower temperatures we make an approximation by our assumption.

Let m be the neutron mass, $\mathbf{k}_0$ and $\mathbf{k}$ the wave vectors for incident and scattered neutrons $\langle\bar{a}\rangle$ and $\langle a\rangle$ the coherent scattering length for the nuclei in the original lattice and for the impurity, both averaged over spin directions and isotopic compositions, $\langle\bar{a}^2\rangle$ and $\langle a^2\rangle$ the corresponding averages for the squares of the cross-sections, $u_R(t)$ the displacement at time t of the nucleus R from its mean position at the temperature considered, $\hbar\nu$ the energy and $\hbar k$ the momentum transferred to the lattice so that

$$\nu = \frac{\hbar}{2m}(k_0^2 - k^2), \qquad \kappa = k_0 - k \tag{1}$$

Using methods introduced by Van Hove we can then write the differential cross-section for the lattice with the impurity as

$$\frac{d^2\sigma}{d\nu\,d\Omega} = \frac{k}{k_0}\frac{1}{2\pi}\int_{-\infty}^{+\infty} dt\, e^{-i\nu t}\sum_{RR'}(b_R b_{R'} + \delta_{RR'} C_R^2)\, e^{2W_{RR'}(t)}\, e^{i\kappa(R-R')} \tag{2}$$

where

$$W_{RR'}(t) = \tfrac{1}{2}\langle(\kappa u_R(0))(\kappa u_{R'}(t))\rangle_T \tag{3}$$

The notation $\langle..\rangle_T$ means that the statistical mean value for the temperature T shall be taken. Because of our assumption concerning the temperature factors we have further the coherent and squared incoherent scattering lengths

$$b_R = \bar{b} + (b - \bar{b})\,\delta_{RR_0}; \quad \bar{b} = \langle\bar{a}\rangle e^{-\overline{W}}; \quad b = \langle a\rangle e^{-W} \tag{4a}$$

$$C_R^2 = \bar{c}^2 + (c^2 - \bar{c}^2)\,\delta_{RR_0}; \quad \bar{c}^2 = \langle\bar{a}^2\rangle e^{-2\overline{W}} - \bar{b}^2; \quad c^2 = \langle a^2\rangle e^{-2W} - b^2 \tag{4b}$$

In our approximation $\exp - \overline{W}$ is the ordinary amplitude temperature factor for the original lattice and $\exp - W$ the same for the impurity nucleus. If we expand $\exp W_{RR'}(t)$ and $\exp 2W_{RR}(t)$ the first terms which are independent of t give in the usual way the elastic (zero-phonon) scattering, the terms linear in the exponents the one-phonon scattering and so on. In order to find the functions $W_{RR'}(t)$ we introduce for the lattice L the normal modes with quantum amplitudes a_s and a_s^*, eigenvectors† e_{Rx}^s and eigenfrequencies ω_s

$$u_{Rx}(t) = \sum_s \left(\frac{\hbar}{2M_R\omega_s}\right)^{1/2}(e_{Rx}^s a_s e^{-i\omega_s t} + e_{Rx}^{s*} a_s^* e^{i\omega_s t}) \tag{5}$$

† The eigenvectors can always be taken as real, but for a perfect lattice are better taken as complex vectors.

Then

$$W_{RR'}(t) = \sum_{\zeta=\pm 1} W^\zeta_{RR'}(t)$$

$$= \sum_{\zeta=\pm 1} \frac{\hbar}{4} \sum_{xx'} \kappa_x \kappa_{x'} \int \frac{d\omega}{\omega} (M_R M_{R'})^{-1/2} \mu^\zeta_{RxR'x'}(\omega) n_\zeta(\omega) e^{i\zeta\omega t} \qquad (6)$$

where

$$\mu^{\zeta=1}_{RxR'x'}(\omega) = \sum_s e^s_{Rx} e^{s*}_{R'x'} \delta(\omega-\omega_s); \quad \mu^{\zeta=-1}_{RxR'x'} = \sum_s e^{s*}_{Rx} e^s_{R'x'} \delta(\omega-\omega_s) \qquad (7)$$

are weighted frequency distributions normalized to unity for $Rx = R'x'$ and

$$n_\zeta(\omega) = \frac{1}{2}\left(\coth\frac{\hbar\omega}{2kT}+\zeta\right) \qquad (8)$$

is for $\zeta = -1$ the mean quantum number for the normal mode s.

Introducing now the Green's functions

$$G_{RxR'x'}(\omega) = (M_R M_{R'})^{-1/2} \int d\omega' \frac{\mu_{RxR'x'}(\omega')}{\omega^2 - \omega'^2} \qquad (9)$$

we have for $\epsilon \to 0$

$$\mu_{RxR'x'}(\omega) = \frac{i\omega}{\pi} (M_R M_{R'})^{1/2} [G(\omega+i\epsilon) - G(\omega-i\epsilon)] \qquad (10)$$

since for $\omega > 0$

$$\frac{1}{(\omega+i\epsilon)^2 - \omega'^2} - \frac{1}{(\omega-i\epsilon)^2 - \omega'^2} = \frac{-i\pi}{\omega}\delta(\omega-\omega') \qquad (11)$$

Using this relation and

$$\frac{1}{2\pi}\int_{-\infty}^{+\infty} dt\, e^{-i\nu t} e^{i\zeta\omega t} = \delta(\nu - \zeta\omega) \qquad (12)$$

we get for the one-phonon cross-section

$$\frac{d^2\sigma'}{d\nu\,d\Omega} = \sum_\zeta \frac{k_\zeta}{k_0} n_\zeta(\zeta\nu)\, \Delta_{\zeta\nu}[\bar{b}^2 L_\zeta(\omega) + 2\bar{b}(b-\bar{b}) M_\zeta(\omega) + \bar{c}^2 N_\zeta(\omega)$$

$$+ \{(b-\bar{b})^2 + c^2 - \bar{c}^2\} P_\zeta(\omega)] \qquad (13)$$

where the meaning of the symbol $\Delta_{\zeta\nu}$ is

$$\Delta_{\zeta\nu}f(\omega) = \frac{i\hbar}{\pi}[f(\omega+i\epsilon) - f(\omega-i\epsilon)]_{\omega=\zeta\nu} \qquad (14)$$

7*

and where 0 is written for the index R_0

$$L_\zeta(\omega) = \tfrac{1}{2} \sum_{xx'} \kappa_x \kappa_{x'} \sum_{RR'} G_{RxR'x'}(\omega)\, e^{i\kappa(R-R')} \tag{15a}$$

$$M_\zeta(\omega) = \tfrac{1}{2} \sum_{xx'} \kappa_x \kappa_{x'} \sum_{R} G_{Rx0x'}(\omega)e^{i\kappa R} \tag{15b}$$

$$N_\zeta(\omega) = \tfrac{1}{2} \sum_{xx'} \kappa_x \kappa_{x'} \sum_{R} G_{RxRx'}(\omega) \tag{15c}$$

$$P_\zeta(\omega) = \tfrac{1}{2} \sum_{xx'} \kappa_x \kappa_{x'} G_{0x0x'}(\omega) \tag{15d}$$

We assume unchanged forces and cubic symmetry as mentioned earlier and introduce the Green's functions for the lattice L (Lifshitz, 1956; Maradudin, Montroll and Weiss, 1963)

$$\bar{G}_{RxR'x'}(\omega) = \bar{M}^{-1} g_{RxR'x'}(\omega) = \bar{M}^{-1}\frac{1}{N}\sum_{qj}\frac{e_{qjx}\,e_{qjx'}\,e^{iq(R-R')}}{\omega^2 - \omega_{qj}^2} \tag{16}$$

Here the e_{qj} are unit vectors (polarization vectors) in the directions of the amplitudes of the lattice waves having wave vectors q and frequencies ω_{qj}. If further the impurity mass M is expressed in the mass of the atoms in the lattice L as

$$M = (1+\eta)\,\bar{M} \tag{17}$$

we have (Waller, 1963)

$$G_{RxR'x'}(\omega) = \bar{M}^{-1}\left[g_{RxR'x'}(\omega) - \frac{\eta\omega^2 \sum_{x''} g_{Rx0x''}(\omega)\,g_{0x''\,R'x'}(\omega)}{1 + \eta\omega^2 g(\omega)}\right] \tag{18a}$$

and in particular

$$G_{0xR'x'}(\omega) = G_{R'x'0x}(\omega) = \bar{M}^{-1}\frac{g_{0xR'x'}(\omega)}{1 + \eta\omega^2 g(\omega)} \tag{18b}$$

and

$$G_{0x0x'}(\omega) = \frac{\bar{M}^{-1} g(\omega)}{1 + \eta\omega^2 g(\omega)}\,\delta_{xx'} \tag{18c}$$

Here

$$g(\omega) = \frac{1}{3N}\sum_{qj}\frac{1}{\omega^2 - \omega_{qj}^2} \tag{18d}$$

Using

$$\sum_{R} e^{i\kappa R} = \frac{8\pi^3}{v_a}\,\delta_p(\kappa); \quad \sum_{RR'} e^{\,i\kappa(R-R')} = \frac{8\pi^3}{v_a}\,N\delta_p(\kappa);$$

$$\sum_{q} = \frac{Nv_a}{8\pi^3}\int dq \tag{19}$$

where $\delta_p(\kappa) = \sum_\tau \delta(\kappa + \tau)$ is a periodic δ-function, τ being the lattice vectors of the reciprocal lattice and v_a the volume of the unit cell.

We then obtain

$$L_\zeta(\omega) = \frac{N}{2\bar{M}} \sum_j \frac{(\kappa \cdot e_{\kappa j})^2}{\omega^2 - \omega_j^2} - \frac{1}{2\bar{M}} \frac{\eta\omega^2}{1 + \eta\omega^2 g(\omega)} \sum_j \frac{(\kappa \cdot e_{\kappa j})^2}{(\omega^2 - \omega_{\kappa j}^2)^2} \qquad (20a)$$

$$M_\zeta(\omega) = \frac{1}{2\bar{M}} \frac{1}{1 + \eta\omega^2 g(\omega)} \sum_j \frac{(\kappa \cdot e_{\kappa j})^2}{\omega^2 - \omega_{\kappa j}^2} \qquad (20b)$$

$$N_\zeta(\omega) = \frac{N}{2\bar{M}} \kappa^2 g(\omega) - \frac{1}{2\bar{M}} \frac{\eta\omega^2 \kappa^2}{1 + \eta\omega^2 g(\omega)} \frac{1}{3N} \sum_{qj} \frac{1}{(\omega^2 - \omega_{qj}^2)^2} \qquad (20c)$$

$$P_\zeta(\omega) = \frac{1}{2\bar{M}} \kappa^2 \frac{g(\omega)}{1 + \eta\omega^2 g(\omega)} \qquad (20d)$$

If a localized mode exists its frequency ω_L has to satisfy the equation

$$1 + \eta\omega_L^2 g(\omega_L) = 0 \qquad (21)$$

We have then for $\omega \sim \omega_L$.

$$1 + \eta\omega^2 g(\omega) = -\eta(\omega^2 - \omega_L^2) K(\omega_L) \qquad (22)$$

where

$$K(\omega) = -\frac{d}{d\omega^2}(\omega^2 g(\omega)) = \frac{1}{3} \frac{1}{N} \sum_{qj} \frac{\omega_{qj}^2}{(\omega^2 - \omega_{qj}^2)^2} \qquad (23)$$

Using (11) we see from (13), (14), (20) and (21) that the contribution of this local mode to the one-phonon cross-section is

$$\frac{d^2 \sigma_L'}{d\nu \, d\Omega} = \sum_{\zeta = \pm 1} \frac{k_\zeta}{k_0} \delta(\nu - \zeta\omega_L) \frac{\hbar n_\zeta(\omega_L)}{2\bar{M}\omega_L K(\omega_L)}$$

$$\left\{ \bar{b}^2 \omega_L^2 \sum_j \frac{(\kappa \cdot e_{\kappa j})^2}{(\omega_L^2 - \omega_{\kappa j}^2)^2} - \frac{2}{\eta} \bar{b}(b - \bar{b}) \right.$$

$$\left. \sum_j \frac{(\kappa \cdot e_{Kj})^2}{\omega_L^2 - \omega_{\kappa j}^2} + \kappa^2 \left[\bar{c}^2 K(\omega_L) + ((b - \bar{b})^2 + c^2) \frac{1}{\eta^2 \omega_L^2} \right] \right\} \qquad (24)$$

In the limit $\eta \to -1$, i.e. when the impurity mass tends to zero, we have $\omega_L \to \infty$. The localized mode then gets more and more confined to the impurity atom. In this limit we get

$$\frac{d^2 \sigma_L'}{d\nu \, d\Omega} = \frac{\hbar}{2\bar{M}\omega_L^3 K(\omega_L)} \langle a^2 \rangle \sum_{\zeta = \pm 1} \frac{k_\zeta}{k_0} \kappa^2 e^{-2\omega\zeta} n_\zeta(\omega_L) \delta(\nu - \zeta\omega_L) \qquad (25)$$

where, for ω_L much larger than the maximum frequency of $\bar{L}$,

$$\omega_L^3 K(\omega_L) = \omega_L^{-1} \sum_{qj} \omega_{qj}^2 \tag{26}$$

The exponent of the temperature factor is the same as that which occurs in the theory of the Mössbauer effect from an isolated impurity nucleus (Waller, 1963); i.e.

$$2\omega_\zeta = \frac{\kappa_\zeta^2}{2\bar{M}} \int \frac{d\omega}{\omega} \frac{\mu(\omega)}{[1 + \eta\omega^2 g(\omega)]^2 + [\pi\eta\omega\bar{\mu}(\omega)]^2/4} \coth \frac{\hbar\omega}{2kT} +$$

$$+ \frac{1}{\eta^2 \omega_L^3 K(\omega_L)} \coth \frac{\hbar\omega_L}{2kT} \tag{27}$$

The neutron scattering seems, according to our results, to be a promising method for investigating local modes and some results in this direction have already been found (Mozer, Otnes and Myers, 1962). As appears from our investigations, it is of advantage to the observation for the impurity nucleus to have a large total cross-section. It seems, therefore, to be worth trying the same type of crystals (alkali halides with hydrogen impurities substituted for part of the alkali ions) that have been used (Schaefer, 1959) for the experimental investigation of local vibrations by infra-red absorption.

The complete formulae for the elastic and one-phonon scattering by an isolated impurity can be deduced by using the general formulae (13) and (20).

As already emphasized by other authors (Krivoglaz, 1961; Maradudin, 1962), local modes will be broadened by anharmonic terms in the crystal Hamiltonian. Our formulae will, however, give a useful result for the total contribution of a local mode.

Acknowledgement

I wish to thank Professor Bernard Goodman for helpful discussions.

REFERENCES

Krivoglaz, M. A. (1961). *Sowjet Phys. JETP*, **13**, 397.
Lifshitz, M. (1956). *Nuovo Cimento* III (X), 716.
Maradudin, A. A. (1962). *Bull. Amer. phys. Soc.* **7**, 451.
Maradudin, A. A., Montroll, E. W. and Weiss, G. H. (1963). "Theory of Lattice Dynamics in the Harmonic Approximation", in press.
Mozer, B., Otnes, K. and Myers, V. W. (1962). *Phys. Rev. Letters* **8**, 278.
Schaefer, G. (1959). *Phys. Chem. Solids* **12**, 233.
Waller, I. (1963). *Ark. Fysik*, in press.

DISCUSSION

S. S. MITRA: Since a vacancy may be considered as an impurity with zero mass, would you expect a sharp localized vibration frequency due to it?

I. WALLER: If you have a vacancy, this theory cannot really be applied directly. You can treat it by the Green's function methods, but I do not know the complete answer yet.

S. S. MITRA: Did you also consider the change of force constants around an impurity?

I. WALLER: Yes, I did; the results will be published shortly. The expressions for the Green's functions are somewhat more complicated but still manageable, if for example only force constants referring to nearest neighbours are changed.

X-Ray Investigation of Long Period Structures of Silicon Carbide and their Growth from Imperfections

P. Krishna† and Ajit Ram Verma

Department of Physics, Banaras Hindu University, India

ABSTRACT

The determination of the structure of a silicon carbide polytype becomes difficult when it has a very large periodicity. Since silicon carbide crystallizes into innumerable modified types with unit cell heights ranging from 5·048 Å in type 2H to nearly 1500 Å in type 594R (and to more in many of the unidentified types), it is necessary to suitably modify the X-ray diffraction methods for their investigation. By these methods, a detailed analysis of the structure of some of the large polytypes has been carried out. The growth of these structures, with a periodicity much larger than the range of any known atomic forces, is discussed on the dislocation theory.

1. Introduction

Silicon carbide is known to crystallize into several modified types, all of which have the same a and b dimensions of the unit cell ($a = b = 3·078$ Å) but differ along c. The unit cell consists of layers of structure stacked along c at constant intervals of 2·518 Å, in a close-packed manner. The repeat period along c varies from 5·048 Å in type 2H (Adamsky and Merz, 1959) to nearly 1500 Å in type 594 R (Honjo *et al.*, 1950), and to more in many of the unidentified types. A simple explanation of the origin and growth of so many different modified types can be found in terms of the screw dislocation theory of crystal growth (Frank, 1951). The direct correlation observed between the step-height of growth spirals and the height of the X-ray unit cell, in different polytypes (Verma, 1952, 1957) left little doubt about the validity of this theory. Using the theory it was possible to explain the origin of the structure series in silicon carbide and it was, therefore, felt that the phenomenon of polytypism had been satisfactorily explained.

However, doubts have been expressed by Jagodzinski (1954) according to whom the structure of a polytype is determined by thermodynamic considerations and screw dislocations play a role only in the later stages of growth. Recently Trigunayat and Verma (1962) have reported a non-correlation between the step-height of growth spirals on cadmium

† U.G.C. Research Fellow.

iodide polytypes and the height of their X-ray unit cells. This has further enhanced the doubts expressed by Jagodzinski regarding the origin of polytypes from screw dislocations.

We, therefore, undertook to isolate a number of silicon carbide polytypes and determine their detailed atomic structure with a view to examine whether the structure conforms with the dislocation theory. This paper describes the experimental methods used for this investigation. The results obtained are discussed on the dislocation theory.

2. EXPERIMENTAL METHODS

A. *Determination of the unit cell*

Since successive unit layers of structure, in silicon carbide, are spaced at intervals of 2·518 Å along the c-axis, it is possible to calculate the number of layers in the unit cell by determining the c-parameter from the oscillation and Weissenberg photographs. The method works quite well with small polytypes like 4H, 6H and 15R, but for larger polytypes the results obtained become ambiguous on account of the limited experimental accuracy of determining c. Honjo *et al.* (1950), as well as Mitchell (1954), identified large polytypes by counting the number of spacings between two known 6H spots. However, this was possible because these polytypes had type 6H in syntactic coalescence.

A simple method of counting the exact number of layers in the unit cell has been used by us in our investigations. It requires only an approximate idea of the number of layers in the unit cell, which can often be had by a comparison of the c-axis oscillation photograph with that of type 6H. The number of layers in the unit cell is obtained from the number of spacings after which the sequence of relative intensities begins to repeat in the 10.l row. The intensity of a 10.l reflection from a silicon carbide polytype nH or nR is given by

$$I_{10.l} \propto (f_{Si}^2 + f_C^2 + 2f_{Si}f_C \cos 2\pi lp)(A_{Si}^2 + B_{Si}^2)$$

with

$$A_{Si} = \sum_{z_A} \cos 2\pi lz + \sum_{z_B} \cos 2\pi(lz + \tfrac{1}{3}) + \sum_{z_C} \cos 2\pi(lz - \tfrac{1}{3})$$

and

$$B_{Si} = \sum_{z_A} \sin 2\pi lz + \sum_{z_B} \sin 2\pi(lz + \tfrac{1}{3}) + \sum_{z_C} \sin 2\pi(lz - \tfrac{1}{3})$$

where z_A, z_B and z_C denote the z-co-ordinates of silicon atoms on the $A:00z$, $B:\tfrac{1}{3}\tfrac{2}{3}z$ and $C:\tfrac{2}{3}\tfrac{1}{3}z$ axes respectively, and $p = 3/4n$ is the displacement of the carbon atoms above the silicon, along c. Now, since $z = r/n$, r being an integer, the values of A_{Si} and B_{Si} are the same for the reflections 10.l and 10.$(l+n)$. The difference in intensity of these spots is due to the change in the factor $(f_{Si}^2 + f_C^2 + 2f_{Si}f_C \cos 2\pi lp)$. But, since f_{Si} and f_C change monotonously with θ and $f_{Si} \approx 3f_C$, the variation in $\cos 2\pi lp$ does not affect the intensity much and the sequence of relative intensities of $10.l$ spots is similar after a change of n in the l-value. Thus the sequence of the intensity of spots $10.(l+n)$, $10.(l+n+1)$, ... etc., would be similar to that of the spots $10.l$, $10.(l+1)$, ... etc. This repetition of relative intensities was first noticed by Ramsdell (1944) in type 21R and applied by us to identify the polytype 90R (Krishna and Verma, 1962c). Thus if the sequence of relative intensities of $10.l$ spots, recorded on a Weissenberg or oscillation photograph repeats after q spacings (counting the absent reflections also), the polytype has q layers in its smallest hexagonal unit cell.

Figure 1 shows the c-axis oscillation photograph of a large polytype of silicon carbide, as recorded on a 3 cm camera. The non-symmetrical arrangement of spots about the zero layer line indicates rhombohedral symmmetry. It can be noticed that the sequence of relative intensities along the $10.l$ row is similar after every 37 spacings. Since each spacing corresponds to a change of 3 in the l-value, the polytype is $37 \times 3 = 111R$. The number of layers can also be determined, with advantage, from the a-axis Weissenberg photographs (Figs. 3 and 4) by observing the above repetition of intensities in the lowest "festoon" of spots. Figure 3 shows the a-axis first layer equi-inclination Weissenberg photograph of type 111R, while Fig. 4 is the a-axis zero layer Weissenberg photograph of a polytype 90R. The relative intensities of $10.l$ spots in Fig. 4 repeat after every 30 spacings.

This method of identifying a polytype, however, requires that the $10.l$ row of spots be both present and well-resolved in the entire range of counting. It can be seen in Figs. 1, 3 and 4 that the first layer equi-inclination Weissenberg photograph provides a much greater resolution than the oscillation or zero-layer Weissenberg. We have obtained still greater resolution by using an oscillation camera of 11·46 cm radius and collimating the X-ray beam further. It is, however, imperative to choose extremely small crystal pieces for taking the X-ray diffraction photographs, so that the width of successive $10.l$ spots may be less than the distance between their centres. Thus a somewhat bigger crystal piece would have produced continuous streaks along the Bernal row lines in Fig. 1, which could be incorrectly taken to have resulted from a random disorder in the structure. The choice of a small crystal piece also reduces errors in the intensity work, due to variable absorption and secondary extinction, the corrections for which are difficult to evaluate. We therefore employed crystal pieces with dimensions of the order of 0·1 mm. Such minute crystal pieces often exhibit no natural faces and, therefore, present some difficulty in setting in a crystallographic direction. In such cases one can adopt the procedure described by Jeffrey (1949); but the peculiarity of the structure of silicon carbide affords a much simpler method. The reciprocal lattice rows parallel to c are densely crowded with reciprocal lattice points. These rows therefore record as a line of closely spaced spots, which are easily recognized even when the crystal is oscillating about a random direction. For adjusting the rotated crystal about [001], these rows were made parallel to the rotation axis, and for adjusting about [100] or [210] they were made perpendicular to the latter.

Having determined the number of layers in the unit cell of a polytype, their probable stacking sequences can be worked out by the methods employed by Ramsdell (1944, 1947), Zhdanov and Minervina (1945) and Krishna and Verma (1962a, b, c). To determine the correct structure from the probable ones so worked out, it suffices to calculate the relative intensity of 10.l reflections and compare these with those observed on Weissenberg photographs (Ramsdell, 1944). It is usually not necessary to perform a quantitative estimation of the observed intensities since the large number of 10.l reflections recorded, themselves, form a scale of relative intensities, whose self-consistency is enough evidence of the correctness of a proposed structure. However, when there are two or more probable structures giving a fairly good qualitative fit with observed intensities it is essential to perform a quantitative estimation. This presents some difficulty on account of the proximity of successive 10.l reflections on the Weissenberg photograph of large polytypes. It is not possible to use Weissenberg photographs of the integrating type since the spots would overlap. It is also difficult to isolate each spot for photometric estimation of relative intensities. We, therefore, employed the following method:

A standard scale of relative intensities was prepared by selecting a single 10.l reflection and then recording it on different portions of the same Weissenberg film. The exposure time for successive recordings was measured in terms of complete oscillations of the crystal. For estimating the spots in different intensity ranges, Weissenberg films of different known exposures were used. For these films also the exposure time was reckoned by counting the number of complete oscillations of the crystal. The different Weissenberg films, as well as the one recording the standard scale were processed under identical conditions. We found that for estimating intensities over such a large range, as that obtained on the Weissenberg photographs of these polytypes, the above method yielded more consistent results than the usual multiple-film method. The excellent agreement obtained between calculated and observed intensities for various structures has confirmed the suitability of the above method (Krishna and Verma, 1962b).

3. RESULTS OF THE INVESTIGATION

Of the many large polytypes discovered during the course of the present investigation special attention was given to the following polytypes of interest:

(i) Type 57R: This crystal is based on the 6H phase with a structure $[(33)_2 34]_3$ (Krishna and Verma, 1962a).

(ii) Type 111R: The oscillation and Weissenberg photographs obtained from this polytype are shown in Figs. 1 and 3. The polytype has been shown to have a structure $[(33)_5 34]_3$ and has enabled a detailed study of the $[(33)_n 34]_3$ series of structures (Krishna and Verma, 1962b).

(iii) Type 90R: A Weissenberg photograph obtained from this crystal is shown in Fig. 4. This polytype was found to have a structure based on the 15R phase with a Zhdanov symbol $[(23)_4 3322]_3$ (Krishna and Verma, 1963a).

(iv) Type 36H: This is a unique polytype within which there has occurred a change in the structure without a change of space group or of the periodicity of the lattice. The two structures have been designated as $36H_a$ and $36H_b$ and were found in a single crystal piece. Figure 2 (a), (b) and (c) show the 10.l row of spots recorded on c-axis oscillation photographs taken from (a) the composite parent 36H crystal, (b) the upper portion, $36H_a$, and (c) the lower part, $36H_b$, respectively.

The lower part $36H_b$ reveals striking structural extinctions on its X-ray diffraction photographs. Thus the 10.l reflections are absent when $l = 36n$, $36n + 6$ and $6n \pm 2$, where $\pm n = 0, 1, 2 \ldots$. This polytype has an unusual structure which could not be determined by the usual methods employed for other polytypes. The structure has been determined in a novel manner from the conditions

$$\sum_{z_A} \cos 2\pi l z = \sum_{z_B} \cos 2\pi l z = \sum_{z_C} \cos 2\pi l z = 0$$
$$\sum_{z_A} \sin 2\pi l z = \sum_{z_B} \sin 2\pi l z = \sum_{z_C} \sin 2\pi l z = 0 \qquad (l = 6n \pm 2)$$

imposed on the structure by the extinctions. The structure so worked out has a Zhdanov symbol $[(33)_2 34(33)_2 32]$ (Krishna and Verma, 1963b).

(v) Disordered Polytypes: In addition to the ordered structures like 90R, 111R and 126R, silicon carbide also forms polytypes with considerable one-dimensional disorder. Fig. 2 (d) shows the 10.l row of spots recorded on a c-axis oscillation photograph of one such crystal. The continuous streak along the row line indicates a random disorder superimposed over the order in the crystal. A tendency towards long-range order can, however, be seen. Figure 2 (e) is the enlargement of a part of Fig. 2 (d) and reveals very closely spaced spots corresponding to a periodicity of about (33×5)H or (33×15)R. The "continuous" streak along the row lines therefore appears to be partly due to a lack of resolution of spots corresponding to a very high periodicity and partly due to a random disorder in the structure.

4. DISCUSSION OF RESULTS—GROWTH OF POLYTYPES

According to Frank's dislocation theory, the different polytypes of silicon carbide grow from basic structures like 6H, 15R and 4H, by the creation of a screw dislocation with a Burgers vector which is a non-integral multiple of the height of the parent unit cell. When the Burgers vector is an integral multiple of the height of the parent unit cell the resulting structure is the same as the basic structure. It has been experimentally demonstrated that the Burgers vector, which is the step-height of the growth spiral, is equal to c for hexagonal polytypes and $c/3$ for the rhombohedral ones (Verma, 1957). It follows, therefore, that the value of c for hexagonal polytypes and $c/3$ for rhombobohedral ones should be a non-integral multiple of the c-spacing of the basic structure. However, we have isolated a number of polytypes with contra-indications, including the types 36H$_a$ and 90R described in this paper.

The polytypes 36H$_a$ and 36H$_b$, as also the types 54H and 66H reported by Verma (1957), give intense X-ray diffraction spots in the 6H positions showing that their structure is based on the 6H phase. The growth of these polytypes could not have taken place by the creation of a screw dislocation in the 6H structure since the Burgers vector of such a dislocation would be an integral multiple of the c-spacing of 6H. A screw dislocation step of 36, 54 or 66 layers, formed in the 6H structure could result only in further growth of the 6H structure itself. All the same the crystals of 54H and 66H shows spirals on their (0001) faces, with a step-height simply related to the height of the unit cell (Verma, 1957).

Similarly, the polytype 90R with a structure $[(23)_4 3322]_3$ is definitely based on the 15R phase but its growth is not possible from a single screw dislocation in 15R, since a ledge of 30 layers exposed in the 15R structure would result in further growth of 15R itself. It would perhaps be possible to explain the growth of these structures from two or more suitably "co-operating" dislocations, but such explanations appear far-fetched in the absence of any surface evidence to this effect. There is no evidence of co-operating dislocations on the surfaces of 36H, 54H, 66H or 90R. On the other hand there is definite evidence of single dislocations in 54H and 66H, while 36H and 90R show no spiral markings. A growth spiral on the surface of 36H would be expected to have a step-height of over 90 Å, which ought to be easily visible under a phase-contrast microscope. Moreover, it is difficult to understand how a system of co-operating

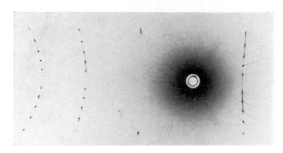

Fig. 1. A 15° c-axis oscillation photograph of SiC type 111R ($r = 3$ cm, $\lambda = 1.54$ Å).

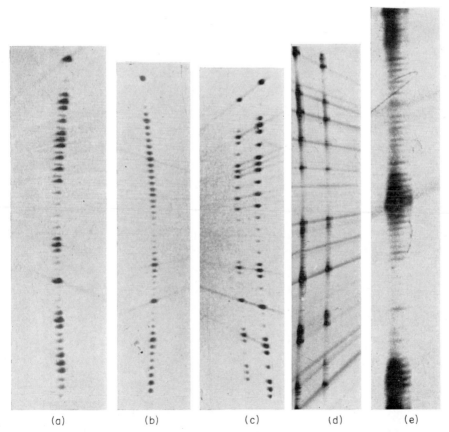

(a) (b) (c) (d) (e)

Fig. 2. The 10·l row of different SiC polytypes, as recorded on 15° c-axis oscillation photographs: (a) 36H parent crystal ($r = 3$ cm, $\lambda = 1.54$ Å, mag. × 3). (b) Type $36H_a$ ($r = 3$ cm, $\lambda = 1.54$ Å, mag. × 3). (c) Type $36H_b$ ($r = 3$ cm, Cu K radiation, mag. × 3). (d) Disordered polytype ($r = 11.46$ cm, Cu K radiation, mag. × 1). (e) Enlargement of a part of Fig. 2 (d).

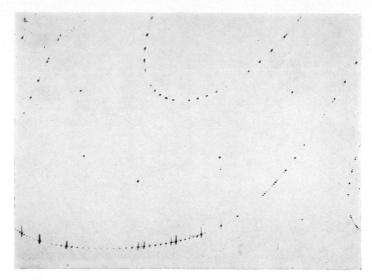

Fig. 3. First layer, a-axis, equi-inclination Weissenberg photograph of SiC type 111R ($r = 2 \cdot 86$ cm, $\lambda = 1 \cdot 54$ Å). The eleven consecutive faint spots near the minimum of the lowest festoon are, from left to right, $01 \cdot \overline{16}$, $01 \cdot \overline{13}$, ..., $01 \cdot \overline{1}$, $01 \cdot 2$, ... $01 \cdot 11$ and $01 \cdot 14$. The l-values of successive spots differ by 3 (mag. × 1).

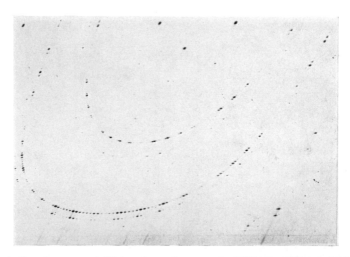

Fig. 4. Zero-layer, a-axis Weissenberg photograph of SiC type 90R ($r = 2 \cdot 86$ cm, Cu K radiation). The lowest festoon records the $10 . l$ row of spots. The ten faint spots near the minimum of the festoon are, from left to right, $10 \cdot 19$, $10 \cdot 16 \ldots$, $10 \cdot \overline{8}$, $10 \cdot \overline{11}$. The l-values of successive spots differ by 3 (mag. × 1).

dislocations, creating the structure $36H_b$, could at a later stage generate a different structure $36H_a$.

Polytypic structures originating from a single screw dislocation ought to have a number of 33, 23 or 22 units in their zigzag sequence, with faults at the end. However, the X-ray diffraction photographs of type 126R show an intensity maxima distribution unlike that of any smaller polytype. This polytype is therefore not based on any smaller structure and could not have grown from a single screw dislocation. All the same it shows a growth spiral with a step 42 layers high (Verma, 1957). The structure, therefore, does not appear to have resulted from the growth of the spiral. Similarly the polytypes 174R with a structure $[(33)_36(33)_54]_3$ (Tomita, 1960), and $36H_b$, with a structure $[(33)_234(33)_232]$ (Krishna and Verma, 1963b) have stacking faults in the middle of a sequence of 33's. They cannot, therefore, result from single screw dislocations in the basic structures. There are, at the same time, structures like 57R and 111R (Krishna, and Verma, 1962a, b), which are most readily understood as originating from single screw dislocations in the 6H structure, but an examination of their surfaces shows no spirals. The existence of random disorder in some SiC crystals (see Fig. 2 (d) and (e)) also cannot be explained on the screw dislocation theory. Table I summarizes the present position of observations regarding the growth of silicon carbide polytypes from screw dislocations, in the light of the above discussion.

TABLE I. Summary of observations on silicon carbide polytypes

Polytype	Structure of unit cell	Surface structure	Remarks
Polytypes conforming with the dislocation theory			
6H	33	Show spirals corre- lated with the unit cell (Verma, 1957)	Growth completely explained in terms of screw disloca- tions
15R	$(23)_3$		
21R	$(34)_3$		
33R	$(3332)_3$		
Structures expected on dislocations but not showing growth spirals			
57R	$[(33)_234]_3$	Show no spirals	Structure readily explained on dis- location theory, but no surface evi- dence of dislocation
111R	$[(33)_534]_3$		
Structures not expected on dislocations			
126R	Not based on any smaller type	Shows spirals with correlation (Verma, 1957)	Surface evidence of dislocation. Struc- ture at variance

Table I—*continued*

Polytype	Structure of unit cell	Surface structure	Remarks
36H$_a$ 54H 66H	Based on 6H. Unit cells integral multiples of the unit cell of 6H	36H No spiral. 54H, 66H show spirals with correlation (Verma, 1957)	Structure not accounted on dislocation theory. Evidence of single screw dislocations in 54H and 66H
90R	[(23)$_4$3322]$_3$. Unit cell 6 times that of 15R	Shows no spiral	Structure based on 15R, but growth not possible from screw dislocation in 15R
36H$_b$	[(33)$_2$34(33)$_2$32]. c-dimension six times that of 6H	Shows no spiral	Structures have stacking faults in the middle of a sequence of 33's.
174R	[(33)$_6$6(33)$_5$4]$_3$ (Tomita, 1960)	No data	
Disordered polytypes	X-ray diffraction photographs show continuous streaks along 10.l row	No data	Not explained on dislocations

1. The polytypes 51R$_a$ (Thibault 1944; Zhdanov and Minervina, 1945), 87R (Ramsdell, 1947), 27R, and 51R$_b$ (Ramsdell and Kohn, 1952), 19H (Ramsdell and Mitchell, 1953), 141R and 393R (Mitchell, 1954), and 16H (Gasilova, 1955) have structures that conform with the dislocation theory, but evidence of their growth from screw dislocations is incomplete since no data regarding their surface structure has been reported.

2. The polytypes 10H (Ramsdell and Kohn, 1951), 75R and 84R (Ramsdell and Kohn, 1952), and 18H (Gliky, 1954) have structures that cannot originate from single screw dislocations in any of the basic structures, but may be thought of as resulting from two or more suitably "co-operating" dislocations (Mitchell, 1957). No surface evidence has however, been put forth.

3. The polytypes 2H (Adamsky and Merz, 1959) and 8H (Ramsdell and Kohn, 1952) appear to be definite phases of silicon carbide, but no structures based on these are, as yet, known.

4. Though β-SiC (Hull, 1919, 1920), which is cubic, can be easily derived from a screw dislocation in any of the basic structures, it does not form in this way since it is, unlike α-SiC, a low-temperature modification.

5. CONCLUSION

It is evident from the above discussion that though the spiral step-height on silicon carbide is simply related to the c-dimension of the lattice, the contents of the unit cell do not necessarily result from a screw dislocation in one of the basic structures. It appears, therefore, that screw dislocations determine the surface structure but not the structure of the unit cell. Jagodzinski (1954) has arrived at a similar conclusion from thermodynamic considerations. According to him the energy required for the creation of a screw dislocation can come from the lattice only after the crystal has acquired a considerable volume, by which time the structure of the crystal has already been determined. Therefore, screw dislocations could cause growth only in the later stages, thereby creating spirals on the surface. Once a polytype is formed the Burgers vector of a screw dislocation in it would be related to its lattice dimension so that there may be no misfit across the slip plane. This would explain the correlation observed between the spiral step-height and the height of the X-ray unit cell; but the structure of different polytypes cannot be understood on the dislocation theory and the cause of so many different modifications of silicon carbide, especially those with unit cell heights much larger than the range of any known atomic forces, has to be reconsidered.

Acknowledgement

One of us (P. Krishna) is grateful to the University Grants Commission of India for the grant of a research fellowship during the tenure of this work.

REFERENCES

Adamsky, R. F. and Merz, K. M. (1959). *Z. Kristallogr.* **111**, 350.
Frank, F. C. (1951). *Phil. Mag.* **42**, 809.
Gasilova, E. B. (1955). *C. R. Acad. Sci., U.R.S.S.* **101**, 671.
Gliky, N. V. (1954). *C. R. Acad. Sci., U.R.S.S.* **99**, 255.
Honjo, G., Miyake, S. and Tomita, T. (1950). *Acta cryst.* **3**, 396.
Hull, A. W. (1919). *Phys. Rev.* **13**, 292.
Hull, A. W. (1920). *Phys. Rev.* **15**, 545.
Jagodzinski, H. (1954). *Neues Jb. Miner. Mh.* **3**, 49.
Jeffrey, J. W. (1949). *Acta cryst.* **2**, 15.
Krishna, P. and Verma, A. R. (1962a). *Acta cryst.* **15**, 383.
Krishna, P. and Verma, A. R. (1962b). *Z. Kristallogr.* **117**, 1.
Krishna, P. and Verma, A. R. (1963a). *Proc. roy. Soc.* **A** (in press).
Krishna, P. and Verma, A. R. (1963b). (in press).
Mitchell, R. S. (1954). *J. chem. Phys.* **22**, 1977.
Mitchell, R. S. (1957). *Z. Kristallogr.* **109**, 341.
Ramsdell, L. S. (1944). *Amer. Min.* **29**, 431.
Ramsdell, L. S. (1947). *Amer. Min.* **32**, 64.
Ramsdell, L. S. and Kohn, J. A. (1951). *Acta cryst.* **4**, 111.
Ramsdell, L. S. and Kohn, J. A. (1952). *Acta cryst.* **5**, 215.
Ramsdell, L. S. and Mitchell, R. S. (1953). *Amer. Min.* **38**, 56.
Thibault, N. W. (1944). *Amer. Min.* **29**, 327.
Tomita, T. (1960). *J. phys. Soc., Japan* **15**, 99.
Trigunayat, G. C. and Verma, A. R. (1962). *Acta cryst.* **15**, 499.
Verma, A. R. (1952). *Phil. Mag.* **43**, 441.
Verma, A. R. (1957). *Proc. roy. Soc.* **A240**, 462.
Zhdanov, G. S. and Minervina, Z. V. (1945). *C. R. Acad. Sci., U.R.S.S.* **48**, 43.

On Variance as a Measure of Line Broadening in Diffractometry: Some Preliminary Measurements on Annealed Aluminium and Nickel and on Cold-worked Nickel

J. I. LANGFORD AND A. J. C. WILSON

Viriamu Jones Laboratory, University College, Cardiff, Wales

ABSTRACT

The 111 line profiles of annealed aluminium and nickel powders and of a cold-worked nickel block have each been recorded several times by means of a counter diffractometer. The reproducibility is found to be good, and by an appropriate choice of background level the asymptotic behaviour of the variance as a function of the range of integration can be made linear within the experimental error. The slope and intercept of the linear portion are discussed in the light of theoretical expectations; the intercept can be accounted for within 10 to 20%, but the slope is about $2\frac{1}{2}$ times as great as expected. Possible explanations are suggested.

INTRODUCTION

The use of the line-profile variance as a measure of diffraction broadening has been the subject of several recent papers (Tournarie, 1956a, b; Wilson, 1962a, b, d). Little attention has, however, been paid to the practical aspects of its determination and application. The following is an account of preliminary work performed at Cardiff on the measurement of profile variances, the assessment of instrumental broadening, and the investigation of strain broadening.

LIST OF PRINCIPAL SYMBOLS

I_i	Observed intensity at angle θ_i
B_i	Background intensity at angle θ_i
L_i	Line intensity at angle θ_i ($\equiv I_i - B_i$)
$\Delta\theta$	Step length
θ_a	Initial limit, step 0
θ_z	Final limit, step n
a	Background intensity at θ_a
z	Background intensity at θ_z
B	Average background intensity $[\frac{1}{2}(a+z)]$

δ	Rise in background over range $[z-a]$
n	Number of steps $[\equiv (\theta_z - \theta_a)/\Delta\theta]$
S_i	Partial sum of I_i's $[\equiv I_1 + I_2 + \ldots + I_i]$
$\sum S$	$\equiv \displaystyle\sum_{i=1}^{n+1} S_i[\equiv I_1 + (I_1 + I_2) + (I_1 + I_2 + I_3) + \ldots]$
Ψ	Defined in text [Eq. 4]
I_T	Total observed intensity $[\equiv (I_1 + I_2 + \ldots + I_{n+1})\Delta\theta = S_{n+1}\Delta\theta]$
I_B	Total background intensity $[\equiv (B_1 + B_2 + \ldots + B_{n+1})\Delta\theta]$
I_L	Total line intensity $[\equiv (L_1 + L_2 + \ldots + L_{n+1})\Delta\theta]$
r	Ratio of total background to total observed intensity (I_B/I_T)
t	Distance of c. of g. of observed profile, G_T, from θ_z
b	Distance of c. of g. of background, G_B, from θ_z
l	Distance of c. of g. of line, G_L, from θ_z
σ	$\frac{1}{2}$ angular range, measured from G_T
W	Variance of line profile
W_0	Intercept of variance-range characteristic
k	Slope of variance-range characteristic
K	Radius of gyration
Δa	Error in a
Δz	Error in z
ΔB	Error in B
$\Delta\theta$	Error in θ
ρ	Error in slope of background $(\Delta\delta/2\sigma)$
$A, \bar{x}, G$	Defined in Fig. 4
ΔW	Defined in text

The general behaviour of the profile variance has been discussed by Wilson (1962a, b). If the profile approaches the background according to an inverse-square law, the variance is a linear function of the range σ, the intercept W_0 and slope k depending on the instrumental aberrations and the physical condition of the specimen. In the region of the tails of the profile this is now verified experimentally, the variance-range characteristic being found to have the form

$$W = W_0 + k\sigma \tag{1}$$

over a considerable range of σ. The intercept W_0 may be, in theory, positive or negative, depending on the magnitude of instrumental aberrations and the behaviour of the emission profile near the origin. The slope k depends on the shape of the emission profile, the particle size, and, if the crystal contains "mistakes", the domain size. Strain broadening, however, only contributes to the intercept (Wilson, 1962a, 1963), provided that the strain nowhere exceeds a few per cent. The following section describes the determination of the parameters W_0 and k from the observed profile.

Experimental Determination of Line-profile Variance

The experimental technique for the determination of the line-profile variance follows closely that established by Pike and Wilson (1959) for the calculation of the line centroid. The observed profile is considered as a true "line" superimposed on a linear background (Fig. 1), an assumption valid provided the angular range is not too great. If angular

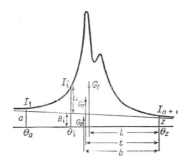

Fig. 1. Observed profile: Line-plus-background.

distances, θ_i, are measured from the upper limit of the range, θ_z, the second moment of the observed profile about θ_z gives

$$K_T^2 = \frac{\sum\limits_{i=1}^{n+1} I_i^3 K_i^2 \Delta\theta}{\sum\limits_{i=1}^{n+1} I_i \Delta\theta} \tag{2}$$

$$= \frac{I_1(n.\Delta\theta)^2 + I_2[(n-1).\Delta\theta]^2 + \ldots + I_n(\Delta\theta)^2}{I_T} \tag{3}$$

or
$$I_T K_T^2 = \psi.(\Delta\theta)^2$$

where
$$\psi = \sum_{i=1}^{n+1} [I_i(n-i+1)^2] \tag{4}$$

The second moment of the observed profile is equal to the sum of the line and background moments taken about the same axis, so that

$$I_T K_T^2 = I_L K_L^2 + I_B K_B^2 \tag{5}$$

Since
$$I_T = I_B + I_L \tag{6}$$

$$\psi \cdot (\Delta\theta)^2 = (I_T - I_B)K_L^2 + I_B K_B^2 \tag{7}$$

If $r = I_B/I_T$,

$$K_L^2 = \left\{ \frac{\psi}{I_T} + \frac{r}{1-r}\left[\frac{\psi}{I_T} - \frac{K_B^2}{(\Delta\theta)^2} \right] \right\} (\Delta\theta)^2 \tag{8}$$

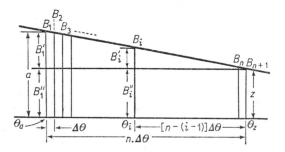

FIG. 2. Assumed background variation.

It therefore remains to determine the radius of gyration of the background, K_B. From Fig. 2, the second moment of the background about θ_z is

$$I_B K_B^2 = \sum_{i=1}^{n+1} B_{i'} K_i^2 \Delta\theta + \sum_{i=1}^{n+1} B_{i''} K_i^2 \Delta\theta \tag{9}$$

where the symbols are defined in the figure. Then

$$K_B^2 = \frac{\begin{aligned}&\{(a-z)n^2(\Delta\theta)^2 + [(a-z)/n](n-1)^3(\Delta\theta)^2 + \ldots + [(a-z)/n](\Delta\theta)^2\} + \\ &+ \{z[n^2(\Delta\theta)^2 + (n-1)^2(\Delta\theta)^2 + \ldots + (\Delta\theta)^2]\}\end{aligned}}{\{(a-z) + [(a-z)/n](n-1) + \ldots + [(a-z)/n]\} + \{z(n+1)\}} \tag{10}$$

$$= \frac{\left\{ \frac{(a-z)}{n}\left[\frac{n}{2}(n+1) \right]^2 + z\frac{n}{6}(n+1)(2n+1) \right\}(\Delta\theta)^2}{\frac{(a-z)}{n}\frac{n}{2}(n+1) + z(n+1)}$$

$$= \left\{ \frac{n(2n+1)}{6} - n(n+2)\frac{\delta}{12B} \right\}(\Delta\theta)^2 \tag{11}$$

Substitution in Eq. (8) for K_B^2 gives

$$K_L^2 = \left\{ \frac{\psi}{I_T} + \frac{r}{(1-r)}\left[\frac{\psi}{I_T} - \frac{n(2n+1)}{6} + n(n+2)\frac{\delta}{12B} \right] \right\}(\Delta\theta)^2 \tag{12}$$

The variance of the line profile about its centroid is given by

$$W = K_L^2 - l^2 \tag{13}$$

where l has been determined by Pike and Wilson (1959, Eq. 27). Then

$$W = \left\{\frac{\psi}{I_T} + \frac{r}{(1-r)}\left[\frac{\psi}{I_T} - \frac{n(2n+1)}{6} + n(n+2)\frac{\delta}{12B}\right]\right\}(\varDelta\theta)^2 -$$

$$- \left\{\frac{\sum S}{I_T} + \frac{r}{(1-r)}\left[\frac{\sum S}{I_T} - \frac{n}{2} + (n+2)\frac{\delta}{12B}\right]\right\}^2 (\varDelta\theta)^2 \qquad (14)$$

From Eq. (14), the variance may be computed from the observed intensities for any desired background conditions. The choice of range of scan is decided in much the same way as that outlined by Pike and Wilson for the determination of the centroid position. A preliminary fast

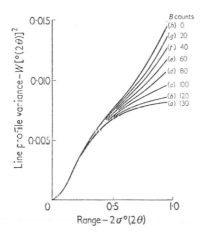

FIG. 3. Aluminium 111 line: Cu $K\alpha$ radiation, β filter, 1° slits. Variance-range variation with different background levels. (Estimated background from observed data is 130 counts.)

chart recording of the line is made, and a starting point chosen well out in the tails of the profile, care being taken to avoid the filter absorption edge. If the range is too great, however, unacceptable statistical errors are introduced. For the lines considered so far, with Cu $K\alpha$ radiation, a range of about ten times the α_1, α_2 peak separation has been found suitable. The upper limit of range is then adjusted until the centroid of the line is within $\pm 0.005°$ (2θ) of the mid-point of the range. This may be done quite simply, provided the effects of dispersion and Lorentz factor on this "symmetry" may be neglected, as is the case for low- and medium-angle lines. Once this optimum range has been established, Eq. (14) may be applied to determine the variance, and by reducing symmetrically the number of steps used, its variation with range may be found.

This calculation is somewhat laborious, and a programme for the Zebra computer has been devised to calculate the optimum range, determine the variance for different ranges for the initial background conditions and then to repeat the calculation for reduced background levels. A typical set of characteristics obtained from one cycle of operation (for the aluminium 111 line) is given in Fig. 3, which shows clearly the strong dependence of the variance on the choice of background level (Tournarie, 1956b), and it is of interest to consider the effects of an error in the choice of background conditions.

EFFECT OF AN ERROR IN THE BACKGROUND ON VARIANCE

If the background has been estimated correctly, the variance-range characteristic in the region of the tails of the line will be reasonably linear. Taking B as $\frac{1}{2}(I_1 + I_{n+1})$ and δ as $(I_{n+1} - I_1)$ gives a characteristic

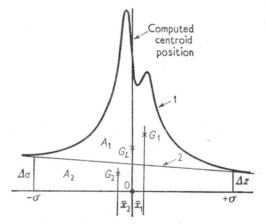

FIG. 4. Line plus error in background.

such as curve (a) in Fig. 3, indicating that this estimate of B is too high—as is of course to be expected. While the effect on the centroid position is insignificant, the variance so determined cannot be interpreted, and it is necessary to know how an error in the estimate of the background influences the variance. In Fig. 4 the line is shown together with an error in background after the estimated background has been removed. The centroid of this profile is at the mid-point of the range, and if suffixes 1 and 2 refer to the line and the error in the background respectively,

$$A_1 \bar{x}_1 = A_2 \bar{x}_2 \tag{15}$$

the symbols being defined in the figure (A = area). Clearly

$$\bar{x}^2 = \rho \sigma^2 / 3 \Delta B \tag{16}$$

and
$$A_2 = 2\Delta B\sigma \qquad (17)$$

whence
$$\bar{x}_1 = 2\rho\sigma^3/3A_1 \qquad (18)$$

The second moment of A_1 about O is
$$J_1 = A_1 W_1 + A_1 \bar{x}_1^2 \qquad (19)$$

and the second moment of A_2 about O is
$$J_2 = \tfrac{2}{3}\Delta B\sigma^3 \qquad (20)$$

giving a total second moment about O of
$$J_{1+2} = A_1 W_1 + A_1 \bar{x}_1^2 + J_2 \qquad (21)$$

The computed variance is then
$$W = \frac{A_1}{A_1+A_2} W_1 + \frac{A_1}{A_1+A_2} \bar{x}_1^2 + \frac{J_2}{A_1+A_2} \qquad (22)$$

Now
$$(1 + A_2/A_1)^{-1} = 1 - \frac{2\Delta B}{A_1} + \left(\frac{2\Delta B}{A_1}\right)^2 \sigma^2 + \ldots \qquad (23)$$

and
$$W = W_1 - \frac{2\Delta B}{A_1} W_1 \sigma + \left(\frac{2\Delta B}{A_1}\right)^2 W_1 \sigma^2 + \left[\frac{2\Delta B}{3A_1} - \left(\frac{2\Delta B}{3A_1}\right)^0 W_1\right]\sigma^3 +$$
$$+ \left(\frac{2\Delta B}{3A_1}\right)^4 W_1 \sigma^4 - \left(\frac{2\Delta B}{3A_1}\right)^5 W_1 \sigma^5 + \left[\left(\frac{2\rho}{3A_1}\right)^2 + \left(\frac{2\Delta B}{3A_1}\right)^6 W_1\right]\sigma^6 + \ldots$$
$$(24)$$

Putting $W_1 - W_0 + k\sigma$ (Eq 1), and also $q = 2\Delta B/A_1$, $Q = (k - qW_0)$, $I_L \sim A_1$,

$$W = W_0 + Q\sigma + qQ\sigma^2 + \left(\frac{q}{3} + q^2 Q\right)\sigma^3 + q^3 Q\sigma^4 + q^4 Q\sigma^5 +$$
$$+ \left[\left(\frac{2\rho}{3A_1}\right)^2 + q^5 Q\right]\sigma^6 + q^6 Q\sigma^7 + \ldots \qquad (25)$$

In many practical cases, including all discussed below, the peak-background ratio is high, giving $q \ll 1$, and for the lines so far investigated, $q \ll k/W_0$. Hence

$$W \sim W_0 + k\sigma + \frac{2\Delta B\sigma^3}{3I_L} + \left(\frac{2\rho}{3I_L}\right)^2 \sigma^6 \qquad (26)$$

The effect of an error in the estimate of the mean level is thus to introduce a cubic term in the experimental variation of variance as a function of range of integration, and an error in the slope introduces a term proportional to the sixth power of the range. Furthermore, if the mean value has been under- or over-estimated, the variance is too large or too small by an amount proportional to the error, and any error in slope causes the variance to be too large by an amount proportional to the square of the error. However, since $\rho\sigma < \Delta B$ by definition, the effect of this last term will be small compared with that involving ΔB. It is thus therotically possible to determine "optimum" values of background level and slope by adjusting them until the variance is as nearly as possible a linear function of the range of integration. In practice this is certainly true of the level (Fig. 3), but the effect of an error in slope is small compared with errors from other sources, and methods so far tried have not been sufficiently sensitive to refine it appreciably.

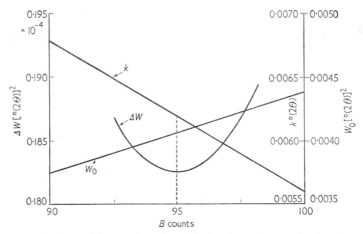

FIG. 5. ΔW, W_0 and k as a function of B in the region of the "optimum" background.

The experimental procedure that has been adopted takes the initial slope and level from the observed values of I_1 and I_{n+1}. For any reduced value of mean level, the variance programme then automatically ascribes a weighted slope based on the initial value. It is found that the "optimum" level is appreciably less than $\frac{1}{2}(I_1 + I_{n+1})$, and it can be determined with an accuracy of better than 5%. The approximate "optimum" level is taken from curves as shown in Fig. 3. To find a better estimate, several regression curves of variance as a function of range are computed, using the same programme as before, to obtain the value of B for which the sum of the squares of the residuals, ΔW, is a minimum. This is always sharply defined, and both the intercept and slope vary linearly with B in the region of the minimum (Fig. 5). After values of W_0 and k have been found in this way for each set of data, the degree of linearity is checked by re-calculating W_0 and k with reduced ranges. If the correct background has been used, these quantities will be invariant with range over a significant region (Fig. 6). If they are not, a slight re-adjustment of B is necessary. The ultimate values for W_0 and k are taken from curves such as those in Fig. 6.

The agreement between the intercepts and slopes computed from various data depends largely on the fluctuations in the background in the region of the tails. This is at present the greatest source of error, but it can be reduced to some extent by reducing the range. The latter, how-ever, must remain well within the linear part of the variance-range characteristic.

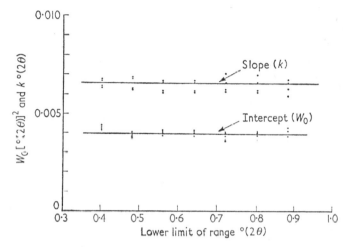

Fig. 6. Aluminium 111 line. Effect on the constants of equation (1) when the "linear range" of the variance characteristic is reduced. (Four sets of data: Upper limit $0.96°$ (2θ).)

BROADENING FROM INSTRUMENTAL ABERRATIONS

When the constants W_0 and k in Eq. (1) have been found by the methods outlined in the previous section, the next step would be to correct them for instrumental aberrations. The residual intercept and slope should then relate entirely to the physical conditions of the speci-men. Expressions for the variances of most of the geometrical aberra-tions, collected from various sources, have been tabulated by Wilson (1961), but the table does not include the variance due to refraction (Wilson, 1962c). A more complete discussion of broadening due to speci-men transparency has been given by Langford and Wilson (1962) and of that arising from axial divergence by Langford (1962). None of these contribute to the slope k, but broadening caused by the wavelength spread of the emission profile affects both W_0 and k. The resulting

8

variance is not known accurately, but an approximation based on two overlapping Cauchy profiles gives

$$W = \tfrac{2}{9}\phi^2 - \langle w^2 \rangle + \frac{2}{\pi} \langle w \rangle \sigma \qquad (27)$$

where $\langle w^2 \rangle$ is the weighted mean of the squares of the half-widths of the components of the α doublet, $\langle w \rangle$ is the weighted mean of the half-widths and ϕ is the doublet separation.

TABLE I. Summary of experimental conditions

Diffractometer radius	17 cm
Equatorial beam divergence:	
(a) aluminium	1°
(b) nickel	$\tfrac{1}{4}°$
Angular mis-setting of 2:1 ratio	$< 0\cdot1°$
Angle of inclination of plane of specimen to axis of rotation:	
(a) aluminium	$\sim 0\cdot1°$
(b) nickel	$0\cdot1°$
Aperture of Soller slits (two sets)	$2\cdot2°$
Width of receiving slit	$0\cdot1$ mm
Distance of receiving slit from focusing circle	< 1 mm
Width of focal line	1 mm
Projected width of focal line (3° take-off angle)	$0\cdot05$ mm
Half height of focal line, specimen, and receiving slit	$0\cdot5$ cm
Centroid position:	
(a) aluminium	$37\cdot68°(2\theta)$
(b) nickel	$43\cdot75°(2\theta)$
Particle size:	
(a) aluminium	$0 < p < 50\ \mu$
(b) nickel (mean)	$4 \leqslant p \leqslant 7\ \mu$

To give an indication of the orders of magnitude involved, the variances arising from instrumental aberrations are listed in Table II for aluminium and nickel 111 lines. Annealed powder specimens were used on a Philips Wide-Angle Goniometer, Type PW1050 with Geiger-Müller detectors, Cu $K\alpha$ radiation, and a monitor count of 10^4 (Pike and Hughes, 1959). The experimental conditions are summarized in Table I.

The mean slope and intercept for the aluminium 111 line, from four different sets of data, are $0\cdot0132°(2\theta)$ and $0\cdot0040[°(2\theta)]^2$, (Fig. 7) and for the nickel 111 line, from five sets of data, are $0\cdot0190°(2\theta)$ and $0\cdot0034[°(2\theta)]^2$ respectively. The experimental error has not yet been estimated statistically, but it is probably in the region of 5 to 10%. There is thus reasonable agreement between the measured intercept and the total instrumental variance in each case. (Strain and other specimen

TABLE II. Variance arising from instrumental aberrations for the 111 lines of annealed aluminium and nickel powder specimens

Source of aberration	Variance $[°(2\theta)]^2 \times 10^6$	
	Aluminium	Nickel
I. *Contributions to intercept*		
(a) Zero-angle calibration	0	0
(b) Specimen-surface displacement	0	0
(c) Specimen transparency (thick, strongly absorbing specimen)	131	16
(d) 2:1 mis-setting	< 9	< 1
(e) Inclination of plane of specimen axis to axis of rotation (assuming uniform illumination of specimen)	10	6
(f) Flat specimen	58	0·16
(g) Focal-line width (assuming uniform intensity across line focus)	24	24
(h) Receiving-slit width	95	95
(i) Cross-term between equatorial extensions of focal line and specimen (assuming uniform intensity across line focus)	0·24	0·0
(j) Cross-term between equatorial extension of specimen and non-equality of source-specimen and specimen-receiving-slit distances	< 3	< 0·2
(k) Axial divergence	676	494
(l) Refraction	17	233
(m) Emission profile (approximation)	2150	2875
II. *Contribution to slope*		
Emission profile (approximation)	5480σ	6800σ
Approximate total intercept contribution		
(a) aluminium	$0·0032[°(2\theta)]^2$	
(b) nickel	$0·0037[°(2\theta)]^2$	
Approximate total slope contribution		
(a) aluminium	$0·0055°(2\theta)$	
(b) nickel	$0·0068°(2\theta)$	

imperfections also contribute to the intercept, but, for the powder specimens used, these effects should be negligible.) The residual slopes, however, are considerable, only about half being attributable to the assumed Cauchy emission profile. Possible explanations are:

(i) The emission profile, though asymptotically inverse-square, has more pronounced tails than a Cauchy profile of the same half-width;

(ii) thermal scattering contributes appreciably to the tails, rather than to the background, when the procedure described above is used to fix the background level;

(iii) the metal specimens, even though annealed, contain residual imperfections [stacking faults or dislocations (p. 221, below)] that contribute to the slope.

It is hoped to undertake further experimental work in order to elucidate the discrepancy.

From Table II it is clear that for the low-angle range the most important broadening aberrations are the emission profile and the axial

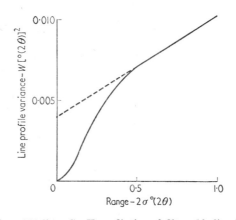

Fig. 7. Aluminium 111 line: Cu $K\alpha$ radiation, β filter, 1° slits. Variance-range characteristic for "optimum" background level. ($B = 95$ counts.)

divergence, the rest amounting to no more than the estimated uncertainties in these two. The relative importance of the different aberrations is, however, a function of the angle of diffraction, and at other angles other aberrations may become important.

STRAIN BROADENING

If a metal is internally stressed, the sharp diffraction lines become broadened, and the original perfection of the crystal lattice has been lost. There have been three main suggestions as to the nature of the imperfections:

(i) That the metal is broken up into "crystallites" so small (10^{-5} to 10^{-6} cm in linear dimensions) that diffraction broadening occurs;

(ii) that the metal is broken up into crystals (about 10^{-4} cm in linear dimensions) with differing lattice parameters; and

(iii) that the crystals of the metal remain fairly large (about 10^{-4} cm in linear dimensions), but are elastically distorted.

Previous experimental evidence is unquestionably in favour of the third suggestion, which implies a variation in lattice spacing throughout the crystal. Different parts of the crystal thus scatter at slightly different angles, resulting in a broadening of diffraction maxima. Based on (iii) above, Wilson (1962a, 1963) has shown that on certain assumptions, the variance of the nth order of the hkl diffraction profile resulting from strain is given by

$$W_s = n^2 \, W_e / d_0^2 \qquad (28)$$

where W_s is measured in terms of distance along the radius vector in reciprocal space and W_e is the variance of the strain. It is thus independent of the range s over which the variance is calculated, instead of containing a term proportional to this range, as is the case for particle-size and mistake variance. The explicit assumptions are:

(i) that the range of s is sufficiently great, and
(ii) that the relative displacements of cells close together are small compared with the cell dimensions.

In terms of the angle of diffraction, the profile variance is

$$W_{2\theta} = W_s \left[\frac{\mathrm{d}(2\theta)}{\mathrm{d}s} \right]^2 \qquad (29)$$

where

$$s = 2 \sin \theta / \lambda - n/d_0 \qquad (30)$$

giving

$$W_{2\theta} = \frac{n^2 \, W_e}{d_0^2} \left[\frac{\lambda}{\cos \theta} \right]^2 \qquad (31)$$

Hence

$$W_e = \frac{d_0^2 \cos^2 \theta}{n^2 \lambda^2} W_{2\theta} \left. \vphantom{\frac{d_0^2}{n^2}} \right\} \qquad (32)$$
$$= \tfrac{1}{4} \cot^2 \theta \, W_{2\theta}$$

and the root-mean-square strain is

$$\bar{e} = d_0 (W_{2\theta})^{1/2} \cos \theta / n\lambda \left. \vphantom{\frac{1}{2}} \right\} \qquad (33)$$
$$= \tfrac{1}{2} (W_{2\theta})^{1/2} \cot \theta$$

To investigate the experimental effects of lattice deformation, the 111 diffraction lines of strained and unstrained nickel specimens were compared. For the unstrained case, annealed powder was used, as described in detail above, and for the strained, the specimen was a machined internally stressed block of the solid metal. Representative profiles are given in Fig. 8 and the corresponding variance-range characteristics in

Fig. 9. As predicted from the simple theory of strain broadening, the latter are both linear in the region of the "tails" and, within the limits of experimental error, both have the same slope. Since the instrumental

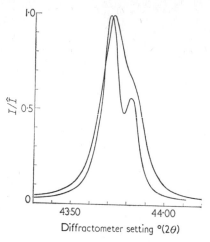

FIG. 8. Nickel 111 line: Cu $K\alpha$ radiation, β filter, $\frac{1}{4}°$ slits. Line profiles for strained and annealed specimens.

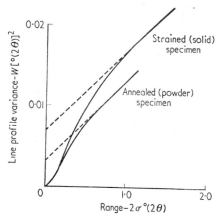

FIG. 9. Nickel 111 line: Cu $K\alpha$ radiation, β filter, $\frac{1}{4}°$ slits. Variance-range characteristics for strained and annealed specimens.

variances in each case are approximately equal, the strain variance is the difference between the intercepts. For five sets of data in each case, the mean intercepts for the powder and solid specimens were $0.0034[°(2\theta)]^2$ and $0.0072[°(2\theta)]^2$ respectively. From Eq. (33), the difference is equivalent to a root-mean-square (r.m.s.) strain of 1.4×10^{-3}.

The behaviour of the solid specimen is in accordance with the second and third suggestions for the nature of the imperfections arising from lattice deformation. The first would give rise to an appreciable difference between the slopes of the strained and unstrained cases. From Eq. (31), in theory the intercept varies as the square of the order of reflection and inversely as $\cos^2 \theta$. To investigate this property, a study of the 222 lines is at present in progress.

EFFECT OF DISLOCATIONS

The theory summarized in the preceding section implies that the strains are nowhere more than a few per cent. In the neighbourhood of a dislocation core, however, the usual models lead to strains of the order of 100%. Wilson (1955) has shown by an elementary argument that the line profiles corresponding to such strains would be of an inverse-cube form, and this has been confirmed from another standpoint by Wilkens (1962). The effect on the profile variance is to add a term varying as the logarithm of the range to the linear terms of Eq. (1):

$$W = W_0 + k\sigma + C \log \sigma \tag{34}$$

where C is a parameter depending on the dislocation density, the order of reflection, as well as other factors. It is proposed to attempt a more refined analysis of the data in order to isolate a logarithmic term, or alternatively to show that it is too small to be detected. For the ranges of σ with which it is practicable to work it may not be possible to separate a logarithmic term from a larger linear one.

SUMMARY OF CONCLUSIONS

Of the available measures of line broadening in crystallography, the mean-square deviation from the mean, or variance, is by far the most amenable to mathematical treatment. The diffracted profile is the convolution of numerous aberration functions arising from experimental conditions, and the total variance has the convenient property of being the sum of the variances of the individual aberrations. For the variance to be finite, the profile must be truncated, and over the "tails" of the profile, the variance is a linear function of range, the resulting slope and intercept depending entirely on instrumental and specimen conditions. Preliminary measurements on line-profiles at fairly low Bragg angles indicate that the variance-range function is in fact linear over a range sufficiently wide to enable consistent slopes and intercepts to be estimated. The function is strongly dependent on the mean level of the background, but this may be "optimized" until reasonable linearity obtains.

An error in background slope has negligible effect on the variance. From this slope and intercept the effects of the instrumental aberrations, strain, particle-size, etc., may be assessed experimentally.

For a specimen that is unstrained and free from "mistakes", provided the particle-size is not too small ($\sim 1 \mu$ or less), the intercept may be considered as arising entirely from instrumental aberrations. The measured value of intercept for the 111 line of a powdered aluminium specimen is $0 \cdot 0040 \pm 0 \cdot 0002 [°(2\theta)]^2$, comparing favourably with the calculated instrumental variance of $0 \cdot 0032 [°(2\theta)]^2$.

To study the effects of lattice deformation, the 111 lines of two nickel specimens were compared, one powdered and annealed, and the other solid and internally stressed. As for aluminium, the intercept for the powder specimen is approximately equal to the sum of the instrumental variances, and for the strained specimen, it is approximately doubled. Since the experimental effects for the two cases are nearly the same, the increase in variance, $0 \cdot 0043 [°(2\theta)]^2$, is attributed to deformation of the crystal lattice. From this increase, the r.m.s. strain in the crystal is estimated to be about $1 \cdot 4 \times 10^{-3}$. The slopes for the two nickel specimens are the same, confirming that the strain variance is independent of the range, provided this is sufficiently large. Work is in progress on higher-order lines.

REFERENCES

Langford, J. I. (1962). *J. sci. Instrum.* **39**, 515.
Langford, J. I. and Wilson, A. J. C. (1962). *J. sci. Instrum.* **39**, 581.
Pike, E. R. (1957). *J. sci., Instrum.* **34**, 355.
Pike, E. R. (1959). *J. sci., Instrum.* **36**, 52.
Pike, E. R. and Hughes, J. W. (1959). *J. sci. Instrum.* **36**, 212.
Pike, E. R. and Wilson, A. J. C. (1959). *Brit. J. appl. Phys.* **10**, 57.
Tournarie, M. (1956a). *C. R. Acad. Sci., Paris* **242**, 2016.
Tournarie, M. (1956b). *C. R. Acad. Sci., Paris* **242**, 2161.
Wilkens, M. (1962). *Phys. Stat. Sol.* **2**, 692.
Wilson, A. J. C. (1955). *Nuovo Cimento* **1**, 277.
Wilson, A. J. C. (1961). *Proc. phys. Soc. Lond.* **78**, 249.
Wilson, A. J. C. (1962a). *Nature, Lond.* **193**, 568.
Wilson, A. J. C. (1962b). *Proc. phys. Soc. Lond.* **80**, 286.
Wilson, A. J. C. (1962c). *Proc. phys. Soc. Lond.* **80**, 303.
Wilson, A. J. C. (1963). *Proc. phys. Soc. Lond.* **81**, 41.

SECTION IV
Anomalous Dispersion

Absolute Configuration and Rotatory Power of the Crystals of NaBrO$_3$ and NaClO$_3$

Gezina Beurskens-Kerssen, J. Kroon,
H. J. Endeman, J. van Laar† and J. M. Bijvoet

*Laboratorium voor Kristalchemie der Universiteit to Utrecht,
The Netherlands*

ABSTRACT

Sodium chlorate and sodium bromate antipodes of same rotation sign are found by X-rays to have opposite configuration. In view of this unexpected result new calculations of the rotatory power are made. In previous calculations the anions were substituted by a single particle. Taking into account the individual oxygen particles, a change of rotation sign is found in the parameter regions involved.

1. Introduction

Our determination by X-rays of the absolute configuration of sodium bromate, and sodium chlorate crystals and the calculation of their optical rotatory power is closely related to the excellent previous investigations of Ramachandran (Ramachandran, 1951; Ramachandran and Chandrasekharan, 1957). Some unexpected results obtained in recent investigations are the subject of this communication.

2. X-Ray Determination of Absolute Configuration

First let us recall briefly the principle of the determination of absolute configuration by means of X-rays. Up to 1949 it was thought to be impossible to attribute to an optical antipode its absolute configuration, i.e. to distinguish by X-rays between model and inverted model (mirror image). Indeed, inversion of a crystal structure not only leaves the diffraction directions unchanged, but also the diffraction intensities:

$$I_H = F_H \cdot F_H^* \quad \text{with} \quad F_H = \sum_j f_j \exp 2\pi i (\mathbf{H} \cdot \mathbf{r}_j) \tag{1}$$

In the transition $\mathbf{r}_j \to \bar{\mathbf{r}}_j$, from antipode A to antipode B, F_H changes into F_H^*, leaving I_H unchanged. In 1949 it was remarked that absolute configuration could be determined by the use of anomalous scattering,

† Now at Philips' Research Laboratory, Eindhoven, The Netherlands.

and the absolute configuration of several optically active compounds has since been determined. The method is based on the introduction of a phase shift in the primary scattering of one of the atoms.

In Eq. (1) it has been assumed that all phase differences in the scattering from the various atoms are caused by path differences only. This holds insofar as all electrons scatter like "free" electrons (resonance frequency $\ll$ frequency of incident beam) or possibly some of them scatter as strongly bound electrons (resonance frequency $>$ incident frequency, inner electrons of heavy atoms). The scattering (oscillation) of the latter category being opposite in phase to that of the other electrons, their contribution simply reduces the value of f_j in Eq. (1). If, however, the incident frequency is near an absorption edge of the atom—on the hard side—a phase jump will appear in the scattering that is different from the above values 0 or π. This anomalous phase shift, which can be made of considerable magnitude by suitable choice of atom and wave-length, changes Eq. (1) into

$$F_{\mathbf{H}} = \sum_j (f_j + i\Delta'' f_j) \exp 2\pi i (\mathbf{H} \cdot \mathbf{r}_j) \qquad (2)$$

From Eq. (2) one obtains

$$F_{\mathbf{H}}(\mathbf{r}_j) \neq F_{\mathbf{H}}^*(\bar{\mathbf{r}}_j)$$

and hence $\qquad I_{\mathbf{H}}(A) \neq I_{\mathbf{H}}(B)$

By the anomalous effect, therefore, the antipodes A and B can be distinguished and identified. Between the anomalous intensities the relations

$$F_{\mathbf{H}}(A) = F_{\bar{\mathbf{H}}}(B); \quad F_{\bar{\mathbf{H}}}(A) = F_{\mathbf{H}}(B) \qquad (3)$$

still hold as seen from Eq. (2), a result at once obvious from the simple inversion of the whole diffraction scene. In such investigations it is therefore essential to attribute the right sign to an index triplet.

As far back as 1916, von Laue observed that Friedel's law, which expresses the equality of reflection and inverse reflection, $I_{\mathbf{H}} = I_{\bar{\mathbf{H}}}$ (see Eq. 1) might be violated by using an appropriate wavelength. Not until 1930 was this effect demonstrated experimentally and used to determine the sense of the polar [111] sequence in zinc sulphide. Again it took about twenty years before one realized that the configuration of optical antipodes could be identified by the same method, viz. from the difference in anomalous intensities between $\mathbf{H}$ and $\bar{\mathbf{H}}$ reflections (or between reflections equivalent to these).

The anomalous scattering not only introduces the imaginary component in the scattering power on which the considerations in the above are based, but also the real part of the scattering power is somewhat changed.

This component $\Delta f'_j$, however, can simply be incorporated in the f_j of Eq. (2).

The mirror-image structures of the two antipodes of sodium chlorate (NaClO$_3$) and sodium bromate (NaBrO$_3$) will be denoted by A and B as given in Fig. 1. In 1957, Ramachandran and Chandrasekharan, using the anomalous scattering effect, established that dextrorotatory NaClO$_3$ has the configuration A. We came to determine the configuration of NaBrO$_3$ and surprisingly found that here configuration A belonged to the laevo-rotatory antipode. At first one suspects a possible error, the determination of absolute configuration having in reserve some rather special pitfalls. Our redetermination, however, this time of the chlorate, was

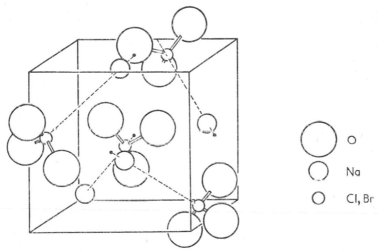

FIG. 1. Crystal structure of NaClO$_3$ and NaBrO$_3$: Model A.

in agreement with the result of the Indian scientists. So it was established that NaBrO$_3$ and NaClO$_3$ crystals of the same rotation sign have opposite absolute configurations; or, the other way round, corresponding configurations of NaBrO$_3$ and NaClO$_3$ crystals have opposite rotation signs.

Let us first consider our results for their reliability in comparing the intensities of hkl and $\overline{hkl}$ reflections. In order to measure these reflections under as equal circumstances as possible, reflections hkl and $hk\bar{l}$ were compared, the latter by the two-fold symmetry being identical with $\overline{hkl}$. In normal beam Weissenberg exposures of cylindrically shaped crystals the $hk1$ and $hk\bar{1}$ reflections were registered simultaneously under identical conditions, by means of a double slit. The ratio of the measured intensities

$$Q_{\exp} = I^+_{\exp}/I^-_{\exp}$$

with $\qquad I(hk1) = I(\overline{h}\overline{k}1) = I(\overline{h}k\overline{1}) = I(h\overline{k}\overline{1}) = I^{+}$

and $\qquad I(hk\overline{1}) = I(\overline{h}\overline{k}\overline{1}) = I(\overline{h}k1) = I(h\overline{k}1) = I^{-}$

were confronted with the corresponding ratio

$$Q_{\text{calc}} = I^{+}_{\text{calc}}/I^{-}_{\text{calc}}$$

calculated for models A and B respectively. All continuous factors being equal, the latter ratio equals $|F^{+}_{\text{calc}}|^{2}/|F^{-}_{\text{calc}}|^{2}$. Hence,

$$(Q_{\text{calc}})_{A} = (Q_{\text{calc}})_{B}^{-1}$$

In Fig. 2 the ratio $I_{hk1}/I_{hk\overline{1}}$ has been plotted for a number of $NaClO_3$ reflections. The small circles denote the calculated values for configuration A, the crosses for the inverted configuration B. The centre of a

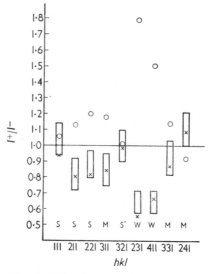

Fig. 2. $I_{hk1}/I_{\overline{hk}\overline{1}}$ for $hk1$ reflections of $NaClO_3$ (Cr $K\alpha$-radiation).

○ calculated for configuration A (Aravindakshan's co-ordinates, 1959)
× calculated for configuration B
▯ measured for $(-)$ crystal
s = strong, m = moderate, w = weak

rectangle gives the observed value for a laevorotatory crystal. The combined estimated inaccuracies in observed and calculated ratios are indicated by the height of the rectangle. Where both circle and cross are inside the rectangle, the anomalous effect is too small to permit a conclusion. Figure 2 shows that for laevorotatory $NaClO_3$ the crosses unambiguously correspond with reality; thus configuration B must be assigned to laevorotatory $NaClO_3$.

In the same way the results of Fig. 3 for laevorotatory bromate attribute configuration A to this crystal.

Considering that the usual way of accounting for the anomalous effect (Eq. 2) is sufficiently well established (Bijvoet, 1962) and that the agreement in Figs. 2 and 3 between calculated and experimental values for the chosen configurations is quite satisfactory, there is no escape from the conclusion that crystals of $NaClO_3$ and $NaBrO_3$ of corresponding configuration differ in sign of optical rotation.

There is an old observation by Marbach (Marbach, 1856)—which we confirmed—pointing to the above conclusion obtained by X-rays,

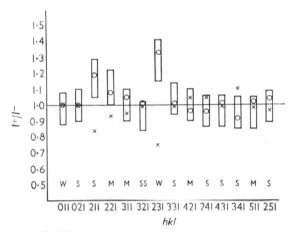

Fig. 3. $I_{hkl}/I_{\bar{h}\bar{k}\bar{l}}$ for hkl reflections of $NaBrO_3$ (Cr $K\alpha$-radiation).

○ calculated for configuration A (Hamilton, 1938)
× calculated for configuration B
☐ measured for (−) crystal
s = strong, m = moderate, w = weak.

though it lacks its conclusive force. He found that if $NaClO_3$ crystallizes from its saturated solution on a crystal of the bromate added to the solution, it appears that laevorotatory chlorate is deposited on the dextrorotatory bromate. This fact becomes plausible by our finding that, in the epitaxy of the chlorate and bromate crystals, the crystalline configuration will continue itself and the rotation therefore changes sign.

3. Results of Optical Calculation

We may proceed to the calculation of the optical rotation. It has been calculated for the crystals of $NaClO_3$ and $NaBrO_3$ by Hermann (1923) and by Ramachandran in 1951. We shall confine ourselves chiefly to the investigations of the last decade. Ramachandran found an excellent agreement between observed and calculated values.

	ρ_{obs}	ρ_{calc}
$NaClO_3$	31·3°	30·0° (deg/cm)
($\lambda = 5893$ Å)		
$NaBrO_3$	13·9°	22·1°
($\lambda = 7188$ Å)		

At that time the absolute configuration had not yet been determined "directly" by X-rays. A completely satisfying situation seemed to have been reached when Ramachandran and Chandrasekharan performed the X-ray determination of absolute configuration and confirmed the former's optical assignation. It was self-evident to attribute to (+)-$NaBrO_3$ the absolute configuration of (+)-$NaClO_3$, the two isotypic crystals differing only very slightly in parameter values:

	ρ_{obs}		ρ_{calc}
(+)-$NaClO_3$	+31° conf. A		+30°
	(direct determination by X-rays)		
(+)-$NaBrO_3$	+13·9° conf. A		+22·1°
	(by analogy)		

The situation was, however, fundamentally disturbed by our direct determination of the $NaBrO_3$ configuration: namely conf. B: (+)-$NaBrO_3$. This changes the above table into:

	ρ_{obs}	ρ_{calc}
(+)-$NaClO_3$	+31°	Conf. A 30°
(+)-$NaBrO_3$	+13·9°	Conf. B $-22\cdot1°$

In view of the rough approximations one has to introduce into these calculations, the disagreement in the bromate structure should not be considered to be too unexpected in itself. Ramachandran already remarked that his excellent agreement between observed and calculated values must be considered fortuitous, as small changes in the parameters used would lead to an appreciable change in the calculated value. It is, however, hard to understand how the optical calculation can provide opposite senses of rotation for structures as similar as the corresponding configurations of chlorate and bromate. The easily polarizable oxygen atoms contribute the greater part to the rotation. In the previous calculations the three oxygens of a chlorate or bromate ion have been substituted by one anisotropically polarizable particle placed on the trigonal axis, in the centre of the oxygen triangle. For this model, calculation reveals that the rotation changes sign only if the anisotropic particle passes through the position $(\frac{1}{2}\frac{1}{2}\frac{1}{2})$ (face-centred configuration), where the configuration changes into its inverted image. Indeed, substitution of the anion by a single particle is in itself highly questionable. In $NaClO_3$ the interionic oxygen distance is only about 1·35 times the intraionic one, and in $NaBrO_3$ this ratio is still smaller. In our calculation we located the induced dipoles at the individual oxygen positions. In

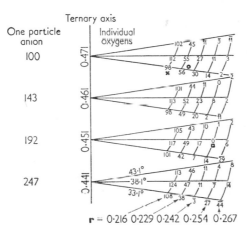

Fig. 4. Calculated rotatory power of sodium bromate:

On the left: as a function of the parameter along the [111] axis for the one-particle model of the anion.

On the right: as a function of the cylindrical co-ordinates for the model with individual oxygens.

The parameter along the trigonal axis is the fractional co-ordinate along this axis.

The parameter perpendicular to it has the cell-dimension as unit. Azimuth in degrees is with reference to the projection of a cubic axis.

× parameter values of Zachariasen (1929)
□   ,,   ,,   ,, Hamilton (1938)
○   ,,   ,,   ,, Beurskens-Kerssen (1961)

this model there appear two more parameters besides that along the trigonal axis, viz. the distance towards this axis and the azimuth around it. Calculation of the rotatory power for this model shows: (i) an extreme sensitivity to small changes in the oxygen parameters, (ii) a new sign reversal boundary, which just traverses the domain of the oxygen location concerned. So our calculation yields the possibility of opposite rotation sign for the highly similar configurations of chlorate and bromate.

Figure 4 is a graph of the calculated rotatory power as a function of the cylindrical co-ordinates of the oxygen atom in which a few parameter sets taken from the literature are marked. One sees the strong dependence on the azimuth, a parameter for which there is no equivalent in the old model. In Ramachandran's calculation the anion had even been given exactly the same location in the chlorate and the bromate; with the extremely small difference in position of the centre of the oxygen triangle this should be considered as fully warranted in his model. One may picture the situation in a one-dimensional scheme in the following way:

Model of anion	B			A
Dipole on trigonal axis	$(-)$			$(+)$
Dipoles beyond trigonal axis	$(-)$	$(+)$	$(-)$	$(+)$
			NaBrO$_3$	NaClO$_3$

We have recently refined the bromate parameters once more, hoping to find somewhat larger differences from those of the chlorate. However, compared with the last determination in the literature, our new co-ordinates—$u_{Br} = 0.4063$; $u_{Na} = 0.077$; $x_O = 0.287$; $y_O = 0.597$, $z_O = 0.508$—approach even somewhat more closely those of the chlorate. The rotation being an extremely sensitive property caused by the loosely bound electrons of the anion, the X-ray data provide but poor information for its calculation. The latter would need the exact distribution of the polarizability over the chlorate and bromate ion. For the time being, we will have to be content with the fact that, by treating the three oxygens separately in the calculation of their rotatory power, the reversal of rotation sign for corresponding configurations loses its mystery. As we have mentioned already, this reversal is not compatible with the one-particle treatment of the anion.

It has been claimed that the sense of rotation of these crystals could be predicted on the basis of the existence of right- or left-handed spirals which one tried to distinguish in the atomic arrangement. It need hardly be stressed that for the NaClO$_3$ structure our result refutes such a rough procedure.

4. OUTLINE OF THE OPTICAL CALCULATION

In order to calculate the rotation one has to investigate the polarization caused by the field of an incident wave. In a cubic non-centro-symmetrical crystal one has the relation

$$\mathbf{D} = \epsilon\mathbf{E} + i\gamma(\mathbf{s} \times \mathbf{E}) \tag{4a}$$

between the electric displacement $\mathbf{D}$ and the electric field strength $\mathbf{E}$; here ϵ denotes the dielectric constant, $\mathbf{s}$ the unit vector in the direction of propagation. Eq. (4a) shows that there is a component in the polarization, perpendicular to $\mathbf{s}$ and $\mathbf{E}$ which differs in phase from $\mathbf{E}$ by $\pi/2$.

Putting $\mathbf{E} = E_x = 1$ and taking $\mathbf{s}$ in the z-direction, Eq. (4a) yields

$$\mathbf{D}_y = i\gamma \tag{4b}$$

The constant γ is connected with the rotation in the following way: Combining the equations

$$\left. \begin{aligned} \mathbf{D} &= \epsilon\mathbf{E} + i\gamma(\mathbf{s} \times \mathbf{E}) \\ \mathbf{B} &= \mu\mathbf{H} \end{aligned} \right\} \tag{5}$$

and

with the Maxwell equations, one derives

$$n_l = \left(1 + \frac{\gamma}{2}\right)\frac{1}{\sqrt{\epsilon}}$$

$$n_d = \left(1 - \frac{\gamma}{2}\right)\frac{1}{\sqrt{\epsilon}}$$

where n_l and n_d denote the refractive index of left and right circular polarized waves respectively. Thus,

$$\rho = \tfrac{1}{2}(n_l - n_d)\frac{\omega}{c} = \frac{1}{2}\frac{\gamma}{\sqrt{\epsilon}}\frac{\omega}{c} = \frac{\pi\gamma}{n\lambda_0} \tag{6}$$

According to Eq. (4b)

$$\gamma = 4\pi P_y' = \frac{4\pi}{a^3}\sum_j (p_j')_y$$

where P_y' denotes the polarization per unit volume (the accent indicates its phase difference of $\pi/2$ relative to E_x) and $(p_j')_y$ the corresponding moment of dipole j, the summation being over the dipoles of the unit cell of volume a^3.

One has to calculate the lattice polarization under the influence of the incident wave and the mutual interaction of the induced atomic dipoles. If one starts with anisotropic oscillators, then in the calculation of the dipole interaction the approximation suffices in which their strength is taken to be equal to that caused by the external field alone. In our case of isotropic particles this approximation gives zero rotation. Here, in calculating the interaction of the dipoles it is necessary to take into account their modification caused by this very interaction (interaction $1 \to 2$, also via 3, etc.). One introduces the final moments $\mathbf{p}_k^l$ (k enumerates the dipoles in the unit cell, l the unit cell) and sets up the equations for their formation:

$$\mathbf{p}_k^l = \alpha[\mathbf{E}_0 \exp i\boldsymbol{\varkappa}.\mathbf{r}_k^l \exp - i\omega t + \sum_{k'l'}' c(\mathbf{r}_{k'}^{l'} - \mathbf{r}_k^l)\,\mathbf{p}_{k'}^{l'}] \tag{7}$$

In Eq. (7) α denotes the polarizability of the oxygen particles, and the term in square brackets the field strength at the particle k, l, this field being the sum of the field of the incident wave and that of all dipoles of the infinite lattice; the accent at the summation sign denotes that in the summation the combination kl occurring in the left-hand member is absent; c is the tensor of the dipole field.

The periodicity of the lattice invites us to assume a plane running-wave for the atomic polarizations

$$\mathbf{p}_k^l = \mathbf{p}_k \exp i(\mathbf{r}_k^l.\boldsymbol{\varkappa}) \exp - i\omega t \tag{8}$$

which reduces the number of unknown atomic polarizations to the number of atoms per cell. The summation in Eq. (7) takes the form of a summation over the n elementary lattices:

$$\mathbf{p}_k = \alpha[\mathbf{E}_0 + \sum_{k'} C(\mathbf{r}_{k'} - \mathbf{r}_k)\,\mathbf{p}_{k'}] \tag{9}$$

In Eq. (9) the tensor C has the form:

$$C(\mathbf{r}_{k'} - \mathbf{r}_k) = \sum_{l'} c(\mathbf{r}_{k'}^{l'} - \mathbf{r}_k^l) \exp i(\mathbf{r}_{k'}^{l'} - \mathbf{r}_k^l.\boldsymbol{\varkappa}) \tag{10}$$

where the accent at the summation sign denotes that for $k = k'$ the term $l = l'$ is missing. Because of the periodicity of the lattice the sum (Eq. 10) is indeed independent of l.

Thus, Eq. (9) gives n linear relations between the n polarizations $\mathbf{p}_k$. One solves these equations for the moments $\mathbf{p}_k$. For that purpose one expands Eq. (10) in powers of $\boldsymbol{\varkappa}$. The real zero-order terms give a real polarization. If $\mathbf{E}_0$ is chosen in the x-direction and $\boldsymbol{\varkappa}$ in the z-direction, then symmetry considerations show that $\sum \mathbf{p}_{kj}^{(0)}$ is directed along $\mathbf{E}_0$: in this approximation the normal refraction is found. The first-order terms in $\boldsymbol{\varkappa}$ give imaginary corrections on the coefficients of Eq. (9) and hence on the solution $\mathbf{p}_k$ of these equations. Here symmetry-considerations show that these corrections, $i\mathbf{p}_k^{(1)}$, have resultant $i\sum_k \mathbf{p}_k^{(1)}$ directed along the y-axis. Calculation of $\sum \mathbf{p}_y^{(1)}$ then directly leads to the rotation.

In $NaClO_3$ there are 12 O-atoms per cell, hence 12 dipoles involving three real and three imaginary components each. This makes 72 unknowns, and the 12 vector equations in Eq. (8) constitute the 72 algebraic equations available for their solution. This number is reduced to 18 by the two-fold symmetry if we choose the incident field along the binary axis. The calculation of the complicated coefficients of these equations and their solution was possible only by electronic computation.

Some fundamental objections can be raised against the above formulation of the wave propagation in the crystal. It may be useful to glance at these after a short outline of the exact, consistently microscopic, theory (Ewald, 1916; Born, 1915). The final equations, however, remain unchanged.

In considering an infinite crystal one proves that a travelling plane-wave can be obtained by composing the spherical waves issuing from the oscillating dipoles of properly chosen amplitudes. This implies the condition that the harmonic oscillation of each dipole is just what is maintained by the field of all other dipoles (no "incident" beam). In the calculation of the dipole field the problem is that the summation over the infinite lattice results in a badly convergent series. Ewald solved this difficulty by a partial Fourier transformation of the series. In the two resulting series, one in ordinary space and the other in Fourier-space, the terms can be expanded in powers of the wave vector. Appropriate splitting results in both series being rapidly convergent. In the zero order approximation of their coefficients, the equations of motion of the dipoles again account for the refraction. In the first-order approximation, these equations appear to be resolved only for a resultant circularly polarized lattice moment in the case of a non-centrosymmetrical cubic structure. The propagation velocities, different for right- and left-handed polarized waves respectively, can be calculated from these equations. The difference between their coefficients of refraction appears to be proportional to what constitutes in the elementary theory the polarization along the y-axis for incident field along the x-axis.

Objections against the elementary deduction are for example:

(1) The rotation is derived on the basis of Eqs. (4a, b) and (5) for the macroscopic electric and the magnetic behaviour of the material respectively. Yet for liquids one can derive a magnetic equation of the form

$$\mathbf{B} = \mu\mathbf{H} + i\frac{\gamma}{2}(\mathbf{s} \times \mathbf{H})$$

which adds a magnetic contribution to the rotation. An analogous contribution can be calculated for the crystal. The difficulties concerning the justification of this procedure are caused by the use of macroscopically defined mean values. These difficulties are not met with in the purely microscopical theory, which rejects a magnetic contribution.

(2) In the elementary theory one employs in the crystal an external field and neglects the retardation. In the exact theory the idea of an "external field" is scrapped by taking into account the retardation.

Acknowledgement

We wish to thank Prof. A. F. Peerdeman for an independent check of the X-ray result.

REFERENCES

Aravindakshan, C. (1959). *Z. Kristallogr.* **111**, 241.
Beurskens-Kerssen, G. (1961). Thesis, Utrecht.
Bijvoet, J. M. (1962). *Acta cryst.* **15**, 620.

Born, M. (1915). *Encyclopädie der mathematischen Wissenschaften*, Band 5, Teil 3, p. 530.
Ewald, P. P. (1916). *Ann. Phys., Paris* [4], **49**, 1.
Hamilton, J. E. (1938). *Z. Kristallogr.* **100**, 104.
Hermann, C. (1923). *Z. Phys.* **16**, 103.
Marbach, H. (1856). *Ann. Phys. Chem.* **99**, 451.
Ramachandran, G. N. (1951). *Proc. Indian Acad. Sci.* **A33**, 217, 309.
Ramachandran, G. N. and Chandrasekaran, K. S. (1957). *Acta cryst.* **10**, 671.
Zachariasen, W. H. (1929). *Z. Kristallogr.* **71**, 517.

DISCUSSION

I. NITTA: I wonder if rotatory dispersion has been measured, because rotatory power sometimes depends strongly on change of frequency.

G. N. RAMACHANDRAN: It was measured by Dr. S. Chandrasekhar in the case of sodium chlorate and by Dr. Rose (Thesis, Gottingen, 1909) for sodium bromate. A table of results of the latter is quoted by C. Hermann (*Z. Phys.* **16**, 103 (1923)).

S. CHANDRASEKHAR: The one other crystal for which similar calculations have been made is beta-quartz (by Ramachandran) and in this case a wrong value was assigned to the anisotropy of the polarizability of the oxygen atom, and yet the theory gave the right order of magnitude for the rotatory power. It is clear, therefore, that caution is necessary in using the polarizability theory for working out absolute configuration. There are two reasons why the theory often fails. Firstly because the optical rotation is very sensitive to the anisotropy of the polarizability of the bonded atoms in the crystal, and there is no really reliable way of estimating the anisotropy. The second reason is more fundamental. All the ultra-violet absorption bands that contribute to the refraction are lumped together into one constant α, the polarizability of the atom, and it is usually assumed in the theory that these bands contribute with the same strengths to the rotatory power, whereas, in fact, it is well known that strong bands may not be optically active at all, and relatively weak bands may be strongly optically active.

J. M. BIJVOET: I fully agree with the remarks of Dr. Chandrasekhar in general. As to the influence of the factors mentioned by him on our special problem, viz. the unexpected difference of the bromate and chlorate respectively, we indeed considered the influence of small anisotropy. Reasonable differences in anisotropy did not result in critical changes. Next, as to the influence of the band structure, it is difficult to assume considerable difference in band structure between our two compounds which are so closely similar.

G. N. RAMACHANDRAN: I may add that we did use the polarizability theory for calculating the optical rotation of the helix. It happens to come out well. In spite of the wide range of assumptions regarding the polarizability tensors, we always got the rotation to be positive for a right-handed α-helix. Now that the study of Kendrew and others has proved that this is so in the case of the natural α-helix, I think one need not be so sceptical about the optical theory as Dr. Chandrasekhar has made out.

The Determination of the
Crystal Structure of Factor V la

DAVID DALE, DOROTHY CROWFOOT HODGKIN AND K. VENKATESAN

Chemical Crystallographic Laboratory, Oxford, England

ABSTRACT

The structure of the compound factor V la, which is an aquo cyanide of the natural vitamin B_{12} nucleus (containing cobalt), has been determined using the anomalous dispersion effect. The compound, which belongs to the space group $P2_1$, exhibited the Bijvoet effect for 1994 of the 4000 reflections, the radiation used being Cu $K\alpha$. Intensities were estimated only visually and the phase angles were calculated from the observed differences in intensities of inverse reflections. The ambiguity in phase angle was resolved by choosing the one nearer to the phase of the cobalt atom. The Fourier thus obtained revealed the structure almost completely. After a few cycles of refinement, the R-factor was brought down to 16·4%. At this stage a difference Fourier map contained peaks which could be identified as hydrogens and the inclusion of these gave an R-factor of 16%.

In the determination of the structure of vitamin B_{12} a critical part was played by the examination of a crystalline hexacarboxylic acid obtained by Todd, Johnson and Cannon by the degradation of the vitamin. This included the cobalt-containing nucleus of the vitamin and corresponded in formula approximately to the naturally occurring nucleus compound factor B. Recently Bernhauer, Wagner and Wahl have obtained in crystalline form a compound, factor V la, which they have shown to be an aquo cyanide of the natural B_{12} nucleus. We started X-ray crystallographic investigation on factor V la about a year ago and our results confirm the views of Bernhauer *et al.* that the compound is to be formulated as cobyrinic acid abcfg hexamide in the mono aquo cyanide form, formula (I). The crystals examined have an asymmetric unit corresponding to the molecule $C_{46}H_{66}O_9N_{11}Co + 11H_2O$. They belong to the space group $P2_1$ with cell dimensions $a = 9·20_4$, $b = 15·80_1$, $c = 19·94_4$, $\beta = 97·067°$.

X-Ray photographs of factor V la using Cu $K\alpha$ radiation exhibited marked anomalous dispersion effects (Fig. 1). It has been shown recently by Ramachandran and Raman, Bijvoet and others that it is possible to calculate the phase angles from an accurate measurement of the intensity differences between hkl and $\overline{hkl}$ reflections. As the Bijvoet effect was

237

quite pronounced over a large number of reflections in factor V 1a we attempted to solve the structure via the anomalous dispersion technique.

The short (9·20 Å) a-axis was chosen as the main axis for the data collection and the unique b-axis as the subsidiary direction. The $0kl - 7kl$ and $h0l - h4l$ layers were photographed using the multiple film equi-inclination film Weissenberg technique with exposures of from six to eight days' duration. Three needle-like prism-shaped crystals of size approximately 0·3 mm × 0·3 mm were used in taking the photographs. These were kept wet in their mother liquor. No change in the intensities was in fact noticeable between the wet and air-dry crystals and the air-dry crystals give photographs nearly as good as those from wet crystals but in the course of time they deteriorate. The final F^2 set contained nearly 8000 terms. No correction for absorption was made. However, correction for the spot-shape variations was made by application of the correction factor

$$I_{\text{true}} = Ie, c(1 \pm k\cos\theta)$$

Wilson plots of $0kl$, $1kl$, $2kl$ and $h0l$ terms provided the absolute scale factor and an average temperature factor of $B = 3·5$ Å^2 for the crystal as a whole. The variation in intensity due to the Bijvoet effect averaged 15–20% and was observed between non-equivalent reflections of the following types

$$hkl = \overline{hk}\overline{l} \neq h\overline{k}l = \overline{h}k\overline{l}$$

$$hk\overline{l} = \overline{hk}l \neq h\overline{kl} = \overline{h}kl$$

Ramachandran and Raman have shown that the phase angle derived using the anomalous technique has two possible values, namely

$$\alpha_{1,2} = \alpha_a + \frac{\pi}{2} \pm \theta$$

where α_a is the phase angle corresponding to the anomalous scattering atoms and θ, the angle between the non-dispersive structure factor F' and the dispersive part F'', is given by

$$\cos\theta = \frac{\Delta|F|^2}{4|F'|\,|F''|}$$

In the case when the anomalous scatterers are centrosymmetrically related, as was the case with factor V 1a, the two possible values for the phase angle are α and $\pi-\alpha$. In the general case of the calculation of a Fourier-type synthesis in which both α_1 and α_2 are employed, the correct phases will reinforce each other to yield the structure while the incorrect terms will give rise to a background. In the case with anomalous scatterers centrosymmetrically distributed, the Fourier computed with

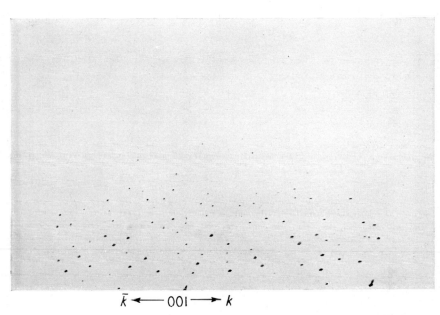

FIG. 1. Weissenberg $0kl$ photograph of factor V 1a using Cu $K\alpha$-radiation. Note the marked anomalous dispersion effect.

both possible phase angles will contain positive and negative peaks in equal numbers, related by an inversion about the inversion centre of the anomalous scatterers. We were somewhat concerned lest a synthesis of such a kind would in practice prove as complicated to unravel as the

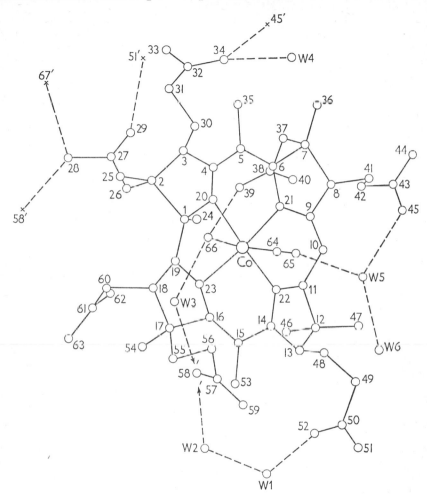

FIG. 2. Projection of structure of factor V 1a on the bc-plane.

heavy-atom type of synthesis, since positive and negative peaks might partly lie over one another in three dimensions. We therefore carried out some trial calculations on phase determination from the data previously collected on the hexacarboxylic acid and observed that, of a total of fifty reflections on which measurements of anomalous scattering had been made, forty-four had the phase angles corresponding to the solution nearest the cobalt phase. We therefore chose in the case of factor V 1a the phase angle lying closer to α_{Co}. It was found possible to compute by a programme devised by Keith Prout phase angles for 1994 terms out of the 4000 observed reflections. At this point, two

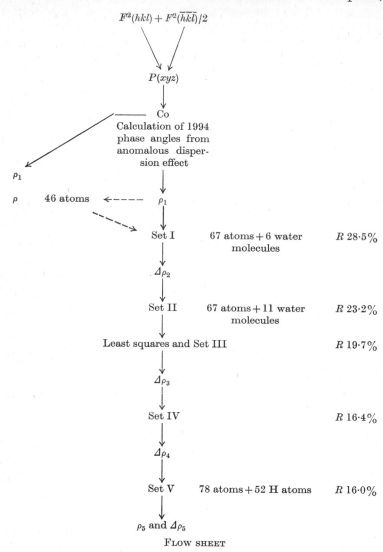

$$F^2(hkl) + F^2(\overline{hkl})/2$$

$P(xyz)$

—— Co

Calculation of 1994
phase angles from
anomalous disper-
sion effect

ρ_1

ρ 46 atoms $\leftarrow ---$ ρ_1

Set I   67 atoms + 6 water   R 28·5%
molecules

$\Delta\rho_2$

Set II   67 atoms + 11 water   R 23·2%
molecules

Least squares and Set III   R 19·7%

$\Delta\rho_3$

Set IV   R 16·4%

$\Delta\rho_4$

Set V   78 atoms + 52 H atoms   R 16·0%

ρ_5 and $\Delta\rho_5$

FLOW SHEET

three-dimensional series were calculated; ρ_1 using those 1994 terms, together with ρ_1' the ordinary heavy atom phased Fourier series. It was immediately clear that ρ_1 was far and away the best. It contained very well defined peaks from $5e/\text{Å}^3$ downwards in addition to that peak of height $43\cdot5e/\text{Å}^3$, due to the cobalt atom. Peaks in similar positions occurred in the heavy-atom series, but doubled by false symmetry and of lower height from $2 \cdot 8e/Å^3$ down, although all 4000 terms were included in this series. It was discarded from further analysis.

A spoke model was made representing the positions of peaks of height greater than $2e/Å^3$ which appeared in ρ_1. Prior knowledge of the probable chemical configuration of the molecule, coupled with distance angle calculations on many of the peaks enabled an approximate and yet almost complete structure to be elucidated. Of the seventy-nine peaks considered, sixty-three appeared at positions consistent with their being atoms of the molecule and a further six peaks corresponded to the sites of water molecules. The remaining four atoms of the molecule appeared at an average height of about $1 \cdot 4e/Å^3$ (Fig. 2). Calculation of the structure

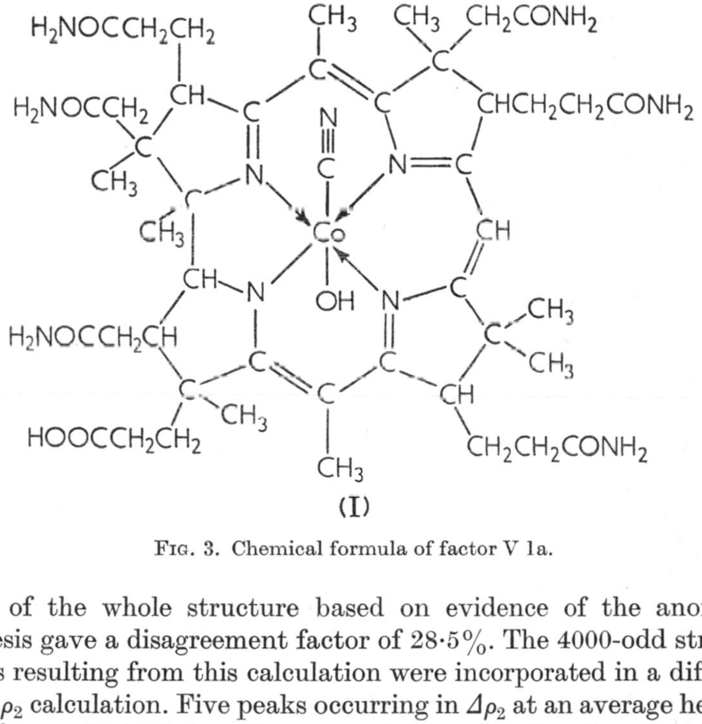

(I)

FIG. 3. Chemical formula of factor V 1a.

factor of the whole structure based on evidence of the anomalous synthesis gave a disagreement factor of $28 \cdot 5\%$. The 4000-odd structure factors resulting from this calculation were incorporated in a difference map $\varDelta\rho_2$ calculation. Five peaks occurring in $\varDelta\rho_2$ at an average height of $2 \cdot 2e/Å^3$ were identified as the extra water molecules, thus making the total number of water molecules eleven per asymmetric unit. Evidence from this map was used to calculate individual isotropic thermal parameters as well as shifts in atomic positions. The R-factor at this stage was $23 \cdot 2\%$. An isotropic least-squares refinement brought down the R-factor to $19 \cdot 7\%$. This was followed by two more difference maps. The $\varDelta\rho_4$ map showed small positive peaks varying in height from $0 \cdot 25$ to $0 \cdot 60e/Å^3$ in the directions to be expected for hydrogen atoms in the molecule. Atomic positions for fifty-two hydrogen atoms were assigned (see flow sheet) and included in the latest structure factor calculation. The projection on the a-plane of the atomic positions found is shown in Fig. 3. It shows the general form of the molecule with the cobalt atom in the centre of the corrin ring. The cyanide group is on the opposite side of the ring to that adopted in vitamin B_{12}, i.e. the same side as in the

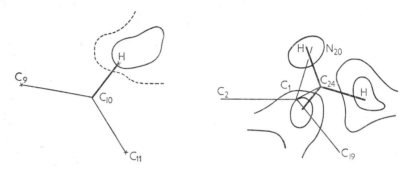

Fig. 4. Electron density maps showing hydrogen atoms.

hexacarboxylic acid. The co-ordination sphere is completed by the oxygen atom 66. It seems more likely that this is present as a hydroxyl group than as a water molecule. The present measurements provide a much more accurate description of the corrin nucleus than that given by any of the other B_{12} compounds. The evidence for many hydrogen atoms is also good and completes the crystallographic determination of the chemical structure, e.g. in relation to the methyl groups present such as C_{24} (Fig. 4).

DISCUSSION

G. N. RAMACHANDRAN: I think it is a very interesting fact that all the structures that have been tackled successfully by the anomalous dispersion technique belong to the space group $P2_1$. I do not know whether the effect is so marked in other space groups, but there is the observation that another derivative of Vitamin B_{12} with space group $P2_12_12_1$ did not show equally marked anomalous dispersion effects. The possible explanation of this seems to arise from the statistical distribution of structure amplitudes. I think that it is not so much the space group $P2_1$ that matters, as the fact that there are just two anomalous scatterers (which are invariably heavy atoms) in the unit cell, and the fact that the intensity distribution for a two-atom case has a peculiar form.

K. VENKATESAN: I think it has been observed in the case of two insulin compounds belonging to the same space group, one containing uranium and the other mercury, that the latter showed more pronounced anomalous dispersion effects than the former, even though theoretically one would not expect this to occur. This seems to indicate that the actual structural features also play some part in this phenomenon.

Some Procedures in the Determination of the Absolute Configuration of Crystals

S. N. Vaidya and S. Ramaseshan

Department of Physics, Indian Institute of Science,
Bangalore 12, India and Department of Physics,
Indian Institute of Technology, Madras 36, India

ABSTRACT

This paper attempts to outline the routine procedures necessary in the determination of the absolute configuration of a crystal by the Bijvoet method using anomalous scattering and employing photographic techniques. The method due to Peerdeman and Bijvoet for assigning correct indices to the reflections recorded by the equi-inclination Weissenberg method has been restated to include trigonal, monoclinic and triclinic classes. The pairs of reflections—named Bijvoet pairs—whose intensities are to be compared for the determination of the absolute configuration have here been listed for all the enantiomorphous space groups. The problem of the determination of the absolute configuration of a crystal when only one crystallographic mounting is possible (as in the case of liquids crystallized at low temperatures), has been discussed. A simple double-layer method of recording reflections of the type hkL and $hk\bar{L}$ has been evolved and its application to various crystal classes given.

1. Introduction

After the classical paper of Bijvoet (1954), the anomalous scattering of X-rays has been used for the determination of the absolute configuration of a good number of crystals. The increased experimental activity in this field is also due to the discovery that there is considerable anomalous scattering with phase change even when the frequency of the K absorption edge is quite far from that of the incident radiation (Peterson, 1955; Dauben and Templeton, 1955). Indeed, this effect is so large that when a suitable atom like iodine is present in the structure as the anomalous scatterer and Cu $K\alpha$ is used, then the simple photographic technique is quite sufficient for establishing the absolute configuration.

In low-temperature cameras using the Fankuchen-Lipscomb type of cooling (Kaufman and Fankuchen, 1949; Abrahams *et al.*, 1950; Singh and Ramaseshan, 1963) the crystal almost invariably grows with a particular crystallographic axis coinciding with the axis of the thin cylindrical capillary tube. It is practically impossible to mount the

243

crystal on any other axis. Hence, techniques are here presented for the determination of the absolute configuration of a crystal (belonging to any crystal system) using only one mounting on an arbitrary axis. In the course of recent investigations by one of the authors and his collaborators on the absolute configurations of orthorhombic, trigonal and triclinic crystal structures (Manohar and Ramaseshan, 1961; Singh et al., 1962) the necessity was again realized of the need to be able to index the diffraction photographs without any reference whatever to the mounting of the crystal.

It was thought that the knowledge gained by these investigations was worthy of record so that the photographic technique could be used as a routine procedure by the X-ray crystallographer for determining the absolute configuration in any crystal system. In each space group, the pairs of reflections that are to be compared are here listed. The indexing procedure given by Peerdeman and Bijvoet (1956) have been extended to cover the monoclinic and triclinic classes, and finally some special but convenient techniques are discussed which facilitate the determination of the absolute configuration of a crystal.

2. The Bijvoet Inequality and the "Bijvoet Pairs"

In the absence of anomalous scattering, the reflections hkl and $\overline{hkl}$ from each of two enantiomorphous crystals A and B are related by

$$\alpha_A(hkl) = \alpha_B(\overline{hkl}) \tag{1a}$$

$$I_A(hkl) = I_B(\overline{hkl}) \tag{1b}$$

However, when they are from one and the same crystal, say A,

$$\alpha_A(hkl) = -\alpha_A(\overline{hkl}) \tag{2a}$$

$$I_A(hkl) = I_A(\overline{hkl}) \tag{2b}$$

If among the atoms there is an anomalously scattering atom, Eqs. (2a) and (2b) are violated while, however, Eqs. (1a) and (1b) are still valid.

From the intensity of the one reflection relative to the other in the inequality $I(hkl) \neq I(\overline{hkl})$, the absolute configurations of structures belonging to the enantiomorphous space groups may be determined.

The phase relations among all those reflections that are equivalent to one another under normal scattering can be one of the following:

(a) $\alpha = \beta$
(b) $\alpha = \pi/2 - \beta$
(c) $\alpha = \pi/2 + \beta$
(d) $\alpha = \pi - \beta$

(e) $\alpha = \pi + \beta$
(f) $\alpha = 3\pi/2 - \beta$
(g) $\alpha = 3\pi/2 + \beta$
(h) $\alpha = -\beta$

TABLE I. Table of Bijvoet pairs in absolute form

Axis of rotation a

Point group	Zero layer WEP 00l / 00l̄	Higher layer WEP H0l / H0l̄	Hkl / Hk̄l	Hkl / H̄kl	Double layer method Hkl / H̄kl̄	Hkl / H̄kl
1						+
2, ‡4, 6	+	+				+
222, 422; 23, 432				+		+
3	+				+	+
32	+				+	+
622					+	+

Axis of rotation b

Point group	Zero layer WEP h00 / h̄00	0k0 / 0̄k0	h0l / h̄0l	h0l̄ / h̄0l̄	Higher layer WEP H0l / H0l̄	Hk0 / Hk̄0	Hkl / Hk̄l	Hkl / H̄kl	Hkl / H̄k̄l	Double layer method hKl / h̄Kl̄	hKl / hK̄l
1											+
2, ‡4, 6	+				+						+
222, 422; 23, 432		+						+			+
3	+	+				+				+	+
32	+	+				+				+	+
622						+				+	+

Axis of rotation c

Point group	Zero layer WEP h00 / h̄00	0k0 / 0̄k0	hk0 / h̄k0	hk0 / h̄k̄0	Higher layer WEP h0L / h̄0L	0kL / 0k̄L	hkL / h̄kL	hkL / hk̄L	hkL / h̄k̄L	Double layer method hkL / hk̄L	hkL / hk̄L
1	+	+									+
2, 4, 6	+	+		+			+			+	+
222, 422; 23, 432			+	+				+			+
3	+		+	+			+				+
32	+		+	+			+				+
622							+			+	+

Axis of rotation c (parallel to c-axis)

Point group	Zero layer WEP hm0 / h̄m0	hm0 / h̄m0	Higher layer WEP hmL / h̄mL	hmL / h̄mL	Double layer method hmL / hm̄L	hmL / hm̄L
3	+			+		+
32	+	+	+		+	+
622					+	+

† + represents that the Bijvoet pair at the head of the column exists. The 0m0 axis is the $h\,h\,\overline{2h}\,0$ axis perpendicular to the h00 axis. Since the Bijvoet pairs are symmetrically disposed about this axis the film is indexed using h00 and 0m0 axes. In 422 and 432 Bijvoet pairs with $h = k$ have equal intensity. In 622 Bijvoet pairs with $h = \pm k$ have equal intensity.

‡ Parallel to c-axis.

With an anomalously scattering atom present, those reflections for which (a), (c), (e) and (g) hold will still be of equal intensity; likewise the reflections for which (b), (d), (f) and (h) hold will be equally intense. Whereas both sets were of the same intensity under normal scattering, they will now differ in intensity.

Two reflections which are of equal intensity under normal scattering, and may become unequal when anomalous scattering is present, are named a "Bijvoet pair". Intensity of Bijvoet pairs must be compared to determine absolute configuration. Under conditions which are easily worked out, the reflections of a possible Bijvoet pair may be accidentally of equal intensity, even when anomalous scattering is present. Again, for certain types of reflections in certain space groups, a Bijvoet pair (in the sense that the pair belongs one each to the two sets of phase relations mentioned above) may not show any difference in intensity. The Bijvoet intensity difference vanishes systematically for them.

3. THE BIJVOET PAIRS IN EQUI-INCLINATION PHOTOGRAPHS FOR VARIOUS SPACE GROUPS

On the above principles, and using the expressions for the structure amplitudes and phases given in the *International Tables for X-ray Crystallography*, Vol. I, it is easy to write down the Bijvoet pairs for the various enantiomorphous space groups. As it is usual to employ the Weissenberg equi-inclination photographs (WEP) for the collection of intensity data, the Bijvoet pairs occurring in the WEP's of the different levels are listed in Table I.

Any WEP may become useless for the purpose of determining absolute configuration owing to any of the following reasons.

(a) There may be no two equivalent reflections in that layer even under normal scattering.

(b) If such a pair exists the reflections may be of equal intensity both under normal scattering and anomalous scattering.

(c) The reflections of a Bijvoet pair may not be recorded on the same side of the central line of the WEP. This is an important consideration since reflections recorded in different halves of the equi-inclination photograph undergo different elongations and are then unsuitable for comparison if intensity is measured visually.

For triclinic crystals of point-group 1, and trigonal crystals of point-group 3 mounted on the unique axis, there are Bijvoet pairs only in the zero-level Weissenberg, and none in the other layers. But for crystals belonging to the point-group 32 there are Bijvoet pairs in any layer, every Bijvoet pair lying symmetrically on either side of the $h\,h\,\overline{2h}\,L$ row of reflections.

For crystals of the point-groups 2, 4 and 6, Weissenberg photographs of any layer taken about the unique axis do not contain Bijvoet pairs to be compared. But in the zero-layer Weissenberg and the higher level WEP's about a non-unique axis, say a, the Bijvoet pairs lie symmetrically about the $Hk0$ row of reflections. If b were the axis of rotation, they lie symmetrically about the $hK0$ row.

For crystals of the point-groups 222, 422, 622, 23 and 432, while the zero-layer Weissenberg about any crystallographic axis does not contain a Bijvoet pair, the higher layer WEP's about any axis have Bijvoet pairs situated symmetrically about the central axial rows; only, for a crystal of point-group 622, and mounted on the hexagonal axis, the Bijvoet pairs in a higher layer WEP are symmetrical about the $h\ h\ \overline{2h}\ L$ row.

4. The Method of Unique Indexing

The correct indexing of the diffraction photographs is extremely important for the determination of the absolute configuration by the Bijvoet method. Since the formulae for the structure amplitudes for any space group are given for a right-handed system of co-ordinates in the International Tables, they can be used only if the right handed system is also chosen for indexing the photographs. Peerdeman and Bijvoet (1956) have clearly laid down the procedure for indexing the reflections from an orthorhombic crystal, and have indicated how they are to be applied to the monoclinic system also. We shall extend them to all the general cases here.

Figure 1 (a) shows the arrangement in a right-handed camera like the Unicam single crystal goniometer S-35, where the clockwise rotation of the graduated drum-head causes the film cassette to move along the axis in the direction of advance of a right-handed screw. The positive direction of the crystallographic axis on which the crystal is mounted and about which it is rotated is taken to point away from the drum-head. The position of the camera with respect to the incident beam of X-rays, and the cut usually made to denote the position of the film in the cassette (at the right-hand top corner as an observer facing the incident beam sees it) are also shown in the figure.

When one uses a right-handed camera (Fig. 1 (a)) and a right-handed system of co-ordinates (Fig. 1 (b)) the indexing of the Weissenberg photographs is quite straightforward and may be done without reference to the crystal or its morphological characteristics. It may be easily verified that the sequence from *right to left* of the axial rows will be a cyclic permutation of the sequence $h00$, $0k0$, $\overline{h}00$ and $0\overline{k}0$ assuming of course that the crystal is rotated about the c-axis. When the axial rows have been identified in this sequence the reflections may all be uniquely

9

indexed (Fig. 1 (c)). The same sequence will obtain in the higher layers as in the zero layer. To obtain the WEP of a particular layer L, the camera has to be turned through a definite angle ν. Depending on the sense of the rotation, one would photograph either the L or the $\bar{L}$ layer. Given

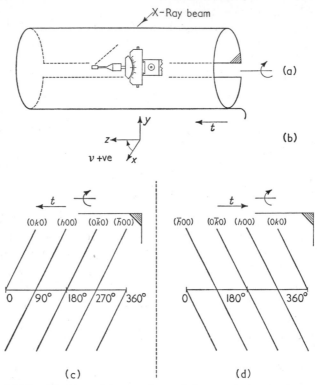

FIG. 1. (a) The direction of the rotation and the translation in a right-handed Weissenberg camera. The direction of the X-ray beam and the position of the cut on the film are also shown. (b) The right-handed system of co-ordinate axes used for indexing. The direction of ν for obtaining positive L layers is also shown. (c) and (d) The sequence of axial reflections as recorded on a film with a right-handed system of co-ordinates using (c) a right-handed camera and (d) a left-handed camera. The actual case illustrated is for an orthorhombic crystal, including all the axial rows for a rotation of 360°.

a right-handed system of co-ordinates, the sense of rotation in a right-handed camera to photograph the layers with positive values of L is apparent from Fig. 1 (b). If a right-handed camera is used, the sequence of the axial rows chosen above (Fig. 1(c)) immediately fixes a right-handed system of co-ordinates (Fig. 1 (b)). This is true, whatever be the symmetry of the crystal, and holds in the zero-level Weissenberg or the higher level WEP.

The appearance of the zero-level Weissenberg photograph from a crystal of any crystal system rotated about its c-axis is as shown in Fig. 2 (a), where γ^* has been chosen acute. In monoclinic, trigonal, tetragonal and hexagonal crystals mounted on the unique c-axis, the

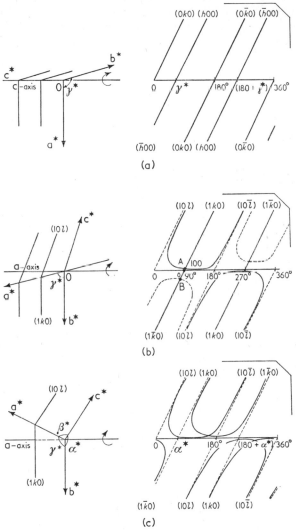

FIG. 2. (a) The zero-layer Weissenberg of a crystal belonging to any crystal system. In the case of crystals with 2-, 3-, 4- and 6-fold axis the zero and higher layer WEP's about the unique axis look alike. (b) The higher layer WEP of a monoclinic crystal about the non-unique axis a. The $Hk0$ spots fall on a straight line, while the $H0l$ reflections form a festoon. (c) The higher layer WEP of a triclinic crystal. The angles β^* and γ^* are computed from the lowest points of the $H0l$ and $Hk0$ festoons.

zero-layer Weissenberg and the higher layer WEP's will all be exactly alike, as in Fig. 2 (a), because the axial rows are always central.

However, if the axis of rotation is not the unique axis c, but either a or b, the zero-layer Weissenberg resembles the zero layer of an orthorhombic crystal (Fig. 1 (c)), but the higher layer WEP is as in Fig. 2 (b). The reciprocal rows $H0l$ and $H0\bar{l}$ being non-central, these reflections record on a festoon and not on a straight line, while the $Hk0$ reciprocal lattice row, being central, records as a straight line on the WEP.

As an illustration, the indexing in the case of a monoclinic crystal is now considered.

The zero layer enables b^* and c^* to be found, but not γ^*. It is customary to choose the angle γ^* to be acute. This may be done by considering the higher layer WEP, say of the first layer. The $1k0$ group of reflections record in a straight line and the $10l$ reflections on a festoon. The distance of the lowest point of this festoon from the central line of the WEP allows us to calculate γ^* (Buerger, 1942). It is rather easier in the case of the monoclinic than in a triclinic crystal to locate the minimum point of the axial festoon, for the point of intersection of the $1k0$ straight line and the $10l$ festoon is the lowest point of the festoon. If γ^* thus found is acute, then on the part of the $1k0$ straight line on which this point lies k is positive, otherwise it is negative. The proper sequence of the axial rows from right to left, mentioned earlier, determines a right-handed system of co-ordinates. This enables the axial rows to be properly identified so that this layer and all other layers can be correctly and uniquely indexed.

It does not matter if the convention for γ^* is ignored. One may then index the zero layer itself first, consistent only with the sequence of axial rows for a right-handed system. The angle γ^* then found from the higher layer may turn out to be either acute or obtuse, and the unit cell is taken as found. In the case of a triclinic crystal it follows that the conventional choice of the angular parameters of the unit cell may be ignored.

5. CORRELATION BETWEEN WEISSENBERG PHOTOGRAPHS FROM TWO DIFFERENT SETTINGS: UNIQUE INDEXING FOR A TRICLINIC CRYSTAL

If the positional parameters of all the atoms are determined from three-dimensional data collected from only *one setting* of the crystal, the absolute configuration of the crystal can be found by comparing the intensity of any Bijvoet pair. However, it is found that, for reason of computational facility, a structure is quite often solved using two-dimensional data obtained by rotating the crystal about each of two different crystallographic axes. It is usual to use two different crystals ground to the form of cylinders along the crystallographic axes which are used as the axes of rotation. This is so, particularly for crystals of the triclinic system. In such cases, when two different crystals are used for collecting intensity data, great care must be exercised in identifying the axes used as the axes of rotation; and the triclinic system is here taken to illustrate the procedure to be followed. Rotated first, say about the a-axis, a normal beam Weissenberg of the zero layer is taken and indexed using a right-handed system of co-ordinates mentioned earlier. The b^*, c^* and α^* values can be determined. Next, about the same axis, a higher layer WEP is taken in which the axial festoons may be identified by comparison of the zero and the higher layer photographs using well-known procedures laid down by Buerger (1942, pp. 342–4). From the lowest points of the axial festoons, β^* and γ^* can be calculated. From the a-axis rotation photograph, a and hence a^*, can be evaluated. Thus all the unit-cell parameters can be found from one setting of the crystal. In the second crystal rotated about, say the b-axis, all the parameters can again be found in the same manner. It is easy to choose the unit cell so that the reciprocal parameters obtained in the second setting are identical with those chosen from the first setting. But it must be pointed out that, if the crystal were mounted along the $-b$-axis instead of the b-axis as assumed, identical reciprocal parameters can be chosen only on a left-handed system and not on a right-handed system.

In actual practice, it is not necessary to take a higher layer WEP in the second setting. Since a^*, c^* and β^* values are already known from the first setting, they can easily be identified in the zero-layer photograph in the second setting also. The sequence of axial rows would show if the co-ordinate system is right-handed or left-handed, i.e. if the axis of rotation is b or $-b$. However, since the angle between c^* and a^* and $-c^*$ and $-a^*$ is the same, the doubt remains whether the axes chosen as c^* and a^* are not really $-c^*$ and $-a^*$ respectively. While this does not matter in centrosymmetric structures ($P\bar{1}$), it is of the utmost importance in non-centrosymmetric crystals for determining the absolute configuration. For the latter, since the $00l$ reflections are common to the zero-layer Weissenberg photographs about the a- and b-axes, the Bijvoet inequality that $I(00l) \neq I(00\bar{l})$ may be used to resolve the ambiguity. If in the first setting $I(00l) > I(00\bar{l})$, the same must be true in the other setting also. If this is not found to be so, then what had been assumed as $00l$ in indexing the photograph about the second setting must now be taken as $00\bar{l}$.

One must draw attention to the fact that all this is necessary only for correlating the data from the two settings and has as yet nothing to do with determining the absolute configuration. To be more explicit, it makes certain that one does not use, say, the a-axis in one projection and the $-a$-axis in the other.

If the unit-cell angles differ sufficiently from 90°, any such mistake may become apparent from unusual interatomic distances, etc. If, however, the unit-cell angles are close to 90°, any differences from accepted interatomic distances will be small and may well be overlooked as being due to errors that are usual in X-ray crystallography.

Having thus fixed the co-ordinate system correctly, the determination of absolute configuration still remains to be done by comparison of intensity between reflections of any Bijvoet pair. It is obvious that if a mistake is made in correlating the photographs in the two settings, the structure and absolute configuration determined will be wrong.

6. Double-layer Weissenberg Photography

One may record on the same film by normal beam photography reflections belonging to two different layers. The necessity was suggested by the following consideration. Since the absorption factors are usually large when anomalous scattering is present, great care should be taken to see that for both reflections of the Bijvoet pair the absorption corrections are identical. This is essential as the differences in the intensity of the Bijvoet pairs is usually quite small. Many crystals belonging to the monoclinic, trigonal, tetragonal and hexagonal classes have a tendency to form needles along the unique axis. In all these systems, excepting the trigonal, there are no Bijvoet pairs in any layer about the unique axis. The reflections to be compared, hkl and $hk\bar{l}$, may, however, be obtained in the Weissenberg photograph of any one layer about a non-unique axis. To cut the crystal in the required direction is impossible where a liquid at normal temperatures has been crystallized in a capillary tube at low temperatures. Even when the substance is a crystal at room temperature it has quite often proved impossible to cut it along the required axis and grind it into a good cylindrical specimen. If the specimen is not perfectly cylindrical, absorption corrections for each of the two reflections of a Bijvoet pair will be different, and if not perfectly corrected may vitiate the comparison of intensity in the determination of the absolute configuration.

To obviate the difficulty, a simple double-layer screen has been devised so that by normal beam Weissenberg photography (Wooster and Wooster, 1933; Buerger, 1942, pp. 242–4) the reflections of the L and $\bar{L}$ layers are recorded on the same film. The reflections hkL and $hk\bar{L}$ are recorded simultaneously on the same film separated by a distance $D(= 2R\tan\mu)$, where R is the radius of the film. If the rotation of the camera is less than the angle corresponding to a translation equal to D, there will be no overlapping of spots of the two layers.

After many trials the design of the double-layer screen which proved most satisfactory is shown in Fig. 3.† The central tube B, between two layer slits A and C, can be varied in length by adding or removing the small stepped rings which fit snugly into one another. It is found that if the rings are made of non-ferrous magnetic alloy and magnetized in the direction of the axis of the tube they hold on to each other quite well, and no other mechanical support is necessary. The beam catcher is permanently fixed to one of the rings, which can always be brought to the centre.

A second method using two vertical variable apertures on either side of the crystal, together with the conventional screen tubes, is also being tried for separating the two layers hkL and $hk\bar{L}$. The double-layer method of recording the Bijvoet pairs has the following advantages. For crystals that have only a 2-, 4- or 6-axis this method may be used. The LP factor

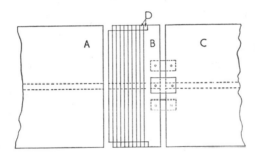

Fig. 3. The double-layer screen, in which A and C are conventional screen tubes and B is attached to C by metal strips. Stepped rings D (if necessary, magnetized) fit on to B to give a central screen tube of variable length.

is identical for the Bijvoet pair hkL and $hk\bar{L}$. If the crystal is cylindrical about the axis of rotation the absorption corrections are also the same. Further, both reflections will be elongated or contracted in the same manner. The reflections also occur simultaneously and so any fluctuations in the intensity of the incident beam will not matter at all. In other cases, where both reflections of a Bijvoet pair are not flashed simultaneously, a stabilized X-ray unit would be essential.

In the triclinic system the reflections to be compared are of the type hkl and $\bar{h}\bar{k}\bar{l}$. These will not be recorded on the same side of the film in any conventional Weissenberg camera. In the double-layer method they may be obtained on the same film and on the same side of the central line as follows. The slots of the double screen are adjusted to photograph the L and $\bar{L}$ layers. One slit is closed and the hkL data is recorded through the other. The crystal is now rotated by exactly 180°. The first slit is now

† This design is due to Dr. G. Suryan.

opened while the other is closed, and $hk\bar{L}$ reflections are recorded in an adjacent part of the same film. The reflections hkl and $\bar{h}\bar{k}\bar{l}$ are now separated by a distance D, and these may be compared for the determination of the absolute configuration, provided the intensity of the incident beam has been constant throughout the experiment and the exposures for the two layers was the same.

Acknowledgements

The authors thank the Council of Scientific and Industrial Research, India, for supporting the project on low and high-temperature crystallography. Thanks are also due to Professor R. S. Krishnan for his interest in the problem, and to Dr. G. Suryan and Dr. S. Swaminathan for many invaluable discussions.

REFERENCES

Abrahams, S. C., Collin, R. L., Lipscomb, W. N. and Reed, T. B. (1950). *Rev. sci. Instrum.* **21**, 396.
Bijvoet, J. M. (1954). *Nature, Lond.* **173**, 888.
Bijvoet, J. M. (1955). *Endeavour* **14**, 74.
Buerger, M. J. (1942). *X-ray Crystallography.* Wiley, New York.
Dauben, C. H. and Templeton, D. H. (1955). *Acta cryst.* **8**, 841.
Kaufman, H. S. and Fankuchen, I. (1949). *Rev. sci. Instrum.* **20**, 733.
Manohar, H. and Ramaseshan, S. (1961). *Tetrahedron Letters* **22**, 814.
Peerdeman, A. F. and Bijvoet, J. M. (1956). *Acta cryst., Camb.* **9**, 1012.
Peterson, S. W. (1955). *Nature, Lond.* **176**, 396.
Singh, A. K. and Ramaseshan, S. (1963). This volume, p. 309.
Singh, A. K., Swaminathan, S. and Ramaseshan, S. (1962). To be published.
Wooster, W. A. and Wooster, N. (1933). *Z. Kristallogr.* **84**, 327.

DISCUSSION

S. RAMASESHAN: The concept of the double-layer line screen is not new. Prof. Bijvoet and his collaborators have used such an arrangement in their studies of the absolute configuration of $NaClO_3$ and $NaBrO_3$ (see this volume, p. 225. See also A. W. Hanson, *J. Sci. Instrum.* **35**, 188, 288 (1958) and the references given therein).

G. KARTHA: While using the double-slit method it seems advantageous to use half slits instead of full slits, so that one could record both hkl and $\bar{h}\bar{k}\bar{l}$ (say) in the same run on the top and bottom halves of the film respectively.

S. RAMASESHAN: Yes. In fact Hanson's double-layer screen has only half slits.

R. SRINIVASAN: I think it is possible to have the hkl and $\bar{h}\bar{k}\bar{l}$ reflections on the same side of the film by changing the ratio of the translation to the rotation, so that instead of the usual coverage of 0–180°, one can have 0–360° on each side of the film.

S. RAMASESHAN: This is of course possible. Prof. Buerger has described an 8°/mm camera in his book. But this involves a major modification of the Weissenberg camera. In this work we devised attachments only for the traditional 2°/mm camera.

D. HARKER: It is to be noted that the point group of the reciprocal lattice is that of the crystal when anomalous scattering is present. In order to observe the Bijvoet inequality, the two reflections must not be related by the true symmetry of the crystal but *must* be related by the Laue point group, that is the true point group plus a centre of inversion.

SECTION V
Electron and Neutron Diffraction

An Electron Diffraction Problem in Phthalocyanine and Its Metal Derivatives

Shizuo Miyake, Kunio Fujiwara

Institute for Solid State Physics, University of Tokyo,
Azabu, Minato-ku, Tokyo, Japan

AND

Fuminori Fujimoto

Institute of Physics, College of General Education,
University of Tokyo, Komaba, Tokyo, Japan

ABSTRACT

The values of Fourier potentials of the indices $(00n)$ and $(2n, 0, \bar{n})$ $(n = 1, 2, 3, 4)$ are calculated for metal-free, nickel, platinum and copper phthalocyanine crystals on the known structural basis, with the use of the tabulations of atomic scattering amplitudes for electrons given by Ibers in 1958 and 1962. With the use of the calculated data, an electron diffraction theory is discussed on $(00n)$-reflections of Pt-phthalocyanine by assuming a harmonic potential which happens to be a fairly good approximation in this case. It is pointed out that, in the geometrical conditions where the (001) reflection is strong, the reflections (002) and (003) can never be neglected and will bear appreciable influences to the feature of the so-called "lattice image" of (001) in electron micrographs.

Introduction

The crystal structures of phthalocyanine and its nickel, copper and platinum derivatives were studied by Robertson (1935) and Robertson and Woodward (1937, 1940). Since Menter's first observation of the "lattice image" in electron micrographs (1956), the metal derivatives, in particular, Pt- and Cu-phthalocyanines have been often used as samples to observe this kind of image. The lattice images for low order reflections of these substances have the spacings near 10 Å and the observation of them plays a role in the performance-tests of electron microscopes.

The spacing for $(20\bar{1})$ of Pt-phthalocyanine, for example, is 11·9 Å, and the lattice image having the same period may appear by the interference of the $(20\bar{1})$ reflection with the primary wave. The experimentally observed interference fringes ("lattice image"), however, seem sometimes too sharp to regard them to be of the sinusoidal form, suggesting the possibility of higher order reflections participating simultaneously in forming the image. Generally speaking, the interactions with higher order reflections are, as was pointed out by Niehrs (1962), often not negligible for a reflection with more or less large spacing, even if the value of the relevant Fourier potential is not so large.

In spite of its wide application to electron microscopic purposes, a comparison in detail of the lattice image with theoretical results has not been made for metal phthalocyanines. In the present paper, the values of some Fourier potentials for metal-free, nickel, platinum and copper phthalocyanines are calculated on the known structural basis, for theoretical needs in future. At the same time, a preliminary consideration of the electron diffraction by Pt-phthalocyanine is given on the basis of dynamical theory.

CALCULATION OF FOURIER POTENTIAL

There have been published several tabulations of atomic scattering amplitudes for electrons expressed in the form

$$f(s) = \frac{8\pi^2 m e^2}{h^2} \frac{Z - f_X(s)}{s^2} \tag{1}$$

where $s = 4\pi \sin\vartheta / \lambda$, 2ϑ the scattering angle, Z the atomic number, and $f_X(s)$ the X-ray form factor (Ibers, 1958; Vainshtein and Ibers, 1958; Ibers and Vainshtein, 1959; Ibers, 1962). The crystal structure factor for a reflection $\mathbf{h}(h_1, h_2, h_3)$ is given by

$$F_\mathbf{h} = \sum_i f_i \exp 2\pi i (\mathbf{h} \cdot \mathbf{r}_i) \tag{2}$$

where i denotes the number specifying the ith atom at the position $\mathbf{r}_i$ in the unit cell; s and the reciprocal lattice point vector $\mathbf{h}$ are related by $s = 2\pi |\mathbf{h}|$. Let the periodic electric potential in the crystal, $V(\mathbf{r})$, be expressed by the following Fourier series

$$V(\mathbf{r}) = \sum_{h_1 h_2 h_3} V_\mathbf{h} \exp 2\pi i (\mathbf{h} \cdot \mathbf{r}) \tag{3}$$

then the Fourier potential $V_\mathbf{h}$ and the structure factor $F_\mathbf{h}$ are known to have the relation

$$V_\mathbf{h} = \frac{1}{v_c} \frac{h^2}{2\pi m e} F_\mathbf{h} \tag{4}$$

where v_c is the cell volume. Values of $V_\mathbf{h}$ in volts are given by

$$V_\mathbf{h} = 300 \frac{1}{v_c} \frac{h^2}{2\pi m e} F_\mathbf{h} = 47 \cdot 9 \times \frac{F_\mathbf{h}(\text{in Å})}{v_c(\text{in Å}^3)} \tag{5}$$

The tabulations of $f(s)$ given before 1959 were based on the Hartree-Fock wave functions for atoms $Z \leq 20$, and on the Thomas-Fermi-Dirac statistical atoms for $Z > 20$. By making use of new calculations of Hartree-Fock wave functions owing to the efforts of A. J. Freeman and R. E. Watson, Ibers (1962) recently gave a recalculation of $f(s)$ for heavier atoms. In evaluating Fourier potentials of phthalocynines, Ibers' tabulations of $f(s)$ given in 1958 and 1962 were utilized, since this combination gives the best theoretical data at the moment.

According to Robertson (1935), phthalocyanines possess the monoclinic symmetry, belonging to the space group $C_{2h}^5 (P2_1/a)$, with the cell dimensions as shown in Table I. The unit cell contains two centrosymmetrical molecules ($C_{32}H_{16}N_8$, $C_{32}H_{16}N_8Ni$, $C_{32}H_{16}N_8Cu$ or $C_{32}H_{16}N_8Pt$), and the metal atom in each metal derivative is situated at the centre of symmetry.

The Fourier potentials of $(00n)$ and $(2n, 0, \bar{n})$ ($n = 1, 2, 3, 4$) for metal-free, platinum and nickel phthalocyanines were calculated by the use of the above crystal data as well as the atomic parameters determined by

TABLE I. Crystal data of phthalocyanines (Robertson)

	Phthalocyanine (metal-free)	Ni-derivative	Cu-derivative	Pt-derivative
a (Å)	19·85	19·9	19·6	23·9
b (Å)	4·72	4·71	4·79	3·81
c (Å)	14·8	14·9	14·6	16·9
β	122·25°	121·9°	120·0°	129·6°
v_o (Å³)	1173	1186	1180	1186

Robertson and Woodward (1937, 1940). The reflections (001) and (20$\bar{1}$) are ones which are most often utilized for observing the "lattice image". It should be mentioned, however, that the contribution of hydrogen atoms was ignored here, simply because their parameters had not been obtained by the X-ray study. The calculated results are shown in Table II. Although the atomic parameters for the copper derivative were not given in Robertson and Woodward's papers, the values of Fourier potentials for this substance have been calculated assuming the same atomic parameters as in the nickel derivative, with a correction due to the difference in cell volumes and are included together in this Table. This assumption is reasonable in view of the small differences in cell dimensions between the copper and nickel derivatives.†

† Hashimoto et al. (1961) quoted the values of the (20$\bar{1}$) Fourier potentials for Pt- and Cu-derivatives, calculated by using the tabulation of Ibers of 1958 and otherwise on the same basis as in the present calculation. Their values, 2·4 volt and 3·3 volt, respectively, differ appreciably from the corresponding values in Table II. The differences do not seem to be due to the use of Ibers' new tabulation of 1962 in the present calculation. It should be mentioned that the value for Pt-derivative should at any rate be larger than that for Cu-derivative.

TABLE II. Fourier potentials for $(00n)$ and $(2n, 0, \bar{n})$ of phthalocyanines

Substance	hkl	$\dfrac{\sin\vartheta}{\lambda}$	Spacing d (Å)	Fourier potential (V)
Phthalocyanine	001	0·040	12·5	1·03
(metal-free)	002	0·080	6·2$_5$	−1·39
	003	0·120	4·1$_7$	−0·58
	004	0·160	3·1$_3$	0·21
	20$\bar{1}$	0·051	9·8	1·31
	40$\bar{2}$	0·102	4·9	−1·46
	60$\bar{3}$	0·153	3·2$_7$	−0·52
	80$\bar{4}$	0·204	2·4$_5$	−0·02
Platinum	001	0·039	13·0	2·18
phthalocyanine	002	0·077	6·5	−0·25
	003	0·116	4·3$_3$	0·15
	004	0·154	3·2$_5$	1·03
	20$\bar{1}$	0·042	11·9	2·10
	40$\bar{2}$	0·084	5·9$_5$	−0·69
	60$\bar{3}$	0·126	3·9$_7$	0·32
	80$\bar{4}$	0·168	2·9$_8$	0·81
Nickel	001	0·040	12·6	1·57
phthalocyanine	002	0·079	6·3	−0·97
	003	0·119	4·2	−0·14
	004	0·159	3·1$_5$	−0·50
	20$\bar{1}$	0·051	9·8	1·82
	40$\bar{2}$	0·102	4·9	−1·06
	60$\bar{3}$	0·153	3·2$_7$	−0·12
	80$\bar{4}$	0·204	2·4$_5$	0·27
Copper	001	0·040	12·5$_7$	1·56
phthalocyanine	002	0·080	6·2$_9$	−0·99
	003	0·119	4·1$_9$	−0·15
	004	0·159	3·1$_4$	0·49
	20$\bar{1}$	0·052	9·6$_3$	1·81
	40$\bar{2}$	0·104	4·8$_2$	−1·08
	60$\bar{3}$	0·156	3·2$_1$	−0·13
	80$\bar{4}$	0·207	2·4$_1$	0·27

The values of Fourier potentials given in Table II are subject to a number of sources of error, as follows.

(i) As already mentioned, the contribution of hydrogen atoms is entirely neglected in the above calculation. Errors due to this approximation are by no means negligible, in view of the relatively abundant number of hydrogen atoms in the molecule, and of the relatively larger ratios of the $f(s)$-value for hydrogen to those for other atoms in the range of small s-values, compared with the same ratios of $f_X(s)$. Errors due to the neglect of hydrogen atoms should, however, be less serious for the metal derivatives, in particular for the Pt-derivative.

(ii) The theoretical calculation of wave functions may not be exact anyway and, as pointed out by Ibers (1962), errors in wave functions may influence the values of scattering amplitudes especially in the range of small s-values.

(iii) Ibers' calculations were made on neutral and spherical free atoms. Atoms in crystals, however, may differ from free ones, and non-sphericity may probably also arise in electron distributions. Such deformations in electron clouds may have again the largest influences on the scattering amplitudes in the range of small s-values (cf. Harada and Kashiwase, 1962).

Exact estimation of errors in the calculated data in Table II, however, is not possible for any of the above mentioned sources. Therefore, it is difficult to insist on a high reliability of the calculated values. Nevertheless, we should have to use these values in any theoretical treatment of electron diffraction by phthalocyanine crystals, inasmuch as neither theoretical values from other sources nor experimental values have been given so far. The values in Table II are based on the best sources available at present. Due caution will be necessary in using these values, but their improvement is a problem to be worked out in the future.

SOLUTION FOR $(00n)$ REFLECTIONS OF PT-PHTHALOCYANINE

The solution of Schrödinger equation for electrons in a crystal is given by the Bloch wave function

$$\Psi_B = \sum_{\mathbf{h}} u_{\mathbf{h}} \exp 2\pi i (\mathbf{k_h} \cdot \mathbf{r}) \tag{6}$$

where $\mathbf{k_h} = \mathbf{k_0} + \mathbf{h}$, $\mathbf{k_0}$ being the wave vector of the primary wave in the crystal and $\mathbf{h}$ the reciprocal lattice point vector. The amplitudes $u_{\mathbf{h}}$ are determined by the well-known simultaneous equations (Bethe, 1928)

$$(\kappa^2 - k_{\mathbf{h}}^2) u_{\mathbf{h}} + \frac{2me}{h^2} \sum_{\mathbf{s} \neq \mathbf{h}} u_{\mathbf{s}} V_{\mathbf{h-s}} = 0 \tag{7}$$

where
$$\kappa^2 = (eV_0 + E)\frac{2m}{h^2} = \frac{1}{\lambda^2}$$

E being the total energy of electron, and κ and λ, the regular values of the wave number and wavelength of electrons within the crystal respectively. The number of the equations (7), or of the amplitudes $u_{\mathbf{h}}$ of the component waves is usually reduced to a finite number by retaining only strong component waves corresponding to the reciprocal lattice points lying close to the Ewald sphere. In problems of electron diffraction by perfect crystals, in contrast to the X-ray cases, the reduction of the number of equations is limited by strong interactions among different reflections due to the large interactions of electrons with matter. If the incident electrons are nearly parallel to some of zone axes of the crystal so that many reciprocal lattice points on a lattice plane passing through the reciprocal space origin happen to come near the Ewald sphere, the interactions take place in a most complicated manner among a large number of different waves. We may avoid such an "accidental" geometrical condition so as to be able to deal primarily with the reflection from a single lattice plane. As was pointed out by Hoerni (1956), however, even in this case it is not always possible to neglect the effect of the "systematic" interactions due to the reciprocal points lying on the point row passing through the reciprocal space origin and the reciprocal lattice point corresponding to the reflection under consideration, since this point row necessarily runs near the Ewald sphere.

The data of Fourier potentials in Table II may be applied to theoretical considerations on low-order reflections of $(00n)$ and $(2n, 0, \bar{n})$ from phthalocyanine crystals taking account of the systematic interactions. Sufficiently accurate solutions of (7) will be available without much difficulty by the use of recent electronic computers. In what follows, however, a preliminary consideration dealing with the solution of the Schrödinger equation for a harmonic potential is given to discuss the reflections $(00n)$ of Pt-phthalocyanine, for which the approximation using a harmonic potential is believed to be fairly good because, as is seen in Table II, Fourier potential for (002) and for (003) are fortunately very small compared with that for (001). The Schrödinger equation is reduced in this case to Mathieu's differential equation, and we can follow Hoerni's procedure (1956) in his treatment on the (111) and (222) reflections of germanium crystal assuming a harmonic potential.

Let us consider a plate-shaped crystal of Pt-phthalocyanine with the thickness D, and assume that the (001) plane is perpendicular to the plate surfaces. We take x and z axes respectively perpendicular to (001) and to the surfaces, and the origin of co-ordinates on the entrance surface. Then, $V(\mathbf{r})$ in the present case is expressed by

$$V(x) = 2V_{001} \cos\left(\frac{2\pi x}{d_{001}}\right) \tag{8}$$

and Ψ_B in Eq. (6) by

$$\Psi_B = \exp 2\pi i(k_{0z}z) \sum_n u_n \exp 2\pi i\left(k_{0x}+\frac{n}{d_{001}}\right)x \tag{9}$$

where k_{0x} and k_{0z} are the x- and z-components of $\mathbf{k}_0$ respectively.† The function

$$v(x) \equiv \sum_n u_n \exp 2\pi i \left(k_{0x} + \frac{n}{d_{001}} \right) x \qquad (10)$$

is proved to satisfy the Mathieu equation

$$\frac{d^2 v}{dx^2} + (a - \tfrac{1}{2} S \cos 2\omega)\, v = 0 \qquad (11)$$

where

$$\omega = \frac{\pi x}{d_{001}}, \quad u = 4 d_{001}^2 (\mathbf{K}^2 - k_{0z}^2), \quad S = -16 d_{001}^2 \frac{2me}{h^2} V_{001} \qquad (12)$$

$\mathbf{K}$ is the wave vector of the incident wave coming to the crystal surface from the outside space, being related to the energy E as follows,

$$\frac{h^2}{2m} \mathbf{K}^2 = E \qquad (13)$$

There are eigenvalues of a for the solutions of (11), so that the wave field $\Psi(x, z)$ in the crystal is given by a superposition of Bloch wave functions of the form (9), namely

$$\Psi(x, z) = \sum_j \Psi_B^j(x, z) = \sum_j \exp 2\pi i (k_{0z}^j z) \sum_n u_n^j \exp 2\pi i \left(k_{0x} + \frac{n}{d_{001}} \right) x \qquad (14)$$

where j is the number specifying the eigenvalues of $a(a^1, a^2, \ldots a^j, \ldots)$. $\Psi(x, z)$ should fulfil the boundary condition on the surface with the incoming wave. By this condition, the relative weight for each of Ψ_B^j for different j is normalized appropriately; we have also the relation

$$K_x = k_{0x} \qquad (15)$$

The values of u_n^j and the corresponding eigenvalue a^j can be known for the discrete values of $K_x(= k_{0x}) = p/d_{001}$ $(p = 0, \pm\tfrac{1}{2}, \pm 1, \pm\tfrac{3}{2}, \ldots)$ by making use of a tabulation of Mathieu functions (U.S. Nat. Bur. Stand., 1951).

Assuming that the amplitude of the incident wave is unity, the values of u_n^j normalized in accordance with the boundary condition were calculated for $K_x = 0$ and $K_x = 1/2d_{001}$. The following values were utilized for the parameters in (12): $d_{001} = 13\cdot0$ Å, $V_{001} = 2\cdot144$ V, $K = 104\cdot2/2\pi$ Å^{-1}. The value of V_{001} has been slightly altered from $V_{001} = 2\cdot18$ V for Pt-phthalocyanine in Table II so as to have a simple figure $S = -40$. The value of K corresponds to the electron energy $41\cdot5$ keV. The results obtained are shown in Table III (A) and (B)

† For clarity the following part of this section will repeat Hoerni's description to some extent.

TABLE III. Data of electron diffraction by a harmonic potential appropriate to $(00n)$-reflections of Pt-phthalocyanine

$d_{001} = 13 \cdot 0$ Å, $V_{001} = 2 \cdot 144$ V, $(S = -40)$

$K = 1/\lambda = 104 \cdot 2/2\pi$ Å^{-1}, amplitude of incident wave being unity

A $K_x = 0$ (symmetrical incidence), $u^j_{-n} = (-1)^{j+1} u^j_n$, $(n \geqslant 0)$

j	$2\pi\zeta^j(10^{-4}\text{Å}^{-1})$	u^j_0	u^j_1	u^j_2	u^j_3	u^j_4
1	$-38\cdot87$	$+0\cdot476$	$+0\cdot332$	$+0\cdot119$	$+0\cdot0024$	$+0\cdot003$
2	$-6\cdot64$	0	0	0	0	0
3	$22\cdot11$	$+0\cdot335$	$-0\cdot129$	$-0\cdot287$	$-0\cdot109$	$-0\cdot020$
4	$48\cdot47$	0	0	0	0	0
5	$58\cdot86$	$+0\cdot185$	$-0\cdot195$	$+0\cdot149$	$+0\cdot119$	$+0\cdot029$
6	$104\cdot36$	0	0	0	0	0
7	$104\cdot68$	$+0\cdot004$	$-0\cdot007$	$+0\cdot019$	$-0\cdot035$	$-0\cdot014$
8	$180\cdot72$	0	0	0	0	0
9	$180\cdot72$	$+0\cdot000$	$-0\cdot000$	$+0\cdot000$	$-0\cdot001$	$+0\cdot002$
$\bar{I}_n = \sum\limits_j |u^j_n|^2$		$0\cdot373$	$0\cdot163$	$0\cdot119$	$0\cdot028$	$0\cdot001$

B $K_x = 1/2d_{001}$ (Bragg condition on (001)), $u^j_{-n} = (-1)^{j+1} u^j_{n+1}$, $(n \geqslant 0)$

j	$2\pi\zeta^j(10^{-4}\text{Å}^{-1})$	u^j_0	u^j_1	u^j_2	u^j_3	u^j_4	u^j_5
1	$-38\cdot87$	$+0\cdot396$	$+0\cdot396$	$+0\cdot196$	$+0\cdot052$	$+0\cdot008$	$+0\cdot001$
2	$-6\cdot69$	$-0\cdot162$	$-0\cdot162$	$-0\cdot217$	$-0\cdot085$	$-0\cdot017$	$-0\cdot002$
3	$22\cdot27$	$+0\cdot093$	$+0\cdot093$	$-0\cdot159$	$-0\cdot110$	$-0\cdot028$	$-0\cdot004$
4	$43\cdot24$	$+0\cdot285$	$-0\cdot285$	$+0\cdot128$	$+0\cdot202$	$+0\cdot063$	$+0\cdot010$
5	$74\cdot65$	$+0\cdot010$	$+0\cdot010$	$-0\cdot036$	$+0\cdot054$	$+0\cdot027$	$+0\cdot005$
6	$77\cdot26$	$+0\cdot052$	$-0\cdot052$	$+0\cdot087$	$-0\cdot111$	$-0\cdot057$	$-0\cdot011$
7	$139\cdot60$	$+0\cdot000$	$+0\cdot000$	$-0\cdot001$	$+0\cdot003$	$-0\cdot007$	$-0\cdot002$
8	$139\cdot62$	$+0\cdot000$	$-0\cdot000$	$+0\cdot001$	$-0\cdot005$	$+0\cdot011$	$+0\cdot004$
9	$227\cdot65$	$+0\cdot000$	$+0\cdot000$	$-0\cdot000$	$+0\cdot000$	$-0\cdot000$	$+0\cdot000$
10	$227\cdot65$	$+0\cdot000$	$-0\cdot000$	$+0\cdot000$	$-0\cdot000$	$+0\cdot000$	$-0\cdot000$
$\bar{I}_n = \sum\limits_j |u^j_n|^2$		$0\cdot276$	$0\cdot276$	$0\cdot136$	$0\cdot078$	$0\cdot009$	$0\cdot000$

where ζ^j is the quantity specifying the position of the tie-points (or wave points) in reciprocal space, which is defined as

$$\zeta^j = K_z - k^j_{0z} \tag{16}$$

and is related, with a sufficient accuracy, to a^j as follows:

$$\zeta^j = \frac{1}{2K}\left(\frac{a^j}{4d^2} - K_x^2\right) \tag{17}$$

DISCUSSION

The case $K_x = 0$ corresponds to the symmetrical condition of incidence that the incident electrons run perpendicularly to the crystal surface (or parallel to the lattice plane (001)), and $K_x = 1/2d_{001}$ corresponds to the Bragg condition on (001).

The intensity I_n of each (00n) reflection is given by

$$I_n = |\sum_j u_n^j \exp 2\pi i(k_{0z}^j D)|^2 = \sum_j \sum_{j'} u_n^j u_n^{j'} \exp 2\pi i(\zeta^{j'} - \zeta^j)\, D \tag{18}$$

In the bottom rows in Table III (A) and (B) are shown the mean intensities, or the average of I_n with respect to the crystal thickness, i.e.

$$\bar{I}_n = \sum_j |u_n^j|^2 \tag{19}$$

The wave field at the exit surface, consisting of the participation of all reflections, is given by

$$J(x, D) = |\Psi(x, D)|^2$$

$$= \sum_n{}' \sum_{n'}{}' \exp 2\pi i\left(\frac{n - n'}{d_{001}}\right) x \sum_j \sum_{j'} u_n^j u_{n'}^{j'} \exp 2\pi i(\zeta^{j'} - \zeta^j)\, D \tag{20}$$

Equation (20) is a generalized expression of the "lattice image".

It is noticed in Table III (A) that the intensity $\bar{I}_1$ is remarkable in spite of this case corresponding to an off-Bragg condition with respect to (001). Further, in Table III (A) and (B), it is observed that the magnitudes of $\bar{I}^2$, as well as of u_2^j, are comparable to those of $\bar{I}_1$ and u_1^j respectively. $\bar{I}_3$, as well as u_3^j, are also not negligible in Table III (B). In other words: (i) The first-order reflection (001) (or (00$\bar{1}$)) continues to have a conspicuous intensity, being the strongest among others, over the whole angular range of incident electrons corresponding to about $|K_x| \lesssim 1/2d_{001}$; and (ii) under these geometrical conditions, the participation of the second- and third-order reflections, at least, can never be disregarded.

The participation of higher reflections will take place similarly or even more remarkably in ($2n$, 0, $\bar{n}$) reflections of this substance and in (00n) and ($2n$, 0, $\bar{n}$) reflections of other metal phthalocyanines, although the approximation using the harmonic potential is not permissible in these cases. Judging from Eq. (20), it is conceivable that the sharpening of fringes and the appearance of fine structure would take place in the lattice image by the higher order harmonics, due to the participation of higher order reflections.

In Table III (A) and (B) the fact should be noted that u_n^j for $j = 4 \sim 5$ have values that are not small when compared with u_n^1 of the corresponding n. The relations $u_n^j = 0$ for even j in Table III (A) can be proved to hold not only for the harmonic potential but for any form of one-dimensional periodic potential under the condition of symmetric incidence ($K_x = 0$).

Niehrs (1962) pointed out that the quantity $d_h^2 | V_h |$ gives a measure of the scattering power of each lattice plane, especially when the strength of the interactions of the relevant reflection with others is to be considered, and that the multiple-beam treatment is essential if the value of this quantity is not small compared with the value 150 VÅ^2. He calculated this quantity for $(00n)$ of lauric acid, for which $d_{001} = 27 \cdot 4$ Å. In the treatment given in the present paper, his quantity corresponds to the parameter S in (12). For (001) of Pt-phthalocyanine, $d_{001}^2 | V_{001} | \approx 370$. Another example is $d_{111}^2 | V_{111} | \approx 120$ for gold, for which $V_{111} = 22 \cdot 6$ V, $d_{111} = 2 \cdot 86$ Å. A comparison of these examples will illustrate how the use of the multiple-beam approximation is required for a reflection with more or less large spacing d_h even if the magnitude of V_h is not especially large, as is in general the case for low-order reflections of phthalocyanines.

A calculation of the intensity distribution of the lattice image due to (001) of Pt-phthalocyanine using the theoretical data given in the present paper, and a comparison with the result of the two-beam approximation, as well as a discussion relating to experiments, will be reported elsewhere.

REFERENCES

Bethe, H. A. (1928). *Ann. Phys., Lpz.* **87**, 55.
Harada, J. and Kashiwase, Y. (1962). *J. phys. Soc. Japan* **17**, 829.
Hashimoto, H., Mannami, M. and Naiki, T. (1961). *Phil. Trans.* **253**, 459.
Hoerni, J. A. (1956). *Phys. Rev.* **102**, 1534.
Ibers, J. A. (1958). *Acta cryst.* **11**, 178.
Ibers, J. A. (1962). Proc. Int. Conf. on Mag. and Cryst., Kyoto, 1961 (*J. phys. Soc. Japan* **17**, Suppl. B-II), 4.
Ibers, J. A. and Vainshtein, B. K. (1959). *Kristallografiya* **4**, 641.
Menter, J. W. (1956). *Proc. roy. Soc.* A, **236**, 119.
Niehrs (1962). Proc. Int. Conf. on Mag. and Cryst., Kyoto, 1961 (*J. phys. Soc. Japan* **17**, Suppl. B-II), 104.
Robertson, J. M. (1935). *J. chem. Soc.* 615.
Robertson, J. M. and Woodward, I. (1937). *J. chem. Soc.* 219.
Robertson, J. M. and Woodward, I. (1940). *J. chem. Soc.* 36.
U.S. Nat. Bureau of Standards (1951). *Tables Relating to Mathieu Functions.* Columbia University Press, New York.
Vainshtein, B. K. and Ibers, J. A. (1958). *Kristallografiya* **3**, 416.

Analysis of Hydrogen-bonded Crystals by Neutron Diffraction Techniques

JAGDISH SHANKAR AND V. M. PADMANABHAN

Chemistry Division,
Atomic Energy Establishment, Trombay,
Bombay, India

ABSTRACT

The paper describes some of the recent work on hydrogen-bonded crystals by neutron diffraction studies. The results are analysed to bring out some of the features of the bond type.

1. INTRODUCTION

The paper describes some recent results on hydrogen-bonded crystals obtained by employing single crystal neutron diffraction techniques. Till recently the neutron diffraction studies were confined to more or less powder specimens. However, with the advent of reactors of high fluxes and due to availability of sophisticated automatic 3-dimensional (3-D) spectrometers the subject has taken a new turn. The earlier studies on heavy metal carbides and hydrides of uranium, thallium and zirconium were undertaken to settle some points of controversy in the structures. Doubts were expressed by Lonsdale (1949, 1950) that Fourier methods cannot be used for crystal analysis from neutron scattering data because of the nature of the nuclear form factors. But the detailed Fourier analysis of potassium dihydrogen phosphate, KH_2PO_4, by Bacon and Pease (1953) and Pepinsky (1953) indicated that neutron diffraction studies on single crystals can be undertaken to obtain a wealth of information.

One of the difficult problems which confronts the experimenter in this field is the actual measurement of the intensity of reflections from all planes of a crystal. Since the neutron detector is heavy it cannot naturally be raised out of the equatorial plane. Of all the instruments developed so far, the Oak Ridge 3-D single crystal orienter which has been put into operation recently by Levy (1961) and his group seems to be the most versatile. The spectrometer is automatic and can record complete three-dimensional data. In this programmed crystal orienter, the three angles θ, ϕ and χ are set according to instructions from a control tape to bring any

269

crystal plane into reflecting position. Data are collected by step scanning and the count at each step position is punched on an output tape. The automatic computer ORACLE is used to produce the control tape, given the cell dimensions, wavelength and orientation information. The output tape is also processed by the computer using a programme which obtains the intensity data and checks the data for various indications of malfunction. It is not necessary to orient the crystal in the usual way. Instead orientation information is supplied to the computer in terms of the measured angular settings required to bring two independent planes into reflecting position. A method of using angle measurements from several reflections to refine both the orientation and cell parameters is also possible.

Since in all the instruments double crystal spectrometers are used, one has to be aware of the effects of the mosaic spread of the monochromator and the minimum aperture which the counter must have to receive the whole of the beam reflected by the crystal. Recently Willis (1960) has made an analysis for the spectrometer design in the absence of Soller slits. It is shown that the choice of θ_B (Bragg angle of monochromator) is particularly important, because of its influence on the widths of the Bragg reflections of the second crystal. To observe weak high-order reflections it would be advantageous to use a relatively high value of θ_B ($\sim 45°$).

Although absorption in neutron diffraction is comparatively small, a correction becomes necessary while doing accurate work. It is customary to make cylindrical specimens and then employ the absorption corrections. Recently Busing and Levy (1957a) have modified Albrecht's method and have written a programme for the computer from which it is possible to get the absorption correction for any reflection.

The problem of obtaining single crystal specimens for neutron diffraction which are free from secondary extinction is a major one. In order to reduce the effect of extinction, the radius of the specimen may be reduced. The ultimate practical limit in this direction is the resulting low diffracted intensity. In practice, at least two sizes of specimens are needed, a small one with a radius of 1 mm on which very intense reflections are measured and a larger one on which the remaining reflections are measured, from which it is possible to see whether any extinction is present. If extinction is important, the experimental structure factors will average smaller than the calculated structure factors, the deviation increasing with intensity. The problem then becomes one of finding the correct function with which to correct experimentally observed intensities.

After deriving a trial structure, the parameters are then refined by least-squares methods. Excellent programmes like that of Busing and

Levy (1960) are available for high-speed electronic computers for refining the positional and temperature factors. It is customary to get all the anisotropic temperature coefficients for each atom to study in detail the thermal movement.

An important aspect of least-squares adjustment is the assignment of correct relative weights to the observation. The sources of error in experimental determination are believed to arise from two principal sources: (1) counting statistics; and (2) instrumental inaccuracies and scale-factor uncertainty caused principally by errors in measurements on the standard samples and in estimated absorption correction. The best atomic parameters are those that result in the minimization of the function

$$R = [\Sigma W(F_o - F_c)^2 / \Sigma W F_o^2]^{1/2}$$

where W is inversely proportional to the variance of the observed structure factor. The variance in F can be easily written down taking into account fluctuations in beam intensity, uncertainty in the absorption correction, etc. The correctness of the weight of each observation can be checked by the relation $[W(F_o - F_c)^2/(m-n)]^{1/2}$, where W is the weight of the observation, m the number of observations and n the number of parameters. The expected value of this quantity is unity, and any deviation from unity indicates that either the assignment of the weights are under-estimated or the thermal movements are incorrectly assumed (Busing and Levy, 1957b).

2. RESULTS ON HYDROGEN-CONTAINING STRUCTURES

We shall discuss some hydrogen-bonded structures that have been solved recently by neutron diffraction from single crystals.

A. *Structure of heavy ice*

The most striking evidence for the existence of the hydrogen bond is in ice, and this has evoked considerable theoretical interest. Peterson and Levy (1957a) have studied the neutron diffraction of heavy ice at −50°C and −150°C. Their results are consistent with the disordered model of Pauling (1935). Fourier projection along b-axis clearly shows the environment of oxygen being surrounded by four other oxygen atoms. Along the bonds which join each pair of oxygen atoms lie what are effectively two half-atoms of deuterium. The distance between the oxygen atoms is 2·76 Å and the deuteriums are at 1·01 Å away from oxygens, and the D—O—D angles are close to tetrahedral. This O—D distance may be compared with 0·96 Å, which is known from other information to be the O—H separation in the vapour state, the increased distance indicating the pull exerted on the hydrogen atom by the more distant of the pair of oxygen atoms. Peterson and Levy analysed the thermal parameters by least-squares refinement and showed that the motion of the deuterium atom was anisotropic. From this, values for the amplitude of the O—D stretching vibration were obtained and these were consistent with the frequency of the motion. The observed H—O—H angle is 109°, which is about 5° more than the vapour value of 104°. A bent-hydrogen model has recently been proposed (Chidambaram, 1961) which uses a value for the H—O—H angle close to 104°. This is obtained by splitting the "half-hydrogen" position into three "one-sixth hydrogen" positions distributed at the vertices of an equilateral triangle perpendicular to the O $\cdots$ O line which will pass through the centroid of the triangle. This model retains the statistical space group (D_{6h}^4) of the "half-hydrogen" Pauling model for hexagonal ice. Each "one-sixth hydrogen" position is shifted from the O $\cdots$ O line by about 0·044 Å. The model is shown to be consistent with the neutron-diffraction data of Peterson and Levy. The splitting suggested may be accommodated as a part of the thermal motion of hydrogen atom perpendicular to the O $\cdots$ O line.

The H-atoms of the water molecule are often involved in forming hydrogen bonds with electronegative atoms like O, N, Cl and F. Rundle and Parasol (1952) have observed a strong correlation between O—H stretching and the distance O—O in a number of hydrogen compounds. In Table I the O—H and O—O distances, as obtained from neutron data, are listed.

Atoji and Rundle (1958) have reviewed the data of some of the above crystals and have indicated an inverse correlation between O—H and O—H $\cdots$ O distances. A closer scrutiny will indicate that if O—H—O is sufficiently short, the hydrogen atom takes up the central position between the oxygen atoms ($NH_4H_2PO_4$, KH bisphenylacetate, sodium sesquicarbonate, KH maleate and KH_2PO_4). The studies do not rule out the second possibility, that of distribution of the hydrogen atom at random between two symmetric non-centred sites along the O $\cdots$ O link. In the case of KH bisphenylacetate, studies at different temperatures show that true centering is alone possible and not the "half-hydrogen" model. Further, the hydrogen atom tends to be collinear with O $\cdots$ O; this tendency being greater the shorter the O $\cdots$ O distance. The mean thermal displacement of the hydrogen atom also shows a correlation, tending to smaller values the shorter the O $\cdots$ O link. In Table II are listed the bond lengths in bonds of type O—H $\cdots$ X (where X is Cl, F or N) and N—H $\cdots$ O.

It can be seen from the table that, in the O—H $\cdots$ X bond type, the O—H distance is about 0·98 Å ($\pm 0·04$) and does not show any large values such as those given in Table I. In all these cases the bond

TABLE I. Data relating to $OH \cdots O$ bonds from neutron data

Compound	Distance (Å)		Whether $O—H \cdots O$ is linear or bent	Reference
	O—H	O—O		
Ice (D_2O)	1·01	2·76	Linear	Peterson and Levy (1957a)
KH_2PO_4 (Room temp.)	1·08	2·48	Linear	Peterson and Levy (1953); Bacon and Pease (1953)
KH_2AsO_4	1.06	2.52	Linear	Peterson and Levy (1961)
$(COOH)_2,2H_2O$:				
(a) hydroxyl-water	1·06	2·52	Linear (symmetrical)	Garret (1954)
(b) water-carboxyl	0·97 0·95	2·82 2·86	Non-linear	
α-HIO_3	0·96	2·68	Nearly linear	Garret (1954)
N-acetylglycine	1·02	2·56	Linear	Peterson et al. (1957)
Li_2SO_4,H_2O:				
(a) water–water	0·95	2·95	Non-linear	Smith (1961)
(b) water–sulphate	0·97	2·80	Non-linear	
$Sr(OH)_2,8H_2O$	0·99	2·80	Linear	Busing and Zocchi (1961)
Resorcinol	1·02	2·66	Non-linear (asymmetric)	Bacon and Curry (1956a)
$CaSO_4,H_2O$	0·99	2·85	Linear	Atoji and Rundle (1958)
KH Maleate	1·05 (half-hydrogen model)	2·44	Linear	Peterson and Levy (1958)
Sodium sesqui-carbonate:				
(a) water molecule	1·01 1·01	2·77	Non-linear	Bacon and Curry (1956b)
(b) hydrogen at the origin	1·12 (half-hydrogen model)	2·5	Linear	
KH bisphenyl-acetate	1·27	2·52	Linear	Bacon and Curry (1957, 1960)
$NH_4H_2PO_4$	1·07 (half-hydrogen model)	2·48	Linear	Tenzer et al. (1958)
Pentaerythritol	0·94	2·74	Non-linear	Hvoslef (1958)
$CuSO_4,5H_2O$	0·96 (mean)	2·76 (mean)	Non-linear	Bacon and Curry (1962)

TABLE II. Data relating to hydrogen bonds of the type X—H$\cdots$Y

Compound	Bond type X—H$\cdots$Y	Distance (Å) O—H	Distance (Å) O$\cdots$Y	Whether O—H$\cdots$Y is linear or non-linear	Reference
CuCl$_2$,2H$_2$O	O—H$\cdots$Cl	0·95	3·00	Non-linear	Peterson and Levy (1957b)
NH$_4$H$_2$PO$_4$	N—H$\cdots$O	1·00 (N—H)	3·17 (N$\cdots$O)	Non-linear	Tenzer $et\ al.$ (1958)
Dimethylgly-oxime	O—H$\cdots$N	1·02	2·77	Non-linear	Hamilton (1961)
FeSiF$_6$,6H$_2$O	O—H$\cdots$F	0·96	2·72	Non-linear	Hamilton (1962)
Urea	N—H$\cdots$O	0·99 (N—H)	3·01 (N$\cdots$O)	Non-linear	Worsham $et\ al.$ (1957)
NH$_3$OHCl	O—H$\cdots$Cl	0·99	3·00	Non-linear	Padmanabhan $et\ al.$ (1962a)
	N—H$\cdots$Cl	1·04 (mean N—H)	3·22 (mean N$\cdots$Cl)		
BaCl$_2$,2H$_2$O	—	0·96	—	—	Padmanabhan $et\ al.$ (1962b)
Ca(OH)$_2$	—	0·94	—	—	Busing and Levy (1957b)

O—H$\cdots$X is bent, and the angle varies from 140° to 170°. Contrary to the observation with crystals in Table I, here no variation of O—H distance with O$\cdots$X is observed.

A close scrutiny shows that (a) in isolated O—H$\cdots$X bonds, the O—H$\cdots$X angle is $\sim$140°, (b) in hydrogen-bonded water molecules O—H$\cdots$X is $\sim$165° and (c) in N—H$\cdots$X bonds, N—H$\cdots$X angle is $\sim$160°.

Apart from giving an idea about the nature of the hydrogen bond, these studies also help to resolve certain controversial points in some cases. Nuclear magnetic resonance studies of cupric chloride, CuCl$_2$,2H$_2$O, give proton positions which are found to be untenable by infra-red workers. The neutron data has revealed that data from N.M.R. studies are definitely wrong and are inconsistent with the geometry of the water molecule.

Bernal and Megaw (1935) by X-ray studies, ruled out the possibility of hydrogen bonding in calcium hydroxide, Ca(OH)$_2$, because of a large O—O distance. But on the basis of infra-red work Mara and Sutherland

(1954) doubted these hydrogen positions. The neutron diffraction studies confirmed the Bernal-Megaw structure, which also explains the softness and easy cleavage of the crystal.

A partial three-dimensional neutron diffraction study of hydroxylamine hydrochloride, NH_3OHCl, showed that the hydrogens of the NH_3 group form an equilateral triangle whose side (proton–proton distance) is 1.66 ± 0.01 Å, the N—O bond direction being normal to the plane of the triangle. The study substantiated the earlier nuclear magnetic resonance investigation (Abrams, 1959).

Hydrogen positions obtained in the case of barium chloride, $BaCl_2,2H_2O$, by three-dimensional data showed that McGrath and Silvidi (1960) have assigned the H—H vectors to wrong water molecules. The electronegative Cl or O were found to be far away from hydrogens. They are either repelled by the two Ba^{++} ions or else these ions attract the unshared electron pairs of the water molecule. The absence of any strong hydrogen bonds may probably explain the easy twinning nature of the crystal.

From a study of proton magnetic resonance of water molecules in eleven hydrates, McGrath and Silvide (1961) conclude that the interproton separations in different hydrated water molecules are all the same. The mean value is 1.589 ± 0.003 Å with a range in values from 1.56 to 1.61 Å. Chidambaram (1962) from a correlation of the structural data on fifteen hydrates showed that it is the H—O—H angle that is more or less unaffected, while O—H distance is increased from the vapour value depending on the bond (which will therefore affect the H—H distance). Taking into account the experimental errors (and thermal motion of the hydrogen) and the recent data on lithium sulphate, Li_2SO_4,H_2O, copper sulphate, $CuSO_4,5H_2O$ and barium chloride, $BaCl_2,2H_2O$, it is not possible to agree with the conclusions of the workers mentioned above. It may be remarked here that the O—H distance varies with O—H $\cdots$ X, but more so in the case of isolated systems than in hydrated salt.

REFERENCES

Abrams, M. C. (1959). Ph.D. Thesis, State College of Washington.
Atoji, M. and Rundle, R. E. (1958). *J. chem. Phys.* **29**, 1306.
Bacon, G. E. and Pease, R. S. (1953). *Proc. roy. Soc.* **A220**, 397.
Bacon, C. E. and Curry, N. A. (1956a). *Proc. roy. Soc.* **A235**, 552.
Bacon, C. E. and Curry, N. A. (1956b). *Acta Cryst.* **9**, 82.
Bacon, C. E. and Curry, N. A. (1957). *Acta cryst.* **10**, 524.
Bacon, C. E. and Curry, N. A. (1960). *Acta cryst.* **13**, 717.
Bacon, C. E. and Curry, N. A. (1962). *Proc. roy. Soc.* **A266**, 95.
Bernal, J. C. and Megaw, H. D. (1935). *Proc. roy. Soc.* **A151**, 384.
Busing, W. R. and Levy, H. A. (1957a). *Acta cryst.* **10**, 180.

Busing, W. R. and Levy, H. A. (1957b). *J. chem. Phys.* **26**, 563.
Busing, W. R. and Levy, H. A. (1960). ORNL Report No. 59-4-37.
Busing, W. R. and Zocchi, M. (1961). Private communication.
Chidambaram, R. (1961). *Acta cryst.* **14**, 467.
Chidambaram, R. (1962). *J. chem. Phys.* **36**, 2361.
Garrett, B. S. (1954). ORNL Report No. 1745.
Hamilton, W. (1957). *Acta cryst.* **10**, 629.
Hamilton, W. (1961). *Acta. cryst.* **14**, 95.
Hamilton, W. (1962). *Acta cryst.* **15**, 353.
Hvoslef, J. (1958). *Acta cryst.* **11**, 383.
Levy, H. A. (1961). American Crystallographic Association Annual Meeting, Boulder.
Lonsdale, K. (1949). *Nature, Lond.* **164**, 205.
Lonsdale, K. (1950). *Sci. J. roy. Coll. Sci.* **21**, 1.
Mara, K. and Sutherland, G. B. B. M. (1954). *J. opt. Soc. Amer.* **43**, 1100.
McGrath, J. W. and Silvidi, A. A. (1960). *J. chem. Phys.* **32**, 924.
McGrath, J. W. and Silvidi, A. A. (1961). *J. chem. Phys.* **34**, 323.
Pauling, L. (1935). *J. Amer. chem. Soc.* **47**, 2680.
Padmanabhan, V. M., Peterson, S. W. and Smith, H. G. (1962a). To be published.
Padmanabhan, V. M., Busing, W. R. and Levy, H. A. (1962b). To be published.
Pepinsky, R. (1953). *Science* **1**, 73.
Peterson, S. W. and Levy, H. A. (1953). *J. chem. Phys.* **21**, 2084.
Peterson, S. W. and Levy, H. A. (1957a). *Acta cryst.* **10**, 73.
Peterson, S. W. and Levy, H. A. (1957b). *J. chem. Phys.* **26**, 220.
Peterson, S. W. and Levy, H. A. and Schomaker, V. (1957). *Acta cryst.* **10**, 844.
Peterson, S. W. and Levy, H. A. (1958). *J. chem. Phys.* **29**, 948.
Peterson, S. W. and Levy, H. A. (1961). Private communication.
Rundle, R. K. and Parasol, M. (1952). *J. chem. Phys.* **20**, 1487.
Smith, H. G. (1961). American Crystallographic Association Annual Meeting, Boulder.
Tenzer, L., Fraser, R. C. and Pepinsky, R. (1958). *Acta cryst.* **11**, 505.
Worsham, J. E., Peterson, S. W. and Levy, H. A. (1957). *Acta cryst.* **10**, 319.
Willis, B. T. M. (1960). *Acta cryst.* **13**, 763.

DISCUSSION

R. CHIDAMBARAM (Atomic Energy Establishment, Bombay): An examination of the more recent neutron diffraction data on crystals containing hydrogen-bonded water molecules seems to indicate that in the crystals in which the water molecules are ligands for transition-metal ions (like Cu^{++}), the H—O—H angle increases by about $5°$ from the vapour value of $104·5°$ while the O—H distance is somewhat lower than what one expects and is about $0·96$ A. In the other crystals, the H—O—H angle is not much altered from the vapour value while there is a tendency for the O—H distance to increase with decreasing O—H $\cdots$ X distance. In the latter case, the lone pair electrons of the water molecule are involved in only weak interactions and one is perhaps justified in assuming (R. Chidambaram, *J. chem. Phys.* **36**, 2361(1962)) that the energy considerations involved in determining the stereochemistry of the water molecule are for the bending of the hydrogen bonds and the distortion of the H—O—H bond angle. In the former class of crystals, due to the partial covalent character of the Cu—OH_2 link, there is perhaps a tendency for the oxygen electrons to rehybridize toward $sp^2 + p_z$ configuration which would lead to an increase in the H—O—H angle and also introduce the possibility of π-bond character in the Cu—OH$_2$ link. This would explain, for example, the observations of S. W. Peterson and H. A. Levy (*J. chem. Phys.* **26**, 220 (1962)) that in cupric chloride dihydrate, the entire CuCl$_2$,2H$_2$O grouping (including the H atoms) is planar.

w. a. wooster: The hydrogen bond picture in which hydrogen atoms may be in one of three positions near to the mid point between two oxygen atoms, might explain the diffuse X-ray pattern given by ice. If the hydrogen atoms can move between these alternative positions and if the movements of neighbouring hydrogen atoms are correlated with one another, then the diffuse pattern may be explained. The movement of the hydrogen atoms in planes all perpendicular to the O—O bond, could explain the diffuse spikes which form an important part of the diffuse pattern of ice.

Neutron Spectrometry at Trombay

P. K. IYENGAR

Atomic Energy Establishment,
Trombay, Bombay, India

ABSTRACT

Neutron diffraction has proved in recent years to be valuable in crystal structure analysis, especially in crystals containing heavy and light atoms together. It is also useful in determining the magnetic structure of alloys and compounds of transition elements, and in the study of thermal oscillations of crystal lattices. Several neutron spectrometers are in operation with Canada India Reactor for study in the above-mentioned fields. The neutron spectrometers have their own special characteristics compared to the conventional X-ray units, due to the smaller intensity of the neutron beam and the method of detection. Details of crystal spectrometers, especially those used for obtaining powder and single crystal data, are described with respect to their mechanical design and data collection.

1. INTRODUCTION

The coherent scattering of slow neutrons by nuclei has made it possible to use neutrons for diffraction experiments in the study of the structure of matter analogous to X-ray diffraction. However, there are important differences between the scattering by X-rays and neutrons which make neutron diffraction specially suitable where X-ray methods are not. One is the fact that the scattering amplitude varies rather irregularly with atomic number of the scattering atoms and is quite significant even for light atoms like hydrogen. This leads to greater precision in the location of light atoms in the presence of heavier ones and also in distinguishing atoms of near atomic number. A second characteristic is the additional scattering due to the magnetic dipole–dipole interaction of neutrons with the atomic magnetic moments in magnetic substances. This additional scattering leads to the precise measurement of the magnetic moments and their orientation at the lattice sites. It is also possible to study the distribution of the electrons responsible for the magnetic moment by Fourier inversion of magnetic intensities similar to the mapping of electron density in X-ray structure analysis.

Another important difference from X-ray diffraction is the fact that the effects of thermal vibrations in a crystal lattice are better studied by neutrons than X-rays. In the case of neutrons, the familiar temperature

10   279

factor arises from the motion of the nucleus while it is due to that of the electron cloud in the case of X-rays. Thus the anisotropy, if any, of the temperature factor can be solely assigned to the thermal vibrations whereas in the case of X-rays, distortion of the electron cloud may contribute to it. A more direct way of studying thermal vibrations is possible with neutrons for, in addition to elastic Bragg scattering, the neutrons exchange energy with thermal vibration leading to inelastic scattering. Experiments on measurement of energy changes of neutrons on scattering provide information on the frequency spectrum of lattice vibrations. Thus neutron spectrometry has three important fields of application, namely, in the precise determination of the position of light atoms in crystals by single crystal and powder diffraction methods, in the study of magnetic structures using powder and single crystal samples, and thirdly in the study of the dynamics of crystal lattices and in general any condensed state of matter. The availability of intense beams of thermal neutrons from the Canada India Reactor at Trombay has enabled us to start a programme of work on neutron diffraction and inelastic scattering of neutrons by solids and liquids. We shall in this paper describe some of the facilities that have been built for work in these fields and some of the work being carried on at present.

2. Neutron Monochromator

Whereas in the case of X-ray diffraction one obtains a monochromatic beam from an X-ray tube, the nuclear reactor provides a beam of thermal neutrons which are in equilibrium with the moderator of the reactor. The wavelength distribution of this white beam is Maxwellian and the intensity is peaked in the region of 1–2 Å. It is therefore necessary to produce a beam of monochromatic neutrons before it can be used for neutron diffraction. This is achieved by reflecting a portion of the incident neutron spectrum by a single crystal about the desired wavelength.

Figure 1 shows a typical arrangement we use at Trombay with most of our set-ups. The surface of the reactor vessel acts as the source of neutron radiation, the thermal neutron flux radiating from this surface being 2×10^{13} neutrons/cm^2 per sec at a reactor power level of 40 MW. A long tube of diameter 4 in and length 12 ft is built into the concrete biological shield of the reactor. The inner gate consists of a cylindrical shield of lead and steel which could be remotely operated to intercept the beam. This shield has a 4-in diameter hole which forms part of the beam channel in the open position. We usually introduce a 3-in thick block of bismuth to attenuate the γ-rays without significantly attenuating the neutron beam. C_1 and C_2 are collimators of wood and steel respectively, each 3 ft long, C_1 carrying a hole 3 in × 3 in, and C_2 a hole of cross-section 2 in × 2 in. C_2 is also provided with a step wherein a soller slit collimator C_3 can be introduced, if necessary.

These collimators are essentially to restrict the neutron beam to an area of 2 in × 2 in. at the exit end of the beam tube, and to have an angular divergence of roughly a degree and a half. By putting a vertical soller slit, C_3, the horizontal divergence could be improved to $\frac{1}{2}°$ or $\frac{3}{4}°$ depending on the length and spacing of the slits. The partitions of the soller slit collimator are made out of thin cadmium sheets. Outside the beam channel the neutron beam enters a monochromator shield. For

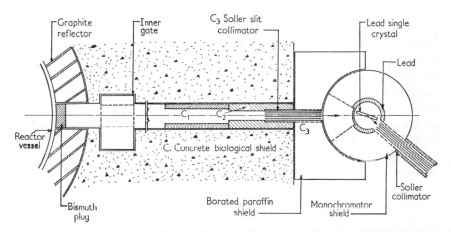

FIG. 1. Typical arrangement of collimators in a beam tube for obtaining collimated beam of neutrons from the Canada India Reactor. The single crystal monochromator housed inside the circular shield reflects a portion of the incident spectrum, providing monochromatic neutrons for diffraction experiments.

convenience we use a large circular shield in the form of a drum, capable of rotation about a vertical axis. It is about 3 ft in diameter with a 5-in diameter central hole. The neutrons enter through a slit in the form of an open sector subtending an angle of 40° at the centre, and the reflected neutrons pass through a hole which accommodates another soller slit to restrict the horizontal divergence of the reflected beam. The monochromatizing crystal is usually a single crystal of lead, in the form of a parallel plate, its large surfaces cut parallel to the reflecting planes chosen, say (111) or (200). It is mounted on a table at the centre of the drum and is capable of rotation from an extended axle at the bottom passing through a set of bearings. The large size of the drum and the additional shielding around are to absorb the scattered neutrons and gamma rays from the beam. The drum is filled with an inch thick of lead nearest to the centre and the rest of the volume is filled with borated paraffin to slow down and absorb the scattered neutrons. The crystal reflects about 1% of the incident neutrons and the remaining 99% have to be absorbed in the surrounding shielding. The construction of the shield in the form of a cylinder makes it easy to change the Bragg angle and hence the wavelength of the reflected neutrons. We use similar set-ups for almost all of our experiments on diffraction or inelastic scattering.

3. NEUTRON SPECTROMETER

There is a vast difference between a conventional X-ray spectrometer and a neutron spectrometer. The differences arise for two reasons. The monochromatic neutron beam is almost 10^5 times smaller in intensity compared to an X-ray beam and hence as large a sample and beam size as possible have to be used. Secondly, the neutron detector used is usually a proportional counter filled with boron trifluoride gas in which the neutron reacts with the boron nucleus resulting in the emission of an alpha particle which ionizes the gas and the ionization pulse is amplified and counted. This counter, which is about 12 in long and of 2 in diameter, has to be adequately shielded from the general neutron background allowing only the neutrons scattered from the sample to enter the counter. This is achieved by enclosing the counter in a shield of boron carbide and paraffin leaving only a hole for the beam to enter the counter axially. A soller slit is introduced in front of the counter to limit the angular acceptance of the scattered neutron beam without limiting the area of the sample. The counter shield in a typical case weighs as much as 200 lb. A sturdy construction is needed so that this weight can be carried on an arm at about 3–5 ft from the centre of the crystal table. Thus the neutron spectrometer is much more massive than the conventional X-ray spectrometer.

In Fig. 2 is shown a typical neutron spectrometer we use for diffraction work. Its design closely follows that of Hurst et al. (1950). It is built on a solid double thrust bearing of large diameter so that the cantilever load of the counter shield can be carried. The angular position of the arm is indicated in the lower graduated brass plate, which moves along with the arm against a vernier fixed to the shaft. The crystal table on the top is driven at half the rate by the pulley arrangement seen in the photograph. The pulley on the right has two discs, the top one having half the diameter of the bottom. The large size of the crystal table, diameter about 15 in is to enable mounting of large cryostats and magnets since very often in the magnetic diffraction work the sample temperature has to be varied or the specimen held in an external magnetic field. We have

FIG. 2. Photograph of a neutron diffraction spectrometer. Monochromatic neutrons emerge through the collimator from the circular shield. The neutron spectrometer with the counter shield, crystal table, the graduated discs for measuring the angles, the belt and pulley arrangement of the half angling device and the motor drive with cam and microswitch are seen in the photograph.

FIG. 6. Photograph of the Triple Axis Spectrometer.

used similar mechanical construction on all our spectrometers, with minor variations.

We normally operate the spectrometer in steps, i.e. the counter measures scattered neutron intensity at discrete scattering angles in steps of a quarter of a degree or less. The spectrometer is driven by a small fractional horse-power motor through a gear box and a tape which is fixed to the outer sleeve of the bearing. A cam disc attached to the shaft of the motor with fixed number of notches determines the magnitude of the angular step. Usually the gear ratios are so adjusted as to make one complete rotation of the motor shaft equal to one degree of angular movement of the spectrometer. A block diagram of the electronics associated with a typical diffraction spectrometer are shown in

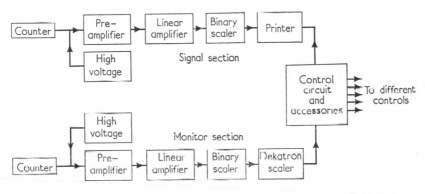

FIG. 3. Block diagram of electronic equipment used with the neutron detectors.

Fig. 3. The counter electronics consists of a high-voltage unit, amplifiers and scalers. A similar set-up is used for the monitor counter which monitors the intensity of the neutron beam in order to be independent of the reactor power fluctuations. It is a thin BF_3 counter held in the monochromatic beam causing very little attenuation, due to its low sensitivity. A pre-set count controller on the monitor channel controls the counting time for each position of the spectrometer. The counts are accumulated in a register, the reading being printed out on a paper tape at the end of the counting period. The programme unit controls the sequence of operations. If necessary, in certain cases a cadmium sheet could be automatically introduced to close the beam and counts taken to determine the background due to the stray neutrons and the fast neutrons in the beam. More sophisticated programming is done for certain special types of experiments. The above is the general philosophy of neutron spectrometer operation.

4. NEUTRON CRYSTALLOGRAPHY

Neutron crystallography is necessarily a supplement to X-ray crystallography because of the larger time involved in collecting sufficient data for solving a problem in structure analysis. Most of the information like lattice parameters and positions of certain atoms in the unit cell should already have been determined by X-ray diffraction. In a few cases the structure could be solved by powder diffraction alone, if the calculations show that intensity of certain reflections should be significantly different for different assumed models for the structure. An example of one such case we have examined is KCN.

Powder samples are easier to obtain in larger quantities, and hence one is able to use larger beam sizes of the order of a few square centimetres in cross-section. In cases where single crystal data are required to establish a structure, the availability of sufficiently large single crystals is very often the limiting factor. Samples at least a few millimetres in size are required to make accurate intensity measurements with neutron fluxes available at present. Due to the small size of the sample crystal, the beam size could also be made small to advantage. The soller slits could be avoided. The angular resolution of the counter for scattering angles could also be relaxed due to the fact that the Bragg peaks do not overlap as with powder samples, and hence the counter can be brought much nearer to the sample table. Higher intensities obtained in single crystal reflections also make it possible to tolerate higher backgrounds, thus reducing the size of the counter shields. These considerations enable one to make the spectrometer much smaller. Because of the low absorption for neutrons, extinction is a major problem in neutron crystallography. Since extinction depends on mosaic structure of the crystal, it is advantageous to increase the mosaic width of the crystal by subjecting the crystal to thermal shocks, for example, by dipping in liquid nitrogen several times. The extinction also depends on the strength of the reflection. Often one has to measure reflections for different thicknesses of the crystal and extrapolate to zero thickness in order to obtain extinction free values for the intensities. Counter method of detection of neutrons introduces complication in the recording of data for a large number of reflections. As the counter and crystal movements are coupled by the half angling device, it is possible to observe higher orders of a given reflection in the zero layer in a single run covering a large range of scattering angle. Even here, the Bragg reflections occur only in smaller regions and it is wasteful to scan the entire region. Hence the programme device is built such that one can preset the angular positions at which the counter will stop and do the normal counting operation and skipping the intermediate regions. A further improvement would be to set the crystal automatically for each reflection in the zero layer. This requires position control of the crystal table and the counter arm independently while setting for the reflection and the half angling device takes over during the counting operation. This could be achieved by an elaborate automation system controlled by a punched paper tape as in SCAND (Prince and Abrahams, 1959). We have, however, designed a simpler mechanical system similar to that of Levy and Peterson (Garrett, 1954), which will allow scanning twenty reflections in the zero layer in succession. This seems to be sufficient when manual resetting of the spectrometer can be done at intervals of at least a day.

Because of the extreme slowness of accumulating data, three-dimensional Fourier analysis for structure determination is not generally attempted. Most of the structures of interest to neutron crystallographers are those in which the hydrogen atom positions have to be located precisely. Very often one is satisfied with two-dimensional projections because the positions of heavier atoms are known from X-ray diffraction. We are studying the hydrogen bonds in the structure of $K_2C_2O_4 . H_2O$ in this way.

5. MAGNETIC SCATTERING

As mentioned in the introduction, the scattering from a magnetic atom is due both to its nucleus and the uncoupled electron spin in its outer orbits which produces a resultant magnetic moment. The scattering amplitude p due to the magnetic moment is given by the relation

$$p = \frac{(e^2 \gamma)}{(mc^2)} Sf$$

where e and m are respectively the charge and mass of the electron, c the velocity of light, S the atomic spin and f the form factor which depends on the angle of scattering and γ the neutron magnetic moment. In cases where there is an orbital contribution, the value of Sf has to be suitably modified. In a para-magnetic substance, magnetic scattering is completely incoherent because of the random nature in the orientation of the atomic spins. The scattered neutron distribution has the same shape as the form factor.

In the case of ordered magnetic materials the differential scattering cross-section per magnetic atom is given by the relation

$$d\sigma = b^2 + 2bp\mathbf{q} \cdot \boldsymbol{\lambda} + q^2 p^2$$

where b is the nuclear scattering amplitude, $\mathbf{q}$ the magnetic interaction vector defined by the relation $\mathbf{q} = \boldsymbol{\epsilon}(\boldsymbol{\epsilon} \cdot \mathbf{K}) - \mathbf{K}$, in which $\boldsymbol{\epsilon}$ is the unit scattering vector and $\mathbf{K}$ the unit vector in the direction of magnetization,

$\boldsymbol{\lambda}$ is the neutron polarization vector. In the case of unpolarized neutrons, the second term averages to zero and the equation above reduces to

$$d\sigma = b^2 + q^2 p^2$$

making the nuclear and magnetic intensities additive. q^2 here is equal to $\sin^2\alpha$, where α is the angle between the scattering vector and the direction of magnetization. The factor q^2 can therefore assume any value between 1 and 0, depending on the alignment of moments in an applied field. In view of the fact that not all the atoms in the unit cell are necessarily magnetic and also because the spin of the magnetic atoms may be aligned parallel or antiparallel or in more complicated fashions among themselves, the symmetry of the magnetic structure is not in general the same

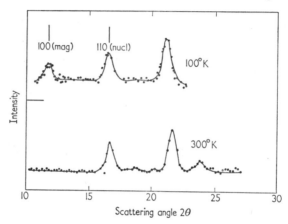

Fig. 4. Low-angle neutron diffraction patterns of $FeGe_2$ at room temperature and liquid nitrogen temperature. The magnetic reflection 100 at the lower temperature indicates an antiferromagnetic alignment of spins.

as that of the chemical unit cell. Lastly, if polarized neutrons are used, the product $\mathbf{q}\cdot\boldsymbol{\lambda}$ can be $+1$ or -1, depending on the direction of the magnetization which makes the cross-section $d\sigma = (b+p)^2$ or $(b-p)^2$. In this case the nuclear and magnetic amplitudes are additive, which results in enhanced intensities for magnetic reflections. This enhanced intensity makes it possible to measure accurately weak magnetic moments and measure form factors very precisely. This incidentally provides a method for obtaining monochromatic polarized neutrons for, by appropriately choosing a crystal reflection for which $b = p$, neutrons in a single polarized state can be reflected.

The above-mentioned properties of magnetic scattering have made the application of neutron diffraction to study of magnetic materials a most fruitful field. One is able to measure quantitatively the magnitude and direction of the magnetic moments in a microscopic scale. It is much more interesting to correlate these values to the gross features of the magnetization curves obtained from macroscopic measurements. Until now the antiferromagnetic structure of at least a hundred alloys and compounds have been studied by neutron diffraction. (For a recent review, see Wilkinson *et al.*, 1962.) Very novel features of the spin orientation in some cases in a helix extending over thirty or forty chemical unit cells have been noticed (Neutron Diffraction Study of Magnetic Materials, 1962).

We have made studies on powder samples of iron–tin (Iyengar *et al.*, 1962*a*) and iron–germanium alloys of composition FeM_2. We have observed antiferromagnetic transformations as predicted by measurements of temperature variation of susceptibility. Figure 4 shows the neutron diffraction patterns at low angles of $FeGe_2$ at room temperature and liquid nitrogen temperature. The antiferromagnetic ordering with the spins along the c-axis produces the 100 reflection at the lower temperature, whereas at room temperature this peak is absent and only the paramagnetic diffuse scattering is present. Our facilities for this type of work include cryostats and furnaces with which we could maintain the temperature of the samples down to liquid nitrogen temperature as a lower limit and up to 600°C on the higher side. The large penetrability of neutrons through small thicknesses of aluminium without significant attenuation makes construction of cryostats and furnaces easy. In the near future we hope to have a cryostat to go down to liquid helium temperature. We are also working on the setting up of a polarized neutron beam spectrometer.

6. Inelastic Scattering

One is familiar with the effect of thermal vibrations on X-ray or neutron diffraction through the Debye-Waller factor which takes into account the loss of intensity of a Bragg reflection due to thermal agitation of the atoms. In single crystal specimens with X-rays it is well-known that the effect of thermal vibrations is to produce diffuse intensity around the Laue spots. Diffuse intensity observed by mis-setting from a Bragg reflection by a known angle can be identified to a definite point in reciprocal space as seen in Fig. 5. The effect of diffuse intensity observed at a point P is due to a thermal wave whose wave vector q is given by the line joining the point to the nearest reciprocal lattice point. The intensity of the diffuse spot is however dependent on the frequency or energy of the thermal wave known as the phonon. The smaller the energy the larger is the intensity of the diffuse spot. By measuring quantitatively the intensity one could calculate the energy. Such types of measurements have been made to determine elastic constants (Ramachandran and Wooster, 1951*a*, *b*), and more recently for measuring

10*

the detailed dispersion relations for phonons (Walker, 1956). A similar
phenomenon exists with neutrons, but in a modified and more suitable
form for measurement of phonon energies. The geometrical conditions
for observing diffuse reflection is not the same as in the X-ray case, for
here the wave vector of the neutron changes rapidly with energy. Thus,
whereas in the case of X-rays the wave vector remained practically the
same on being scattered by the thermal wave, it is not so in the case of
neutrons. In Fig. 5 is shown the conditions for observing diffuse reflections in X-ray and neutron case at the point P in reciprocal space. The

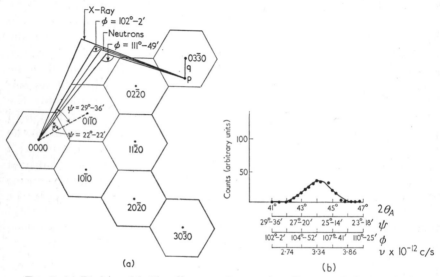

Fig. 5. (a) Reciprocal lattice diagram of magnesium (hexagonal close-packed
lattice). Conditions for observing inelastic scattering of neutrons and
X-rays due to a phonon of wave vector $\mathbf{q}$ at point P are shown. Limits of the
values of the three variable parameters ψ, ϕ and $2\theta_A$ for the "constant Q"
method of observing the phonon is also indicated in the figure. (b) A typical
phonon observed is shown, the counts being plotted against the three parameters.

conditions can be written down mathematically in the case of the neutron
scattering by the relations:

$$E_0 - E' = \pm h\nu \quad \text{and} \quad \mathbf{k}_0 - \mathbf{k}' = 2\pi\boldsymbol{\tau} \pm \mathbf{q}$$

with the additional constraint that $\nu = \nu_j(q)$, $\nu_j(q)$ being the dispersion
relation for phonons. Here E_0 and E' are the energies and $\mathbf{k}_0$ and $\mathbf{k}'$ the
wave vectors of the incoming and outgoing neutrons respectively; $\boldsymbol{\tau}$ is a
vector of the reciprocal lattice, $\mathbf{q}$ the wave vector and ν the frequency
of the phonon. The first two equations are essentially the equations for
conservation of energy and momentum for the scattering process. Since
the dispersion relation is unknown, it is not possible to pre-set conditions

for observing the diffuse spot at any chosen point in reciprocal space. However, this could be done experimentally by a process of trial and error. In a method introduced by Brockhouse (1961) this is done in a systematic way by the constant momentum transfer method. The process essentially consists in assuming for a given $\mathbf{q}$ various values for ν in the third relation within limits which could be judged from the elastic constants and other theoretical considerations. Using these values for the ν's, and the value of $\mathbf{k}_0$ and E_0 appropriate to the incident neutrons, the value of E' and k' satisfying the two conservation conditions are calculated. If now, the geometry of the experiment is arranged successively to conform to the different assumed values of ν and the scattered neutron intensity in each case is measured, the intensity corresponding to one of the settings will be a maximum. The frequency corresponding to this maximum is the true frequency of the phonon. Figure 5 illustrates the method. The angle ψ defines the direction of the incident neutrons with respect to the crystallographic axis, Φ the scattering angle and θ_A the Bragg angle at which the analysing spectrometer should be set in order to reflect neutrons of wave vector k' or energy E'. The result of such a run is shown on the right side of the figure.

As is evident from above, in order to perform this experiment it is necessary to be able to vary ψ, Φ and $2\theta_A$ independently and in a predetermined manner automatically. Figure 6 shows the spectrometer which we use for such experiments. Neutrons of energy E_0 and wave vector $\mathbf{k}_0$ fall on the sample crystal mounted on the crystal table which is capable of rotation in steps of 3 minutes of arc. The analysing spectrometer sits bodily on the arm of the first spectrometer. A collimator in the vertical shield defines the direction of the scattered beam. The scattering angle is measured on a scale, and could be changed in steps of $\frac{1}{8}°$ by the motor and cam arrangement seen at the extreme bottom. The analysing spectrometer uses a single crystal of aluminium with its (111) planes orientated for Bragg reflection. After computing the values of ψ and Φ for each value of $2\theta_A$ assumed, the increments in ψ and Φ are rounded off to the nearest multiples of 1/20th degree and $\frac{1}{8}$th of a degree respectively. The spectrometer is set at the initial values of ψ, Φ and $2\theta_A$. Counts are taken for predetermined monitor counts in the normal way. The background is measured in this case by flipping the aluminium single crystal a few degrees off the Bragg reflection position, using an electromagnetic device. At the conclusion of the counting period, the $2\theta_A$ motor moves one step to the next value, whereas the ψ and Φ motors run for such a time as to cover the predetermined number of steps. This is achieved by a programme unit which makes use of a stepping switch of 256 positions each for ψ and Φ. These contacts of the stepping switch are brought out on a programme panel, consisting of banana sockets.

The increments are achieved by plugging to ground appropriate banana sockets in proper sequence. The contacts of this stepping switch control a relay which controls the motors. The motor will come to a stop when the next position which is plugged in the programme board is reached. When all the three motors come to a stop, the counting operation starts again.

Measurements have been made on a single crystal of magnesium using the above instrument. Figure 7 gives the experimentally measured dispersion curve for transverse acoustic phonons propagating in the [10$\bar{1}$0] direction in the basal plane of the hexagonal close-packed lattice. The neutron measurements can also give information about the polarization vector of the phonon. Extensive measurements have been made for

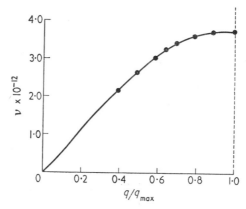

FIG. 7. Measured dispersion curve for transverse acoustic phonons in the [10$\bar{1}$0] direction of magnesium.

various directions and polarizations in the crystal. The results will be published elsewhere (Iyengar *et al.*, 1962*b*).

Coherent inelastic scattering is possible also from liquids and magnetic materials. The analysis of scattered neutron spectrum is quite complicated in the case of liquids. However, for neutrons there occurs incoherent scattering from certain nuclei. This comes mainly from different scattering amplitudes connected with the compound states, which the neutrons can form with non-zero spin nuclei. Hydrogen is a familiar incoherent scatterer. Inelastic scattering from such nuclei have no interference conditions as in coherent scatterers and hence will be directly related to the frequency spectrum of thermal vibrations. The vibrations and rotations of a large class of molecules which contain an incoherent scatterer can be studied by this technique. We have made measurements on various ammonium compounds to investigate the nature of vibrations of the ammonium ion by the methods of neutron spectrometry (Venkataraman *et al.*, 1962).

So far we have described experiments in which we make use of the diffraction phenomenon to study elastic and inelastic scattering of neutrons. The neutron wavelength can also be measured conveniently by the time of flight technique since the speed of thermal neutrons is only a few thousand metres per second. We use this technique in some of our measurements on inelastic scattering (Venkataraman *et al.*, 1962).

Acknowledgements

I am grateful to Dr. R. Ramanna for his keen interest and constant encouragement in this work. A number of my colleagues have actively participated in the work described here. My sincere thanks are due to all of them. I am also obliged to Shri V. Surya Rao, Superintendent, Canada India Reactor, and the Reactor Operations Division for their co-operation.

References

Brockhouse, B. N. (1961). In *Inelastic Scattering of Neutrons from Solids and Liquids*, p. 113. International Atomic Energy Agency, Vienna.

Garrett, B. S. (1954). ORNL Report 1745.

Hurst, D. G., Pressesky, A. J. and Tunnicliffe, P. R. (1950). *Rev. sci. Instrum.* **21**, 705.

Iyengar, P. K., Dasannacharya, B. A., Vijayaraghavan, P. R. and Roy, A. P. (1962a). *J. phys. Soc. Japan* **17**, 247.

Iyengar, P. K., Venkataraman, G., Rao, K. R., Vijayaraghavan, P. R. and Roy, A. P. (1962b). Dispersion Relations for Phonons in Magnesium, SM 30/58. Proceedings of Symposium on Inelastic Scattering of Neutrons in Solids and Liquids. Chalk River, Canada (to be published).

Neutron Diffraction Study of Magnetic Materials (1962). Proceedings of the International Conference on Magnetism and Crystallography. *J. phys. Soc. Japan* **17**, Supplement BIII.

Prince, E. and Abrahams, S. C. (1959). *Rev. sci. Instrum.* **30**, 581.

Ramachandran, G. N. and Wooster, W. A. (1951a). *Acta cryst.* **4**, 335.

Ramachandran, G. N. and Wooster, W. A. (1951b). *Acta cryst.* **4**, 431.

Venkataraman, G., Usha, K., Iyengar, P. K., Vijayaraghavan, P. R. and Roy, A. P. (1962). Study of Ammonium Halides by Neutron Spectrometry. Proceedings of Symposium on Inelastic Scattering of Neutrons in Solids and Liquids. Chalk River, Canada (to be published).

Walker, C. B. (1956). *Phys. Rev.* **103**, 547.

Wilkinson, M. K., Woollan, E. O. and Koehler, W. C. (1962). *Ann. Rev. nucl. Sci.* **11**, 303.

SECTION VI
Instrumentation

An Automatic X-Ray Diffractometer

W. A. Wooster, A. M. Wooster and G. A. Wooster,

Brooklyn Crystallographic Laboratory, Cambridge, England

ABSTRACT

This diffractometer is based on a four-circle design originally described in 1936 by Wooster and Martin. The X-ray detector rotates in a horizontal plane between 2θ values $0°$ to $170°$. The crystal is brought to the reflecting position automatically by the setting of three circles. The unit cell dimensions are first determined and then the four angles required for each setting are worked out on a digital computer. This information is stored on punched tape. The tape is fed into the diffractometer and the circles are set by means of digitizers which ensure an absolute correspondence between the setting of a particular circle and the information on the punched tape. The time required for setting the four circles for a given X-ray reflection is 15 to 45 sec depending on how large are the required angles of rotation. Recording and registration may be on punched tape or by typewritten characters.

INTRODUCTION

The instrument described here is based on the instrument developed by Wooster and Martin (1936), which was the first automatic X-ray diffractometer. The base of the instrument carries two 360-teeth worm wheels denoted 2θ and ω respectively (Fig. 1). The 2θ-wheel carries the detector which may be a Geiger counter, proportional counter or scintillation counter. The ω-wheel carries a vertical shaft on which is mounted the χ-circle. The plane of the χ-circle is vertical and on it is mounted the ϕ-circle which has its axis intersecting both the ω- and χ-axes. The crystal is placed at this point of intersection, mounted on a goniometer head supported on the ϕ-axis. It is an important feature of this arrangement that the goniometer head is mounted on one side of the χ-circle and not so that the ϕ-axis lies in the plane of the χ-circle.

The great development of crystal structure analysis in recent years has made it necessary to collect data more quickly than non-automatic instruments permit. A decade ago it was common to carry out structure analyses by two-dimensional Patterson and Fourier projections. Each projection might involve 50 to 500 reflections depending on the unit cell dimensions. Today some structure analyses require the measurement of 10 000 to 30 000 reflections. What was possible by hand ten years ago is now only possible if automatic instruments are used. The electronic digital computer has introduced a revolution in X-ray crystallography.

The calculations involving very large numbers of reflections can only be carried out because of this mathematical tool. As well as dealing with the calculations involved in the determination of crystal structures, the digital computer can also be employed in the setting of the crystal in the reflecting positions. This has affected the design of diffractometers by making it easy to calculate the 2θ-, ω-, χ- and ϕ-angles for any given reflection hkl. The data can be punched on to tape or cards and fed into the diffractometer to set the various circles. When the scaler has recorded the number of counts the information can be punched on to tape. This can be fed into a digital computer which applies the necessary corrections

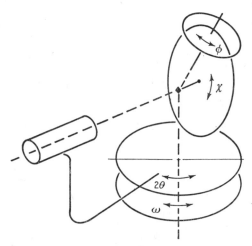

Fig. 1. Diagrammatic representation of the four circles used in setting the crystal and counter on the automatic diffractometer.

and proceeds with the further computations. Thus, the automatic diffractometer in combination with the electronic digital computer is an essential tool in the modern analysis of crystal structure.

MECHANICAL DETAILS

The 2θ- and ω-worm wheels are of 9 in. diameter and are cut with an accuracy such that, starting from any point, the inaccuracy between that point and any other point round the wheel does not exceed $1'$. These wheels are driven by worms which are mounted so that there is no backlash in excess of $1'$. The worms are mounted on stiff springs which ensure no change in the backlash even if the worm wheels are mounted slightly eccentrically. The χ- and ϕ- worm wheels have 180-teeth each and are driven by worms mounted in the same way as the 2θ- and ω-wheels. Each of the four circles has its own electric motor. On the shaft of each worm is mounted a revolution counter or digitizer, which gives the angle of rotation by four digits, representing hundreds, tens, units and tenths of a degree respectively. The system is thus an absolute one, each reading applying only to a given setting of the circle. (Some diffractometers use circular scales with fine rulings and count, by an electronic device, the number of lines which cross a given point. This system is a *relative* device since every setting can only be defined relative to some other setting.)

DEFINITION OF THE ORIENTATION OF A REFLECTING PLANE

The orientation of a reflecting plane of indices hkl can be defined in relation to (a) the crystallographic axes a, b, c, or $a*, b*, c*$; (b) the diffractometer axes. It is best to calculate the angles defining the orientation (a) and then to apply these to determine the orientation (b). In Fig. 2 the

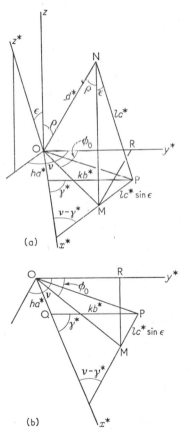

FIG. 2. (a) Perspective drawing of axes to which the reflecting plane, normal to ON, can be referred. (b) Plan drawing of same axes (Wooster, 1962).

various Bravais lattice and reciprocal lattice directions which are employed are shown. The axis z is taken vertical so that the reciprocal axes x^* and y^* are horizontal. The axis z^* is not vertical in general but is inclined to z at an angle ϵ. The plane containing z and z^* is inclined to the plane containing z and y^* at an angle ν. The vector ON is perpendicular to the reflecting planes and its length is d^*. If the spacing of the lattice planes is d then we take

$$d^* = \lambda/d$$

The direction of ON makes an angle ρ with the z-axis and the plane containing z and ON makes an angle ϕ_0 with the plane containing z and y^*. The three quantities d^*, ρ and ϕ_0 thus define the position of any reciprocal point relative to the axes of the reciprocal lattice. The point N refers to a plane of indices hkl and therefore the co-ordinates of N referred to the reciprocal unit cell dimensions are ha^*, kb^* and lc^*. It is a matter of elementary geometry to arrive at the well-known relations (Wooster, 1962)

$$\text{ON} = d^* = (h^2 a^{*2} + k^2 b^{*2} + l^2 c^{*2} + 2klb^* c^* \cos \alpha^* + 2lhc^* a^* \cos \beta^* + 2hka^* b^* \cos \gamma^*)^{1/2} \tag{1}$$

$$\text{OM} = (h^2 a^{*2} + k^2 b^{*2} + l^2 c^{*2} \sin^2 \epsilon + 2klb^* c^* \cos \alpha^* + 2lhc^* a^* \cos \beta^* + 2hka^* b^* \cos \gamma^*)^{1/2} \tag{2}$$

$$\text{NM} = lc^* \cos \epsilon \tag{3}$$

$$\text{MR} = ha^* \sin \gamma^* - lc^* \sin \alpha^* \cos \beta \tag{4}$$

$$\text{OR} = ha^* \cos \gamma^* + kb^* + lc^* \cos \alpha^* \tag{5}$$

From the relations (1) to (5) we obtain

$$\sin \rho = \text{OM}/\text{ON} \tag{6}$$

$$\cos \rho = \text{NM}/\text{ON} \tag{7}$$

$$\sin \phi_0 = \text{MR}/\text{OM} \tag{8}$$

$$\cos \phi_0 = \text{OR}/\text{OM} \tag{9}$$

It is necessary to calculate on the electronic digital computer both the sine and the cosine because the angular values derived from the sine are not accurate enough between 60° and 90° and the angular values derived from the cosine are not accurate enough between 0° and 30°. The computer chooses the value of the angle which is given by the sine when the angle lies between 0° and 30° and the value given by the cosine when the angle lies between 60° and 90°. When the angle lies between 30° and 60° the computer takes the mean of the values given by the sine and the cosine respectively.

The relation between the Bragg angle θ and d^* is given by the expression

$$d^* = 2\sin\theta \tag{10}$$

Thus, starting from $a^*, b^*, c^*, \alpha^*, \beta^*, \gamma^*$ and λ we obtain ρ, ϕ_0 and θ. This completes the step (a) in the determination of the orientation of the reflecting plane.

(b) We shall suppose the crystal to be set up on the goniometer so that the z-axis coincides with the ϕ-axis, i.e. the axis about which the goniometer head can rotate. This axis is denoted G in subsequent stereograms. Figure 3 is a stereogram in which the point N represents the direction ON

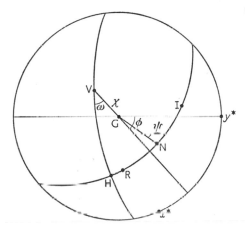

Fig. 3. Stereogram showing the orientation of directions: G, the axis of the goniometer head; V, the vertical direction; and I, R, the directions of the incident and reflected X-rays respectively.

of Fig. 2. The corresponding positions of y^* and x^* on the stereogram are also shown. Although the goniometer head rotates with respect to the base of the diffractometer it is a convenience to maintain G at the centre of the stereogram and to rotate other directions as may be required. Through N (Fig. 3) a great circle is drawn and on it two points I and R are marked each making an angle of $\{(\pi/2) - \theta\}$ with N. The directions I and R correspond to those of the incident and reflected beams for which the Bragg angle is θ. In Fig. 3 the incident beam is going downwards while the reflected beam is travelling upwards. The angle GNI is denoted ψ and is called the *azimuthal* angle. It is hardly ever of importance in X-ray crystal structure analysis but for neutron studies on magnetic crystals it can be very important.

In this diffractometer the directions I and R are always horizontal, so

that the plane INR is horizontal. The vertical direction V of the diffractometer is the pole of the great circle INR. We take as the starting orientation of the circles that in which (i) G (i.e. the ϕ-axis) coincides with V,
(ii) the χ-axis coincides with I. The angle VG corresponds to the rotation
round the χ-circle and is denoted χ. The great circle VH has I as its pole
so that H is a horizontal direction, perpendicular both to directions V
and I. The rotation of the χ-circle about V is denoted ω. Initially the
direction y^* is taken to lie parallel to the plane of the χ-circle, i.e. to VG.
The angle through which it has had to be rotated, namely, $\phi = \pi - V\hat{G}y^*$
is shown in Fig. 3. Thus, given the angles ω, χ and ϕ, the normal N can be
brought into the reflecting position. In general, there are an infinite

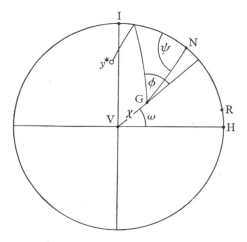

FIG. 4. Stereogram giving the same information as Fig. 3 but plotted with V at
the centre of the stereogram and the line IV drawn vertically on the diagram.

number of combinations of the angles ω, χ and ϕ which will satisfy the
required conditions. To each such combination of ω, χ and ϕ there
corresponds a particular value of ψ. This is of importance in a diffractometer for the study of neutron scattering.

The stereogram of Fig. 4 shows the same orientations as are given in
Fig. 3 but I, V and H are brought into the usual orientation for an
observer looking down on the diffractometer from above. The incident
X-rays travel in the plane of the diagram from I towards V. The reflected
X-rays travel in the plane of the diagram from V towards R. The reflecting normal N lies mid-way between I and R. The angles ω, χ, ϕ and ψ
have the same values in Figs. 3 and 4. Out of the infinite number of
combinations of ω, χ and ϕ we normally select two. The first, called the
symmetrical setting is indicated by the stereogram of Fig. 5. It is obtained
from Fig. 4 by rotating the crystal about the normal to the reflecting

planes N until G lies in the line VN. It is clear that in this setting $\omega = \theta$, $\chi = (\pi/2) - \rho$ and $\psi = \pi/2$. The other common setting is that in which $\psi = 0$. The stereogram of Fig. 6 shows this orientation which is obtained from Fig. 5 by a rotation about N through 90°. It will be seen that $\omega = \theta - \rho$, $\chi = \pi/2$, $\psi = 0$.

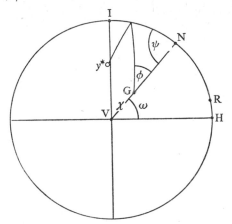

FIG. 5. Stereogram for the setting defined by $\psi = \pi/2$.

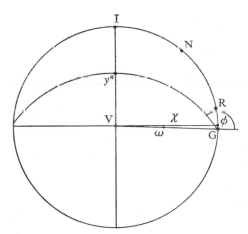

FIG. 6. Stereogram for the setting defined by $\psi = 0$.

It is also possible to arrange that G lies between N and I instead of between N and R, when $\omega = \theta + \rho$. Thus, using any of these three settings which we shall call the $\psi = \pi/2$, 0 and π settings respectively, it is possible to determine the setting angles on the diffractometer, i.e. ω, χ and ϕ from the angles ρ, ϕ_0 and θ calculated for the crystal. If it were necessary to make $\psi = \pi/4$ or some other fixed angle it would be possible to compute by a slightly different programme all the values ω, χ and ϕ for each hkl reflection.

The Overcoming of the Obstruction offered by a Complete Circle

The three alternative settings of the instrument corresponding to $\psi = \pi/2$, 0 and π make it possible to overcome to a great extent the

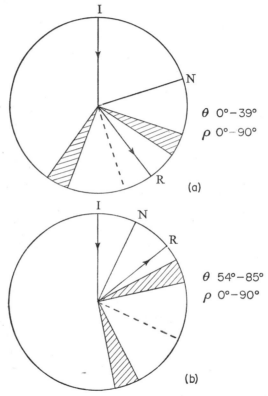

FIG. 7. (a) Diagram representing a section through a crystal by a horizontal plane. The shaded regions are those within which no reflected X-rays can lie. $\theta = 0°$ to $39°$. (b) Same as for Fig. 7 (a) except that $\theta = 54°$ to $85°$.

obstruction offered by the complete χ-circle. The mechanical parts of this circle lie within two cones having a common apex at the crystal and semi-angles of $39°$ and $54°$ respectively. For values of θ lying in the ranges $0°$ to $39°$ and $54°$ to $85°$ (the highest θ-value obtainable), the $\psi = \pi/2$ setting is suitable for all values of ρ from $0°$ to $90°$. This is shown in Fig. 7 (a), (b), which are sections through the apparatus in the plane containing the incident and reflected rays. In Fig. 7 (a) the reflected beam passes *through* the χ-circle and in Fig. 7 (b) it passes *in front of* the χ-circle. The range of θ from 39° to 54° is obstructed when $\rho = 0°$, but as ρ increases the obstructed region decreases until when $\rho = 7\frac{1}{2}°$, no reflections are obstructed. This is due to the fact mentioned on p. 301 that $\omega = \theta \pm \rho$ in the $\psi = 0$ and π settings. Thus when $\theta = 46\frac{1}{2}°$ and $\rho = 7\frac{1}{2}°$, ω may have the value 39° and the reflected rays can pass by the vertical circle and enter the detector (Fig. 8). When ρ lies in the range $7\frac{1}{2}°$ to 90° there is no obstruction in one or other of the settings $\psi = 0$ or π. The easiest way of describing the region of reciprocal space which cannot be studied because of the complete χ-circle is in terms of the reciprocal lattice and the limiting sphere of radius 2 reciprocal units. The ranges 0°

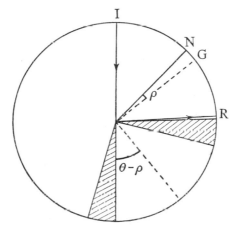

FIG. 8. Diagram representing a central section through the diffractometer by a horizontal plane for the $\psi = \pi$ setting.

to 90° in ρ and 0° to 360° in ϕ correspond to all possible reciprocal points lying within a hemisphere of radius 2. Within this hemisphere the volume which corresponds to excluded reflections is a small region lying on the axis G. Figure 9 is a central section through this hemisphere and the excluded region is shaded. To obtain the complete hemisphere Fig. 9 must be rotated about the axis ϕ. The shaded region has a volume which is less than $\frac{1}{4}\%$ of the volume of the hemisphere. Thus the number of reflections which can be recorded in more than $99\frac{3}{4}\%$ of the possible reflections, or, out of 800 reflections, only one or two are likely to be excluded.

The great advantage of using a complete χ-circle rather than a quarter, or some other fraction of a complete circle, is that mechanically a complete circle retains its shape and accuracy much better than any part of a circle. It is also easier to construct and it can be made lighter. Since the provisions which have to be made in order to overcome obstruction can be applied to the programme of a digital computer, it makes almost no difference to the time required for punching the tape. Thus for an automatically operated diffractometer there is more to be said in favour of a complete circle than there is in favour of an incomplete circle.

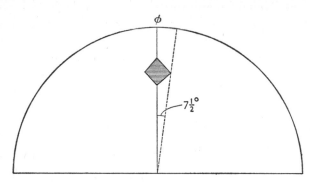

FIG. 9. A section through the limiting sphere showing the region (shaded) which cannot be recorded with a given setting of the crystal.

THE STUDY OF CRYSTALS LACKING A CENTRE OF SYMMETRY

When a crystal lacks a centre of symmetry and has any anomalous dispersion-effects, the intensity of reflection from hkl need not be the same as that from $\bar{h}\bar{k}\bar{l}$. This failure of Friedel's law is a powerful means of solving crystal structures and is applicable to a considerable number of acentric structures when using Cu $K\alpha$ radiation. It can be applied in nearly every acentric structure analysis if the kind of radiation is specially selected to give a well-marked anomalous scattering. The most suitable diffractometer for this purpose would be one which enabled not merely the usual hemisphere of the limiting sphere to be investigated, with a single setting of the crystal, but the whole of the limiting sphere. This cannot be achieved because the crystal must be carried on some finite size of goniometer head. In the present instrument the ϕ-worm wheel subtends at the crystal a cone of semi-angle 20°. This prevents certain reflections from being recorded. The corresponding reciprocal points lie in a spherical cap centred on the ϕ-axis having a volume of 11% of the hemisphere. Thus 89% of the $\bar{h}\bar{k}\bar{l}$ reflections can be recorded and as only a selection of the total number is required this will usually be adequate for the structure analysis.

THE METHOD OF SETTING THE FOUR CIRCLES

Each setting circle is driven by a worm and this worm also drives a revolution counter or digitizer. This digitizer (Wooster, 1961) consists of four wheels which are linked to one another by a Geneva-type gear so that when one wheel moves from position "9" to position "0", the wheel on one side of it advances by one-tenth of a rotation. The four wheels correspond respectively to hundreds, tens, units and tenths of degrees. Each of these wheels carries a thin metal disc in which is an opening subtending about 30° at the centre of the wheel. On one side of this wheel is a metal plate from which a signal is taken and on the other side is an insulating plate supporting ten sector-shaped electrodes. These electrodes are supplied with 50-cycle pulses of the same voltage but differing phases. The phase difference between successive sectors round the plate is $\pi/10$. The rotating wheel is earthed and the signal reaching the output plate corresponds in phase to that of the sector opposite the opening in the rotating disc.

The punched tape carries in code the setting angles, each line of holes corresponding to one digit. The tape reader closes switches which correspond to the punched holes and four uniselectors, with ten contacts in each wafer, are set in positions corresponding to the four digits of any one of the angles 2θ, ω, χ and ϕ. Only one circle is set at a time. The four digits from the tape are conveyed to the uniselectors which give out pulses having phases corresponding to the positions of the wipers on the uniselectors. The motor drives the corresponding circle towards the setting in which the digitizer has the same setting as the uniselector. This is carried out in the sequence hundreds, tens, units and tenths of degrees. If the motor overshoots or starts up from a position where the digit in the digitizer has a greater value than the corresponding digit in the memory, then the motor drives in the opposite direction. Only when the memory and the digitizer settings are identical can the motor come to rest. This procedure follows automatically for all four circles.

ELECTRONIC DETAILS OF THE SETTING DEVICE

A block diagram of the parts of the electronic setting device is shown in Fig. 10. The 20-phase generator is based on a 3-phase transformer. Many separate coils are wound on the three arms of this transformer and by combining the 6-phase voltages available in appropriate amounts, it is possible to obtain twenty sinusoidal outputs each of the same voltage and differing in phase by $\pi/10$ from one another. The ten phases between 0 and π are passed through a square wave generator, and pre-amplifier to the plates of the digitizer. All digits of the same number on the four plates are connected together. The output from the digitizer is amplified and passed to a "NAND of 3" gate, which has the property that a signal only passes through it if all three inputs are present.

The other two inputs to the "NAND" gate correspond to the holes punched in the tape. Any given row of holes in the tape sets a uniselector wiper in a position corresponding to the digit implied by the holes. The twenty phases are fed to other wafers of the uniselector so that the phases 0 and π correspond to digit 0, the phases $\pi/10$ and $11\pi/10$ to digit 1, etc. The outputs from the 0 to π phases are delayed by $1\frac{1}{2}°$ and the outputs from the π to 2π phases are advanced by the same angle so that there is a 3° overlap between these two outputs. The sinusoidal waves are converted into square waves. When the digit in the digitizer corresponds to the digit in the uniselector the "NAND" gate opens and a pulse is transmitted to the "OR" gate. This allows first the hundreds digit, then

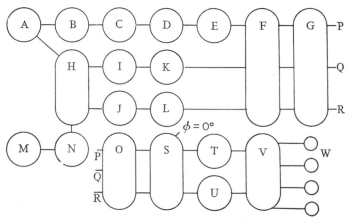

Fig. 10. A block diagram of the electronic setting device used in correctly aligning all four circles. A, 20-phase sinusoidal generator; B, 10-phase square-wave generator; C, pre-amplifier; D, digitizer; E, amplifier; F, "NAND OF 3" gates; G, "OR" gates; H, uni-selectors; I, delay circuit; J, advance circuit; K, L, square-wave generators; M, tape reader; N, decoder; O, pulse decapitator; S, double "NAND" gate; T, "forward" relay; U, "backward" relay; V, distributor; W, motors.

the tens digit, then the units digit and finally the tenths digit to pass through but rejects all other pulses than the particular one required at any given instant. After passing through a pulse decapacitor, which cleans up the signal, it passes into a double "NAND" gate. The necessity for this arises from the fact that the digitizer not only produces spikes having the phase to be expected from the position of the opening in the rotating plate but also spurious spikes mid-way between them. This is due to the effect of the trailing edge of the square wave. This difficulty is overcome by paralysing the Q and R lines (Fig. 10) during half the cycle. This is achieved by feeding in the phase 0° signal on lines Q and R which permits only pulses having phases 0 to π to pass through the "NAND" gate. This position of the circuit also operates a "forward" relay if the digitizer digit is less than that in the memory and a "backward" relay if the digitizer digit is greater than that in the memory. The motor circuit operated is determined by the distributor which moves round in the sequence 2θ, ω, χ and ϕ. Thus each motor is set in motion and continues until both relays open, at the point where the digits are the same in the digitizer and the uniselector memory.

CONCLUSION

To sum up the characteristics of this diffractometer we may consider how the experimenter would proceed to make observations on the intensities of reflection. The cell dimensions must first be determined either by a Weissenberg or other goniometer. It may be useful to employ the diffractometer to study high-angle reflections for the purpose of obtaining accurate values of the cell dimensions.

Next, a suitable form of crystal must be prepared. In many cases this form will be spherical. Various grinding devices are used for preparing spherical crystals, particularly those in which the crystal is blown round an abrasive cone or cylinder. The size of crystal should be related to the absorption coefficient, though as *International Tables for Crystal Structure Determination* (1959, 1962) show there is no optimum size. In any case the crystal must not be larger than the X-ray beam at the point where the X-rays strike the crystal.

The crystal must be orientated carefully so that the z axis, or some other chosen axis, is parallel to the ϕ-axis. The accuracy with which this orientation must be carried out is related to the unit cell dimensions and to the size of window in the detector. If the window is $11\cdot4$ cm from the crystal, a rotation of $1°$ of the crystal corresponds to 2mm movement of the reflected beam. As the window is likely to be about 5×2 mm, or smaller, it is advisable to effect the orientation with an accuracy of $0\cdot1°$. The same accuracy is required in setting the y^* or other chosen direction, parallel to the plane of the χ-circle. The z-axis setting is made most conveniently by narrowing the window of the counter in the vertical direction and ensuring that $hk0$ reflections occur centrally with respect to the window. The y^*-axis setting may be made by ensuring that $0k0$ reflections occur when the ω-setting has the calculated value. When using monoclinic and triclinic crystals it is also very important to ensure that z^* has the inclination to the χ-circle which has been assumed in calculating ω, χ and ϕ. There are, of course, two settings differing by π in ϕ for both of which the z-axis and the y^*-axis have the correct orientation with respect to the diffractometer. Care must be taken to distinguish between these alternatives.

The crystal is now ready for the automatic determination of the intensities. A sub-programme is carried out by a mechanical device fixed to the vertical shaft which supports the χ-circle. This is the Arndt, Faulkner and Phillips' (1960) rocking device, and when the four circles are set the motor driving the rocking device comes into operation. A complete rotation of the cam takes 60 sec. During 15 sec the background on one side of the reflection is counted, during the next 30 sec the crystal is rotated through an angle of between 1° and 5°, which can be pre-set, and during the last 15 sec the background on the other side of the reflection is counted. Switches are actuated by the rotating cam so that the scaler determines the mean value of the background and subtracts this from the count for the reflection. The difference is either recorded on a print-out unit or, in code, on a punched tape. Further processing of the information can thus be carried out as desired.

REFERENCES

Arndt, U. W., Faulkner, T. H. and Phillips, D. C. (1960). *J. sci. Instrum.* **37**, 68.
International Tables for Crystal Structure Determination, Vol. II (1959), Vol. III (1962). Kynoch Press, Birmingham.
Wooster, A. M. (1961). British Patent No. 9935/61.
Wooster, W. A. (1962). *J. sci. Instrum.* **39**, 103.
Wooster, W. A. and Martin, A. J. P. (1936). *Proc. roy. Soc.* **A155**, 150.

DISCUSSION

G. N. RAMACHANDRAN: Has the instrument been tried with an actual crystal, and if so, how long does it take to collect the three-dimensional data of a typical crystal?

W. A. WOOSTER: We have not actually put it through a given crystal problem, but have tested the different parts. It takes 15–60 sec for a reflection.

D. C. PHILLIPS: There are a great many developments of this kind in many laboratories, including at least three which involve diffractometers of the Woosters' own manufacture (cf. D. C. Phillips, (1963). In *Aspects of Protein Structure*, ed. by G. N. Ramachandran, p. 57. Academic Press, London). Some of these make use of Moiré fringe gratings on the actual circles as a means of detecting and controlling their rotation. Has Dr. Wooster any comments to make on this system as compared with his own use of digitizers?

W. A. WOOSTER: The difficulty about the use of Moiré fringes is that practically all scalers, at any rate in my experience, drop counts sooner or later. In order to avoid trouble on this account, it is usual to return to the starting point after 10 or 20 reflections to make sure no serious zero error has been introduced, whereas if you use an absolute method, this can be avoided.

An Integrating Weissenberg Camera
for Low and High Temperature Studies

A. K. Singh and S. Ramaseshan*

*Department of Physics, Indian Institute of Science,
Bangalore, India*

ABSTRACT

The paper describes the construction of an integrating Weissenberg camera. The mechanism of the angular integration is very similar to that used in the original Wiebenga design. The linear integration is effected by a rack and pinion arrangement. Both these are made repetitive, so that one complete integration takes place in about one hour. A Fankuchen-Lipscomb cooling arrangement has been incorporated into this camera for the study of crystals at low temperatures. The problem of removing the cassette for loading and developing without disturbing the cooling arrangement has been solved by making the jacketed cold and warm air leads thin enough to pass through the slot of a conventional cassette. A high temperature attachment for study of crystals up to 500°C has been made using a nickel foil both as a heater element and an X-ray filter.

1. Introduction

It is now accepted that for extremely accurate determinations of crystal structures in which photographic techniques are used, the recording of intensity data on integrating cameras of the Wiebenga type is perhaps the best. Many eminent crystallographers have advocated the precise determination of atomic and thermal parameters of crystals at low temperatures. There is no doubt that the Fankuchen-Lipscomb (Kaufman and Fankuchen, 1949; Abrahams *et al.*, 1950) arrangement for cooling the crystal has many advantages over other methods, particularly when one is interested in the study of the crystal structures of substances which are liquids at room temperature.

As the present writers had no access to any camera that combined the essential features of these two techniques, it was decided to design and construct such a camera. As this camera has some novel features, its constructional details have been described in this paper. The problem of removing the cassette for developing the X-ray film without interfering with the cooling arrangement has been solved in a simple manner.

* Present address of authors: Department of Physics, Indian Institute of Technology, Madras, India.

2. Details of Construction

A. *The integrating process*

The process of integration consists of imparting two types of movements to the cassette during the exposure. At the end of every to-and-fro traverse of the carriage a cylindrical cassette rotates through a small angle ($\approx 0.1°$) about its axis and at the same time it is translated parallel to its axis by about 0·05 mm. In the present camera the mechanism for angular movement is very similar to the one used by Wiebenga (Wiebenga and Smits, 1950). However, a rack and pinion arrangement is used for the linear integration. Unlike Wiebenga's original design both the movements are made repetitive and one complete integration takes about an hour.

B. *The carriage design*

A carriage consisting of two parallel plates of brass AA (12 cm × 8 cm × 0·6 cm) separated by another brass plate B (12 cm × 3·8 cm × 0·6 cm) is capable of moving freely on rollers $R_1 R_1$ supported on parallel cylindrical rails (RR), one being placed vertically above the other (Fig. 1).

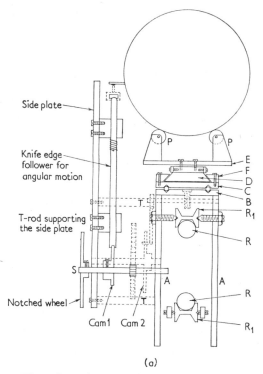

(a)

FIG. 1 (a). The end-on view of the integrating Weissenberg camera.

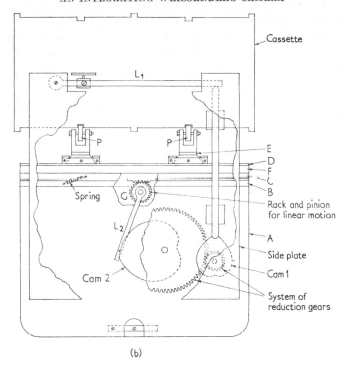

(b)

Fig. 1 (b). Diagram showing the arrangement for angular and linear movement.

On the upper side of the plate B there are two V-grooves parallel to the length and 1·5 cm apart. A similar plate C having identical V-grooves on the lower side is kept on plate B. Four balls kept in the grooves minimize the friction so that plate C becomes a platform capable of sliding parallel to the length of the carriage. On this platform are mounted two pairs of ball-bearings for supporting the cassette (only one pair is shown in sectional diagram). The assembly of ball-bearings is capable of a movement parallel to the length of the carriage (by D sliding over C). This movement is necessary when taking equi-inclination Weissenberg photographs and it also makes it possible to remove the cassette without disturbing the cooling arrangement which is described later. Each set of ball-bearings can move, independent of each other, in the transverse direction—a feature essential for fine adjustment while properly aligning the camera.

C. The mechanism for angular movement

As in the Wiebenga design, a notched wheel having fourteen teeth is mounted on the side of the carriage by means of a horizontal shaft, S.

11

At the end of every oscillation of the carriage the tooth of the notched wheel is engaged by a pin which causes a rotation of the notched wheel. A spring and roller arrangement makes the rotation of the notched wheel uni-directional and in equal steps. Thus at the end of every oscillation of the carriage, the notched wheel rotates through (360/14) degrees causing the rotation of a cam mounted on the common shaft. A vertical knife-edge follower moves through a distance (0·4 mm) for every (360/14) degrees rotation of the cam. This movement is further reduced by a lever arrangement and it is imparted by an adjustable pin to the cassette sitting on the four ball-bearings described earlier. Total rotation of the cassette can be adjusted by changing the position of the pin on the lever arm.

D. *The mechanism of linear movement*

The rotation of the notched wheel is transmitted to cam 2 by a system of reducing gears (ratio 5:1). A lever L_2 (Fig. 1 (b)) kept pressed against cam 2 follows the motion of the cam. As cam 2 rotates the lever oscillates with an amplitude of 20°. This oscillating lever rotates a pinion G which is fixed just below C between the plates AA. On the lower side of plate C is attached a spur rack which through a slot in plate B is engaged to pinion G. A spring pulls the plate C so that the lever L_2 is always pressed against the cam 2 and any possible backlash is avoided. The slightest movement of cam 2 and thus of lever 2 results in a linear movement of the plate C. In this particular arrangement the total movement of C is 1·5 mm. Different amplitudes can be obtained by using cams of different sizes which are mounted on the common shaft. However, a continuous variation in the amplitude is not possible.

It is possible to take with this camera, Weissenberg photographs, without any integration, with either angular integration or linear integration only or with both simultaneously.

In this camera both movements complete an integral number of oscillations in about 70 min, the angular movement completing five oscillations while the linear movement completes one. Thus the exposure time chosen must always be an integral multiple of 70 min.

3. Low Temperature Attachment

The Fankuchen-Lipscomb arrangement of cooling consists of blowing a jet of dry cold air on to the crystal. The cold air jet is surrounded by a sheath of dehydrated air at room temperature and this prevents any condensation of moisture on the crystal. This method is simple and extensively used in the X-ray investigation of crystals at low temperature. However, one has to face the difficulty of removing the cassette (for loading and developing purposes) without disturbing the cooling arrangement—a feature essential when one wishes to study crystals of substances which are liquids at room temperature. This difficulty is often overcome by using a split cassette. The use of a split cassette in an integrating

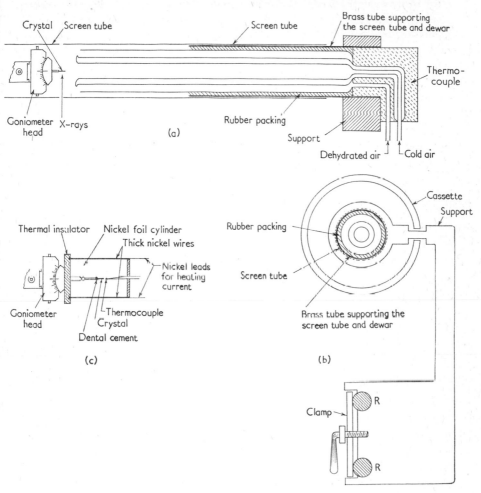

FIG. 2 (a) The cooling attachment. (b) End-on view of the screen tube holder which permits the removal of the cassette. (c) Heater attachment to the goniometer.

camera is, though not impossible, yet sufficiently complicated to make one look for some simpler arrangement. Recently Viswamitra (1962) has designed a special camera which permits the removal of the cassette from the goniometer end of the camera. The camera employs a large number of bevel and spur gears wherein the possibility of backlash cannot be so easily avoided.

The low temperature attachment described here permits the removal of an ordinary cassette without disturbing the cooling arrangement. This is achieved by making the screen tube holder support and cold-air lead thin enough to pass through the slot of the conventional cassette.

As shown in Fig. 2(a), cold air is passed through the Dewar tube which is surrounded by another glass jacket. Dehydrated air at room temperature is passed through the gap between the Dewar tube and outer jacket. The whole assembly is mounted inside a brass tube which also serves as the screen tube holder. This screen tube holder is held in position by a bracket-like brass support bent twice at right angles (Fig. 2(b)). The lower part of this support is clamped on to the camera. From Fig. 2(b) it is clear that cassette can be removed without disturbing the cooling system.

Some of the important features of the new design of the cooling attachment are:

(i) It permits the removal of a conventional cassette without disturbing the cooling arrangement, so that crystals of the substances which are liquids at room temperature can be studied.

(ii) Since the Dewar tube is enclosed by the screen tubes, the removal of the cassette does not change the condition of cooling so the temperature does not rise.

(iii) The mounting of the Dewar tube inside the screen tube makes it quite safe against mechanical shock.

(iv) This low temperature attachment can be used in any other commercially available Weissenberg camera (integrating or ordinary) with equal facility provided the screen tube holder (Fig. 2(b)) is made.

4. HIGH TEMPERATURE ARRANGEMENT

Steward (1949) suggested a heating arrangement using a nickel foil both as heater element and as a filter for Cu $K\beta$ radiation. This heater-cum-filter arrangement has been slightly modified to suit the present camera, and it is illustrated in Fig. 2 (c). The base of the furnace is an insulating material which forms a part of the goniometer head and it holds a cylinder (diameter 2 cm) of this nickel foil. This foil is heated up by passing current at low voltage. The cylinder is closed by another insulator and this effectively prevents any fluctuations in temperature due to convection currents. A thermocouple placed near the crystal records the temperature.

Acknowledgements

The authors' grateful thanks are due to Professor R. S. Krishnan for his kind interest in the work and to Dr. M. A. Viswamitra for helpful discussion. They are also grateful to the Council of Scientific and Industrial Research for sponsoring the research scheme on "Low and High Temperature X-Ray Crystallography".

REFERENCES

Abrahams, S. C., Collin, R. L., Lipscomb, W. N. and Reed, T. B. (1950). *Rev. sci. Instrum.* **21**, 396.

Kaufman, H. S. and Fankuchen, I. (1949). *Rev. sci. Instrum.* **20**, 733.

Steward, E. G. (1949). *J. sci. Instrum.* **26**, 371.

Viswamitra, M. A. (1962). *J. sci. Instrum.* **39**, 381.

Wiebenga, E. H. and Smits, D. W. (1950). *Acta cryst.* **3**, 265.

DISCUSSION

V. M. PADMANADHAN: I think the Nonius integrating Weissenberg camera of the latest design incorporates a symmetric cam. How is the apparatus described different from the Nonius model?

A. K. SINGH: The mechanical process of integration is different. The symmetric cam has the disadvantage of reducing the number of steps in the integration.

G. N. RAMACHANDRAN: Has the instrument been tried on an actual crystal? How do the intensities compare on the two sides of an equi-inclination photograph for a higher layer?

A. K. SINGH: Zero layer photographs were taken and the performance of the camera was very satisfactory. Higher layer photographs have not been taken.

D. C. PHILLIPS: What type of densitometer is used for the measurement of intensity?

A. K. SINGH: The camera has not yet been used for structural investigations.

G. N. RAMACHANDRAN: I would like to add a comment that not many in India use a densitometer for intensity measurements. We usually go by visual estimation of intensities with a set of standard spots.

G. BORRMANN: To what extent can the temperature of the crystal be kept constant?

S. RAMASESHAN: Although very accurate measurements have not yet been taken, the temperature could be kept constant to 1° to 2° at -120°C.

SECTION VII
Other Physical Studies

The Elasticity of Metallic Crystals of Cubic Symmetry

Jean Laval

College de France, Paris, France

ABSTRACT

The present studies devoted to the binding force in the metallic crystals show that the potential energy of these crystals includes a part which exclusively varies with the condensation. This part is due to the conduction electrons that form a medium which, like a fluid, has a pure compressibility. Therefore the interatomic forces have a component which arises from this compressibility. Consequently the static elastic coefficients c_{11} and c_{12}, of the cubic metallic crystals have two components: one is related to the lattice formed by the positive ions, the other to the pure compressibility. On the other hand, in the same crystals, the harmonic oscillations of the atoms produce pressing interatomic forces which have an intensity proportional to the condensation made by the oscillation, to the square of the wave number, and to a coefficient smaller than unity, which decreases when the wave number increases.

1. Introduction

The metallic crystals have an electronic structure that is quite their own. They are composed of positive ions which have a spherical symmetry, or are nearly spherical, and of conduction electrons which are uniformly distributed on the atomic scale. These electrons constitute a medium which, like a fluid, has pure compressibility (Fuchs, 1935). Therefore, the potential energy of a metallic crystal includes a component which exclusively varies with the condensation χ:

$$\chi = -\frac{\Delta V}{V} = -\sum_\alpha t_{\alpha\alpha}; \quad \alpha = 1, 2, 3 \tag{1}$$

that is, a component which remains constant when the expansions or the contractions† $t_{\alpha\alpha}$ vary individually but in such a way that their sum remains unchanged.

This study will be confined to the elasticity of metallic crystals with cubic symmetry. The positions of their atoms will be defined by double

---

† If **u** is the displacement of a point in equilibrium position **x**

$$t_{\alpha\gamma} = \frac{\partial u_\alpha}{\partial x^\gamma}; \quad \alpha, \gamma = 1, 2, 3$$

translations: $\mathbf{m} + \mathbf{u}^m$, $\mathbf{p} + \mathbf{u}^p$, ... where $\mathbf{m}$, $\mathbf{p}$, ... are translations of the crystalline lattice, and $\mathbf{u}^m$, $\mathbf{u}^p$, ... are the displacements of the total oscillations made by the atoms in mean positions $\mathbf{m}$, $\mathbf{p}$, ... The potential energy of a metallic crystal with cubic symmetry can then be expressed in its stable state† by Eq. (2a), using Hooke's approximation and neglecting thermal stresses and denoting Θ as the absolute temperature:

$$W(\Theta) = W_0(\Theta) + \frac{1}{2}\left[\sum_{mp} \sum_{\alpha\beta} C_{mp}^{\alpha\beta} u_\alpha^m u_\beta^p + \mathscr{C} \int_V \chi^2(\mathbf{x})\, \mathrm{d}^3 x\right]_\Theta \qquad (2a)$$

where $\alpha, \beta = 1, 2, 3$.

$W_0(\Theta)$ is the potential energy of the crystal, without any external stress, with the atoms at rest in their mean positions; $u_\alpha^m, u_\beta^p, \ldots$ are the Cartesian components of the displacements $\mathbf{u}^m$, $\mathbf{u}^p$, ... perfomed by the positive ions from their mean positions. These spherical or nearly spherical ions are bound by cohesive forces which are central or nearly central. Therefore, the interatomic forces produced by the displacements u^m, $u_\beta^p \ldots$ are derived from elementary potential energies, w^{mp}, connecting two atoms and which are only functions of the distance $r = |\mathbf{m} - \mathbf{p}|$ between their mean positions $\mathbf{m}$ and $\mathbf{p}$; thus:

$$C_{mp}^{\alpha\beta} = \left[\frac{\partial^2 W_0(\Theta)}{\partial x_\alpha^m \partial x_\beta^p}\right]_{(\mathbf{x}^m = \mathbf{m};\, \mathbf{x}^p = \mathbf{p})}$$

$$= -\frac{a^\alpha a^\beta}{r}\frac{\mathrm{d}}{\mathrm{d}r}\left(\frac{1}{r}\frac{\mathrm{d}w^{mp}}{\mathrm{d}r}\right) - \delta_{\alpha\beta}\frac{1}{r}\frac{\mathrm{d}w^{mp}}{\mathrm{d}r}$$

where $\qquad \mathbf{a} = \mathbf{m} - \mathbf{p}; \quad r = |\mathbf{m} - \mathbf{p}|$ $\qquad\qquad$ (2b)

Finally, $\mathscr{C}$ is the isothermal compressibility coefficient which exclusively concerns the conduction electrons;

$$\mathscr{C} = \frac{1}{V}\left[\frac{\partial^2 W_0(\Theta)}{\partial \chi^2}\right]_{(\chi = 0)} \qquad (2c)$$

where V is the volume of the crystal.

2. Static Elasticity

In order to impart a homogeneous isothermal elastic deformation $(t_{\alpha\gamma})$ to a cubic metallic crystal‡, an energy E must be applied to the

---

† Thus, the potential energy does not include first-order terms in u_α^m, $u_\beta^p \ldots$ and in χ.

‡ $(t_{\alpha\gamma})$ represents the strain tensor which includes nine elementary deformations $t_{\alpha\gamma}$ $(\alpha, \gamma = 1, 2, 3)$.

crystal which, according to Eqs. (1) and (2a), takes a density per unit volume (Laval, 1957)

$$E = -\frac{1}{4V} \sum_{\alpha\beta} \sum_{a} C_a^{\alpha\beta} \left(\sum_{\gamma} t_{\alpha\gamma} a^{\gamma} \right) \left(\sum_{\delta} t_{\beta\delta} a^{\delta} \right) + \tfrac{1}{2}\mathscr{C} \sum_{\alpha\beta} t_{\alpha\alpha} t_{\beta\beta}$$

$$\mathbf{a} = \mathbf{m} - \mathbf{p}; \quad \alpha, \beta, \gamma, \delta = 1, 2, 3$$

where V is the volume of the unit cell.

Setting

$$c_0^{\alpha\gamma, \beta\delta} = -\frac{1}{2V} \sum_{a} C_a^{\alpha\beta} a^{\gamma} a^{\delta} \tag{3}$$

we obtain:

$$E = \tfrac{1}{2} \sum_{\alpha\beta} (c_0^{\alpha\alpha, \beta\beta} + \mathscr{C}) t_{\alpha\alpha} t_{\beta\beta} + \tfrac{1}{2} \sum_{\alpha\beta\gamma\delta} c_0^{\alpha\gamma, \beta\delta} t_{\alpha\gamma} t_{\beta\delta}$$

where $\gamma \neq \alpha; \delta \neq \beta$.

Thus the elastic coefficients of a metallic crystal with cubic symmetry are defined by:

$$c^{\alpha\alpha, \beta\beta} = c_0^{\alpha\alpha, \beta\beta} + \mathscr{C}$$

$$c^{\alpha\gamma, \beta\delta} = c_0^{\alpha\gamma, \beta\delta} \tag{4}$$

where $\gamma \neq \alpha; \delta \neq \beta$.

Or, in Voigt's symbols with two indices as:

$$c^{11} = c_0^{11} + \mathscr{C}; \quad c^{12} = c_0^{12} + \mathscr{C}$$

$$c^{44} = c_0^{44} \tag{4a}$$

The cohesive forces between the ions being nearly central, we obtain roughly†

$$c_0^{44} = c_0^{12}$$

and, therefore

$$c^{12} - c^{44} = \mathscr{C} \tag{5}$$

In this way, we arrive at the elastic coefficients defined by Fuchs (1936).

However, the potential energy formula (2a) does not take into account the isotropic thermal stress, T, (Laval, 1959, 1961), which occurs in the metallic crystals of cubic symmetry. In fact, their effective (or apparent) elastic coefficients are (Laval, 1961):

$$c'^{11} = c^{11} + T; \quad c'^{12} = c^{12} + T; \quad c'^{44} = c^{44}$$

and

$$c'^{12} - c'^{44} = \mathscr{C} + T \tag{6}$$

† The pure compressibility of the metallic crystals which have a cubic symmetry, a compressibility defined by the coefficient $\mathscr{C}$ (Eq. (2c)) does not bring any component to the cohesive forces between positive ions. Therefore the elastic coefficients peculiar to the lattice formed by the ions—designated $c_0^{\alpha\gamma, \beta\delta}$—satisfy Cauchy relations. Upon this matter I disagree with B. Dayal and B. B. Tripathi (Dayal and Tripathi, 1962).

3. THE DYNAMICS OF ELASTIC WAVES†

According to Wigner and Seitz (Wigner and Seitz, 1933, 1934; Seitz, 1935), the conduction electrons have a density—measured by the square of the modulus of their wave function—which remains almost constant in all the space occupied by an atom, except in the central core of the positive ions, and which identically repeats without discontinuity in all the atoms at their boundaries. We shall suppose that the harmonic oscillations made by the positive ions repeat in this medium; and, as Wigner and Seitz have done, we shall substitute for atoms of polyhedral shape‡ spherical atoms which have the same volume (the unit cell volume).

A harmonic oscillation of the atoms§

$$u_\alpha^m = A c_\alpha \cos 2\pi(\nu t - \mathbf{S} \cdot \mathbf{m}) \tag{7}$$

where

$$\alpha = 1, 2, 3; \quad \sum_\alpha c_\alpha^2 = 1$$

which by substituting

$$\zeta_\alpha = A c_\alpha \tag{8}$$

may also be expressed as

$$u_\alpha^m = \zeta_\alpha \cos 2\pi(\nu t - \mathbf{S} \cdot \mathbf{m}) \tag{9}$$

induces in the medium formed by the conduction electrons, at point $\mathbf{m} + \mathbf{x}$, an oscillation:

$$u_\alpha^m(\mathbf{x}) = \zeta_\alpha \cos\left[2\pi(\nu t - \mathbf{S} \cdot \mathbf{m}) - \sigma \sum_\beta q^\beta x_\beta \right] \tag{10}$$

and a condensation:

$$
\begin{aligned}
\chi^m(\mathbf{x}) &= -\operatorname{div} \mathbf{u}^m(\mathbf{x}) \\
&= -\sigma(\sum_\beta q^\beta \zeta_\beta) \sin\left[2\pi(\nu t - \mathbf{S} \cdot \mathbf{m}) - \sigma \sum_\beta q^\beta x_\beta \right] \\
&= -\sigma A_S \sin\left[2\pi(\nu t - \mathbf{S} \cdot \mathbf{m}) - \sigma \sum_\beta q^\beta x_\beta \right]
\end{aligned}
\tag{11}
$$

where $\beta = 1, 2, 3$

† These dynamics had already been the subject of a remarkable study by Jules de Launay (de Launay, 1953); this study has been developed by Dayal and Sharan (Dayal and Sharan, 1960), and by Dayal and Singh (Dayal and Singh 1961); besides, A. B. Bhatia has taken up the same study (Bhatia, 1955). I deal with the same subject but according to a method completely different from that followed by Jules de Launay, and my results differ from those he obtained.

‡ These atoms have been defined by Wigner and Seitz (Wigner and Seitz, 1933, 1934; Seitz, 1935).

§ By harmonic oscillation of the atoms we mean the whole of the oscillations piloted by the same fundamental wave vector $\mathbf{S}$, having the same frequency ν, and made by all the atoms of the crystal.

and where q^1, q^2 and q^3 are the direction cosines of the fundamental wave vector $\mathbf{S}$†; $\sigma = 2\pi|\mathbf{S}|$, i.e. the number of waves in the length 2π; and where

$$A_S = A \sum_\beta q^\beta c_\beta \tag{12}$$

is the orthogonal projection, upon the wave vector $\mathbf{S}$, of the vector $\mathbf{A}$, directed along the displacement, of modulus equal to the amplitude A, and forming with vector $\mathbf{S}$ an angle smaller than or at the very most equal to $\pi/2$.

However, it is not possible to define the compressibility and the condensation in a space within the body of an atom and thereby having a smaller volume than the latter. In fact, upon taking an average in time, this space does not contain all the conduction electrons included in a particular atom, according to Wigner and Seitz's theory (Wigner and Seitz, 1933, 1934; Seitz, 1935). But, except for their mass differences, all the atoms which constitute the same metal of cubic symmetry have the same compressibility, that is the one for the complete crystal, and the compressibility coefficient $\mathscr{C}$ (Eq. (2c)) is related to this *average* compressibility and therefore to the *average* condensation in the space occupied by an atom. The average condensation produced by a harmonic oscillation of the crystalline medium (Eq. 7) in the space occupied by an atom is equal to the condensation that would be produced in the same space filled with a homogeneous fluid by an oscillation of the same frequency, of the same polarization, and of the same amplitude as the harmonic oscillation made by the positive ions. Thus the average condensation $\bar{\chi}^m$ in the space which contains an atom in position $\mathbf{m}$ is expressed by:

$$\bar{\chi}^m = -\frac{\sigma}{V} A_S \int_0^R \int_{\theta=0}^{\pi} \int_{\phi=0}^{2\pi} \sin\left[2\pi(\nu t - \mathbf{S}\cdot\mathbf{m}) - \sigma r \cos\theta\right] r^2 \sin\theta \, dr \, d\theta \, d\phi$$

where R is the atomic radius.‡

If we write

$$y = \sigma R$$

and

$$\phi(\sigma) = 3 \frac{\sin y - y \cos y}{y^3} \S \tag{13}$$

we obtain

$$\bar{\chi}^m = -\sigma\phi(\sigma) A_S \sin 2\pi(\nu t - \mathbf{S}\cdot\mathbf{m}) \tag{14}$$

† The wave vectors which direct the harmonic oscillations of the atoms are only defined to a translation $\mathbf{M}$ of the polar lattice. The vectors which have the smallest moduli are called fundamental vectors; they may be inscribed in a first Brillouin zone, with their origin at the zone centre and the termini distributed with a uniform density.

‡ $V = \frac{4}{3}\pi R^3$.

§ When σ tends towards zero, $\phi(\sigma)$ tends towards 1, and for all the metallic crystals with cubic symmetry, $\phi(\sigma)$ remains a constantly decreasing function of σ.

The potential energy of a harmonic oscillation (Eq. (7)) contains a part which is related to the pure compressibility due to the conduction electrons, and taking account of Eqs. (2) and (14), this part, referred to the unit cell volume, and therefore to an atom, becomes:

$$w(\sigma, \nu) = \tfrac{1}{2}\mathscr{C}V\sigma^2\,\phi^2(\sigma)\,A_S^2\sin^2 2\pi(\nu t - \mathbf{S}\cdot\mathbf{m})$$

Thus its average magnitude in the course of time is:

$$\bar{w}(\sigma, \nu) = \tfrac{1}{4}\mathscr{C}V\sigma^2\,\phi^2(\sigma)\,A_S^2 \tag{15}$$

Moved by the harmonic oscillation (Eq. (7)), the medium formed by the conduction electrons exerts upon each atom an interatomic force which we shall call a pressing force, in order to emphasize that it arises from the pure compressibility.

The oscillations of the positive ions being linear, this pressing force keeps a constant direction. It is the resultant of elementary pressures exerted upon the atom by the surrounding electrons, and directed along the gradient of the condensation χ (Eqs. (11)–(14)) and therefore along the wave vector $\mathbf{S}$. It would have this precise direction if the atoms were spherical. Actually, the atoms are polyhedral but nevertheless they preserve the cubic symmetry. Consequently, if the wave vector $\mathbf{S}$ is directed along a (two-fold, three-fold or four-fold) axis of symmetry, then the pressing interatomic force has exactly the same direction. Thus it can only make very small angles with the wave vector $\mathbf{S}$, when this is in a general direction. These angles being neglected, the pressing interatomic force, thus supposed always to be directed along $\mathbf{S}$, has the amplitude A_S (Eq. (12)), that is the amplitude taken by the orthogonal projection, upon the wave vector $\mathbf{S}$, of the oscillation made by the positive ions (Eq. (7)). On the other hand, the crystalline medium being stable, this pressing interatomic force is in opposite phase to the harmonic oscillation (Eq. (7)) which develops it ($\mathscr{C} > 0$). Thus the pressing interatomic force $\mathbf{f}_e^m$, which acts upon an atom in position $\mathbf{m}$, is expressed by:

$$\mathbf{f}_e^m = -c\mathbf{A}_S\cos 2\pi(\nu t - \mathbf{S}\cdot\mathbf{m}) \tag{16}$$

Here, $\mathbf{A}_S\cos 2\pi(\nu t - \mathbf{S}\cdot\mathbf{m})$ is the orthogonal projection of the harmonic oscillation upon the wave vector $\mathbf{S}$ and c is a constant which is to be determined. Now, the average potential energy of a harmonic oscillation which would be kept up by the interatomic force $\mathbf{f}_e^m$ is:

$$\tfrac{1}{4}c\mathbf{A}_S^2$$

It is the part which is related to the pure compressibility in the average potential energy of the oscillation (Eq. (7)) made by an atom. Thus this part is equal to the average potential energy $\bar{w}(\sigma, \nu)$ (Eq. (15)), which likewise is related to an atom. This equality determines the constant c:

$$c = \mathscr{C} V \sigma^2 \phi^2(\sigma) \tag{17}$$

Let us write:

$$\eta^{\alpha\beta} = \mathscr{C} V \sigma^2 q^\alpha q^\beta \tag{17a}$$

Taking account of Eqs. (8), (12), (16) and (17a), the component of the pressing interatomic force, $\mathbf{f}_e^m$, along the Ox^α co-ordinate axis, is:

$$\mathbf{f}_e^{m\alpha} = -\phi^2(\sigma) \sum_\beta \eta^{\alpha\beta} \zeta_\beta \cos 2\pi(\nu t - \mathbf{S}\cdot\mathbf{m}) \tag{18}$$

4. THE HARMONIC COMPONENTS OF THE THERMAL AGITATION

Taking the atomic harmonic oscillation into account, we obtain

$$u_\alpha^m = \zeta_\alpha \exp i2\pi(\nu t - \mathbf{S}\cdot\mathbf{m}); \quad \alpha = 1, 2, 3 \tag{19}$$

This oscillation is kept up by interatomic forces which have two components $\mathbf{f}_i^m$ and $\mathbf{f}_e^m$; the first one is produced by the displacements of the positive ions:

$$f_i^{m\alpha} = -\sum_p \sum_\beta C_{mp}^{\alpha\beta} \zeta_\beta \exp i2\pi(\nu t - \mathbf{S}\cdot\mathbf{p}) \tag{20}$$

the second one is produced by the condensation χ^m (Eq. (4)) of the medium formed by the conduction electrons. Taking account of Eq. (18), its expression is

$$f_e^{m\alpha} = -\phi^2(\sigma) \sum_\beta \eta^{\alpha\beta} \zeta_\beta \exp i2\pi(\nu t - \mathbf{S}\cdot\mathbf{m}) \tag{21}$$

Let μ be the mass of an atom and write

$$\gamma_i^{\alpha\beta} = \frac{1}{\mu} \sum_a C_a^{\alpha\beta} \exp i2\pi(\mathbf{S}\cdot\mathbf{a}); \quad \mathbf{a} = \mathbf{m} - \mathbf{p} \tag{22}$$

$$\gamma_e^{\alpha\beta} = \frac{1}{\mu} \phi^2(\sigma) \eta^{\alpha\beta} \tag{23}$$

The d'Alembert's principle applied to the oscillation (Eq. (19)) gives three linear and homogeneous equations:

$$\omega^2 \zeta^\alpha = \sum_\beta (\gamma_i^{\alpha\beta} + \gamma_e^{\alpha\beta}) \zeta_\beta; \quad \alpha, \beta = 1, 2, 3; \quad \omega = 2\pi\nu \tag{24}$$

Now, if we take into account the matrices γ_i and γ_e, of order 3×3, formed by the elements $\gamma_i^{\alpha\beta}$ and $\gamma_e^{\alpha\beta}$, and the matrices ζ, of order 3×1, formed by the elements ζ_β, these three equations reduce into only one

$$\omega^2 \zeta = (\gamma_i + \gamma_e) \zeta \tag{24a}$$

Like the interatomic forces, the Fourier matrix composed of the elements $\gamma_i^{\alpha\beta} + \gamma_e^{\alpha\beta}$ has two components; one γ_i is related to the displacements of the positive ions, the other γ_e to the condensation (Eq. (1)) of the medium formed by the conduction electrons.

5. The Acoustic Oscillations of Low Frequency

When the fundamental wave vector S is small compared with all the radii of the first Brillouin zone, the thermal oscillations are propagated with an almost constant velocity $\mathscr{V}$, the coefficient $\phi^2(\sigma)$ (Eq. (13)) is roughly identical with unity, and the interatomic forces are nearly proportional to σ^2. Consequently, the tensorial components $\gamma_i^{\alpha\beta}$ (Eq. (22)) and $\gamma_e^{\alpha\beta}$ (Eq. (23)), taking account of Eq. (3), are approximately expressed by:

$$\gamma_i^{\alpha\beta} = -\frac{\sigma^2}{2\mu} \sum_{\gamma\delta} \left(\sum_a C_a^{\alpha\beta} a^\gamma a^\delta \right) q_\gamma q_\delta$$

$$= \frac{V\sigma^2}{\mu} \sum_{\gamma\delta} c_0^{\alpha\gamma,\beta\delta} q_\gamma q_\delta$$

$$= \frac{\sigma^2}{\rho} \sum_{\gamma\delta} c_0^{\alpha\gamma,\beta\delta} q_\gamma q_\delta \quad (\rho = \mu/V \text{ is the specific mass of the crystal)};$$

$$\gamma_e^{\alpha\beta} = \frac{\sigma^2}{\rho} \mathscr{C} q^\alpha q^\beta$$

As
$$\omega = \mathscr{V} \sigma$$

we obtain:

$$\rho \mathscr{V}^2 \zeta^\alpha = \sum_\beta [(c_0^{\alpha\alpha,\beta\beta} + \mathscr{C}) q_\alpha q_\beta + \sum_{\gamma\delta} c_0^{\alpha\gamma,\beta\delta} q_\gamma q_\delta] \zeta_\beta$$

$$= \sum_\beta [c^{\alpha\alpha,\beta\beta} q_\alpha q_\beta + \sum_{\gamma\delta} c^{\alpha\gamma,\beta\delta} q_\gamma q_\delta] \zeta_\beta$$

where $\gamma \neq \alpha$, $\delta \neq \beta$.

We again meet with the equations, defined by the classical theory of elasticity, which are related to the propagation of elastic waves, but in which the static elastic coefficients $c^{\alpha\gamma,\beta\delta}$ (Eq. (4)) are taken into account, that is, in Voigt's symbols, the coefficients c^{11}, c^{12} and c^{44} (Eq. (4a)).

However, the harmonic oscillations, due to the thermal agitation or to excitation, and whose fundamental wave vector S is small compared with all the radii of a first zone, refer to these static elastic coefficients so long as their wavelength Λ [$\Lambda = (1/|S|)$] remains small compared to the order of the radius of action, r_Θ, of the repulsive thermal forces (Laval, 1959).

Let us consider a harmonic oscillation of increasing wavelength. When this wavelength increases from r_Θ. the elastic coefficients, related to the oscillation and to the expansions and contractions, $t_{\alpha\alpha}$, slowly increase, and when the wavelength becomes very large compared to the radius r_Θ, they become equal to the effective adiabatic elastic coefficients $c_\sigma'^{11}$ and $c_\sigma'^{12}$:

$$c_\sigma'^{11} = c^{11} + \epsilon + T; \quad c_\sigma'^{12} = c^{12} + \epsilon + T$$

$$(c_\sigma'^{44} = c^{44} = c_0^{44})$$

Here, $\epsilon = (T\lambda)/(c\rho)$; $\lambda = dT/d\Theta$ and c is the specific heat at constant volume (Laval, 1957).

Thus we find again the classical equations which determine the propagation of elastic waves, except that the adiabatic elastic coefficients, defined by the classical theory of elasticity, do not take the thermal stress T into account.

REFERENCES

Bhatia, A. B. (1955). *Phys. Rev.* **97**, 363.
Dayal, B. and Tripathi, B. B. (1962). *Proc. roy. Soc.* **A266**, 122.
Dayal, B. and Sharan, B. (1960). *Proc. roy. Soc.* **A259**, 361.
Dayal, B. and Singh, S. P. (1961). *Proc. phys. Soc. Lond.* **78**, 1495.
de Launay, J. (1953). *J. chem. Phys.* **21**, 1975.
Fuchs, K. (1935). *Proc. roy. Soc.* **A151**, 585.
Fuchs, K. (1936). *Proc. roy. Soc.* **A153**, 622.
Laval, J. (1957) *J. Phys. Radium* **18**, 247, 289, 369.
Laval, J. (1959). *J. Phys. Radium* **20**, 577.
Laval, J. (1961). *J. Phys. Radium* **22**, 783.
Seitz, F. (1935). *Phys. Rev.* **47**, 400.
Wignor, E. and Seitz, F. (1933). *Phys. Rev.* **43**, 804.
Wigner, E. and Seitz, F. (1934). *Phys. Rev.* **46**, 509.

DISCUSSION

s. PANCHARATNAM (University of Mysore, Mysore): The Cauchy relations between the elastic constants are not satisfied by many crystals, indicating that the forces are *not* central. In view of the fact that the Cauchy relations appear to have been assumed in the theoretical discussion, could you indicate how the theory can be tested against experiment?

J. LAVAL: Cauchy's relations, which I take into account, exclusively concern the lattice formed by the positive ions; and to these ions I ascribe a spherical symmetry.

From the experimental point of view, it is possible to compare the compressibility coefficients calculated according to the theory I have set forth with the compressibility coefficients measured by Bridgman. The agreement is satisfactory.

s. K. JOSHI (University of Allahabad, Allahabad): Can you give us an estimate of the modification in the relation $c_{11} - c_{12} = e$, because of (a) correlation and exchange effects and (b) the shape of the Fermi surface, which deviates appreciably from the spherical form?

J. LAVAL: The reactions between the positive ions do not sensibly bring in the shape of the Fermi surface. The correlation and exchange energies between the electrons which belong to distinct positive ions are very small for the alkaline metals formed of light atoms (e.g. sodium) because, in these metals, the positive ions have a volume which is small compared with the volume of an atom.

The relations $c_0^{12} = c_0^{44}$ and $c^{12} - c^{44} = \mathscr{C}$ are verified with good accuracy as regards these metals.

The correlation and exchange energies between the electrons and two different ions are important only for metals composed of heavy atoms (e.g. gold, lead). I have only taken cubic crystals into consideration. On account of their cubic symmetry, the correlation and exchange energies, even when large, do not strongly alter the spherical symmetry of the positive ions which constitute the heavy metals. However, for these metals, the relations $c_0^{12} = c_0^{44}$ and $c^{12} - c^{44} = \mathscr{C}$ are probably only roughly satisfactory.

Infra-red and Raman Spectra of Glycine and its Addition Compounds

R. S. KRISHNAN AND P. S. NARAYANAN

Department of Physics, Indian Institute of Science, Bangalore, India

ABSTRACT

A knowledge of the infra-red and Raman spectra of molecules and crystals is known to be invaluable in the study of their vibration spectra, the nature of the interatomic forces, the configuration of the ions present, the changes that occur during any transition that may exist and the strength and orientation of the hydrogen bonds in crystals. A systematic study of the infra-red and Raman spectra of glycine and its addition compounds was therefore undertaken in this laboratory.

α-Glycine, γ-glycine triglycine sulphate, diglycine hydrochloride, diglycine hydrobromide, diglycine nitrate, glycine barium chloride and triglycine selenate have been investigated so far. The spectroscopic observations show the following:

(1) The SO_4 ion in G_3S has at best a plane of symmetry in the crystal and does not play any significant role in the ferro-electric behaviour of G_3S.

(2) The lowering of the frequencies of the stretching vibrations N—H $\cdots$ O, etc., in G_3S is in conformity with the bond distances revealed by X-ray analysis, though there exist also a number of bands in the region 2400–2700 cm^{-1} which cannot be accounted for by the known bond distances.

(3) While, in α- and γ-glycines, the glycine exists in the form of a zwitterion ($NH_3^+CH_2COO^-$), in all other cases, both the glycine with un-ionized COOH group and zwitterions are present.

(4) Infra-red absorption in the region of 2400 cm^{-1} in DGCl is in agreement with the known short O—H $\cdots$ O bond of 2·57 Å in this crystal; however, in DGBr the theoretically expected absorption corresponding to the O—H $\cdots$ O bond of 2·46 Å in this crystal is not observed. It is suggested that this bond, being unusually short, may be completely covalent in character and is therefore very weak in absorption.

(5) The orientation of the CH_2 groups in α-glycine, deduced from the polarization studies in Raman effect, is slightly different from that given by Marsh by X-ray analysis and a quantitative estimate of this deviation has been made.

(6) In $DGNO_3$, the NO_3 groups acquire an O—NO_2 configuration as in alkalyl nitrates and it cannot therefore be freely rotating in this crystal. One should find only a disordered arrangement of such groups in the crystal.

(7) When the Raman spectrum of G_3S was studied just above and below the Curie point, the actual changes observed were not as striking as was hoped for; it was however found that C—H frequency at 2958 and COO$^-$ frequency at 1675 cm^{-1} both increase in frequency on passing through the Curie point to the para-electric phase.

1. INTRODUCTION

The utility of the infra-red and Raman spectra in the study of the vibration spectra of molecules and crystals is well-known and has served particularly in the field of organic chemistry in the identification of the functional groups in large molecules and has been extensively used for qualitative and quantitative analyses. It was on account of these possibilities that a systematic study of glycine (G) and its addition compounds by spectroscopic methods was undertaken in this laboratory, in the hope that they would enable us to understand better, the configuration of the ions present in these series of crystals, the forces between them, the changes that occur during any transition that may exist and the strength and orientation of the hydrogen bonds in these crystals. To restrict the length of the account, we have chosen to present here only some of the significant new results obtained and reference may be made to other publications by us and our co-workers for the experimental details, theoretical basis of interpretation and the earlier results.

Mathias, Miller and Remeika (1956) discovered ferro-electricity in trigylcine sulphate (G_3S) even at room temperature and subsequently the phenomenon was found in triglycine selenate (G_3Se) and also in triglycine fluoberyllate by Hoshino et al. (1957). Since then there has been a growing interest in all the physical properties of these compounds. It has been found that a partial deuteration of G_3S raises its Curie point from 47°C to 60°C, thus indicating that a special arrangement of the glycine molecules and the system of hydrogen bonds in this crystal are responsible for the ferro-electric behaviour. Diglycine nitrate ($DGNO_3$) is also found to be ferro-electric below -67°C (Pepinsky et al., 1958) and though a complete structure analysis has not yet been reported, the nitrogen atoms of the $-NO_3$ groups are believed to be on centres of symmetry.

Among these compounds, the Raman spectrum of solid glycine alone was studied by the earlier workers, the most notable investigations being those by Edsall (1936), Kahovec and Kohlrausch (1936), Ananthakrishnan (1937) and Baba et al. (1949). However, the substance was used by them in the form of powder and the spectrum was excited by λ4046 radiation of mercury. Our knowledge of the spectrum, particularly in the lattice region was therefore meagre. Consequently, using the powerful resonance radiation of mercury (2536·5 Å) as exciter, the Raman spectra of single crystals of glycine (Krishnan and Balasubramanian, 1958a), G_3S (Krishnan and Balasubramanian, 1958b), diglycine hydrochloride (DGCl), diglycine hydrobromide (DGBr), G_3S, $DGNO_3$ (Balasubramanian, 1961), γ-glycine (Balasubramanian et al., 1962) and glycine barium chloride have so far been investigated and orientation and polarization measurements were also made in all of them, except G_3Se, γ-glycine and $DGNO_3$. The spectrum of G_3S has also been studied both above and below the Curie point. Taurel *et al.* (1958) studied the Raman spectrum of G_3S and found evidence for a lowering of the symmetry of the SO_4 ions in G_3S and the existence of glycine as a zwitterion $NH_3^+ CH_2COO^-$) and arrived at the conclusion that the SO_4 ions do not play any significant role in the ferro-electric behaviour of G_3S. Independently Krishnan and Balasubramanian (1958b) also came to the same conclusion.

On the other hand the infra-red absorption spectrum of glycine had been studied earlier in powder form by Blout and Linsley (1952), Klotz and Green (1948), Lenormant (1952), and Tsuboi *et al.* (1958). The study of the infra-red absorption spectra of single crystals of glycine and its addition compounds is rendered difficult by the fact that extremely thin sections of the crystals are required to get the spectral details. Realizing the advantage of studying the reflection spectra in such cases, Robinson and Price (1955) have investigated the reflection spectrum of glycine using polarized radiation and deduced the orientation of the transition moments for various vibrational modes which assist in interpreting the spectrum. More recently, Dodd (1959) has studied the infra-red absorption spectra of glycine and G_3S and their deuterated analogue in the region 625–3200 cm^{-1}. Of these, G_3S alone has been investigated in single crystal form and for different orientations. Narayanan and Khanna (1959), who independently studied the absorption spectra of G and G_3S in the form of mull, came to conclusions in harmony with those of Dodd. Bernard (1961) investigated the infra-red absorption in G_3S in a restricted region to locate the valence vibrations of the very short O—H $\cdots$ O groups in it. Since then, employing KBr disc technique and single crystals in the case of glycine and DGCl and DGBr, a detailed study of infra-red absorption and dichroism has been made and only the salient features will be discussed here. The infra-red absorption spectra of DGCl, DGBr and $DGNO_3$ have not been reported so far.

2. Theoretical Basis of Interpretation

Though the theory of vibrations of molecules is well-developed, it is still not possible to calculate *a priori* the frequencies of the normal modes of vibration in the case of large molecules. Fortunately, the pioneering work of Coblentz and all subsequent investigations in a large number of compounds have shown that each molecular group or ion is characterized by absorption at certain frequencies and this simplifies the problem of interpretation and also, these absorption frequencies serve as tracers for the identification of such groups in molecules or crystals of unknown structures. Further, the small but significant shifts in the frequency of a radical from one compound to another provide additional information regarding the exact nature and influence of the neighbouring groups on the one in question. But it is essential to emphasize also the fact that the correlation rules and charts for the identification of chemical bonds are partly empirical and are based on the experimental observations on the spectra of many compounds; a theoretical justification can however be provided for the near constancy of frequency of end group vibrations and those involving hydrogen. Also, on account of partial overlapping, the bending vibrations cannot often be identified unambiguously. Several correlation charts and excellent accounts have been given by Barnes *et al.* (1944), Colthup (1950), Berl (1950), McMurray and Thornton (1952), Randall *et al.* (1952), Sutherland (1952), Bellamy (1954), West (1956), Lecomte (1958) and Lawson (1961). This approach has been employed in the study of glycine and its addition compounds also and to establish the existence of glycine in the zwitterion configuration ($^+NH_3CH_2COO^-$) in all of them.

In principle, it is necessary to treat the vibrations of the atoms in the unit cell of a crystal to account for their infra-red and Raman spectra. In the harmonic oscillator approximation, it has been shown by Bhagavantam and Venkatarayudu (1948) that only the "limiting vibrations" or "principal vibrations" corresponding to $k \approx 0$, where k is the wave vector, are effective in first order Raman effect and fundamental infra-red absorption. One can therefore apply standard group theoretical methods developed for molecular vibrations to the study of the vibrations of the unit cell of the crystal. But in practice it is found that this procedure always leads to a large number of frequencies, and in the words of Halford (1946), this is due to the fact that "the method introduces and emphasizes distinctions that are without meaning in relation to the available experimental techniques". Therefore Halford (1946) and Hornig (1948) and their co-workers prefer to interpret the spectra in terms of the vibrations of the complex ion in a potential field reflecting the symmetry of the surrounding crystal. This amounts to stating that, when there is more than one such complex group in the unit cell, the homologous ions are not expected to show appreciably different frequencies for the fundamental modes and one can therefore neglect the coupling of the internal vibrations of the different ions in the unit cell. Mathieu and his co-workers (Mathieu, 1945; Couture, 1947) have in fact been utilizing the idea of local or site symmetry to interpret the Raman spectra of crystals and take into consideration the coupling of the vibrations only in those cases where the experimental results justify it. Thus their approach provides the connecting link between the site symmetry idea of Halford and Hornig and the unit cell approach of Bhagavantam and others.

If we consider a molecule in which only one normal mode is excited, then the polarizability can vary during the oscillation and can be expressed as

$$[T] = [T]_0 + \left(\frac{\partial[T]}{\partial Q}\right)_0 Q$$

where $[T]$ is the polarizability tensor, the subscript indicating the value at equilibrium and $\left(\frac{\partial[T]}{\partial Q}\right)_0$ represents the polarizability derivative in the neighbourhood of the equilibrium configuration. Q is the normal co-ordinate. One may also, in the first approximation, suppose that the molecule or ion in the crystal has the same symmetry as in the free state or, in other words, that it is not perturbed by the crystalline field. A comparison of the calculated and observed depolarization values and intensities of the Raman lines in single crystals will then enable us to estimate the nature and perturbation by the crystalline field. By this method, the orientation of water molecules in a large number of crystals (Weil-Marchand, 1957) and also the orientation of the C=O bond in oxalic acid dihydrate and that of the C—N bond in potassium cyanide have been studied. Recently this principle has been employed in our laboratory to study the orientation of the –CH$_2$– groups in glycine and will be dealt with below.

In general, the absorption of infra-red radiation by a crystal can be represented in a manner similar to that employed for refractive index. If the absorption coefficient is small, then in the case of a monoclinic crystal like glycine or G$_3$S or DGNO$_3$, the principal axes of the absorption tensor are the same as those of the refractive index ellipsoid, with one axis coinciding with the crystallographic b axis. But the other two axes of the absorption tensor, though restricted to the (010) plane, need not coincide with those of the principal axes of the refractive index ellipsoid in this plane. Moreover, one has to take into account the dispersion of the axes with wavelength. Hence in principle it is necessary to examine a large number of sections in a monoclinic crystal to draw any definite conclusion regarding the orientation of the transition moments associated with any particular vibration (Mathieu, 1955). It is also necessary that the infra-red absorption should be studied taking into account the fact that only when the plane of polarization coincides with the neutral lines or principal planes of the crystal that the radiation will pass through the crystal without change of state. For other directions, the beam acquires an ellipticity and the interpretation of the spectrum is no longer easy. These points have been well emphasized by Robinson and Price (1955). Another source of error is that if the beam is not normal to the crystal plate, then on account of refraction the beam traverses a direction inside the crystal different from the incident beam and although a calculation is possible, the data necessary for that, namely, the refractive index for the wavelength of the absorption band and its variation over its width are not easy to obtain. Convergence of the incident radiation can also affect the polarized infra-red spectra to a marked extent. (Fraser, 1953; Wood and Mitra, 1958). It is for these reasons and also because of the difficulty in the preparation of extremely thin specimens of large area that reflection methods are preferred (Simon, 1951; Simon and McMahon, 1953; Robinson and Price 1955). The orientation of the transition moments of the fundamental vibrations of a crystal can be determined by standard group theoretical methods. For crystals containing complex ions or molecular groups, a correlation of the transition moments (m) of the internal vibrations or characteristic bond frequencies with the transition moments (M) of the unit cell is possible (Mathieu, 1945, 1955) taking into account also in the process the coupling of the vibrations of the different ions of the same kind. The presence of more than one ion of the same kind on sites of different symmetry can sometimes make the interpretation difficult. The structure of glycine being simple, can be expected to yield spectra capable of easy interpretation. By an analysis of the reflection maxima from a (010) section of glycine, they concluded that for the different azimuths of polarization of the incident light, the beam acquired only a small ellipticity and the vibrations can therefore be regarded as being predominantly in the plane of the $N^{+}CCOO^{-}$ skeleton of the glycine zwitterion. It is therefore reasonable to presume that in sufficiently thin specimens, the azimuth of maximum infra-red absorption for polarized radiation will give a direct indication of the orientation of the transition moment associated with that vibration.

In regard to lattice vibrations, a feature of the glycine compounds worthy of special mention is the "dipolar" nature of the zwitterion and this may result in an appreciable intensity for the absorption arising from the rotatory type of lattice oscillations. Though such oscillations fall outside the range of the prism spectrometer employed by us, the possibility of their interacting with other modes and leading to a widening of absorption maxima exists. On account of its low symmetry and also because of the dipolar nature, the glycine units in these crystals will not librate about their principal axes of inertia (Rousset, 1947); but their high optical anisotropy will lead to a large intensity in Raman spectra for the librations. Unlike in the case of naphthalene and similar crystals it is, however, not easy to work out the variation of intensity with orientation.

3. Results and Discussions

The Raman shifts of glycine and its addition compounds are given in Table I along with the assignments based on the ideas outlined above. In a similar manner, Table II contains the results on infra-red absorption.

TABLE I. Observed Raman shifts in glycine and its addition compounds†

DGCl	DGBr	DGNO$_3$	γ-G	G$_3$S	α-G	Assignment
37 (6)	36 (2)					
	49 (5)	42 (4)	43 (10)	45 (6)	53 (7)	Lattice Oscillation
60 (5)	65 (7)	60 (4)	58 (15)	63 (10)		,,
73 (11)			89 (45)	73 (10)	74 (6s)	,,
	86 (8)	88 (20)			90 (1)	,,
101 (8)	97 (11)	105 (9)	106 (20)	102 (10)	109 (9)	,,
116 (3)	108 (6)					
141 (6)	139 (5)	141 (6)	137 (15)	129 (5)		,,
	158 (7)	153 (13)	152 (40)			,,
171 (7)	169 (5)	168 (5d)	170 (6)	171 (8)	164 (5s)	,,
191 (4)	187 (4)	186 (4d)	186 (8)		183 (4s)	,,
203 (2d)	207 (3)	211 (3d)		220 (4d)	199 (3s)	,,
221 (2d)		250 (1d)	217 (9)			,,
330 (2d)	330 (3d)	311 (1d)		330 (6d)		} C—C torsion
354 (6)	354 (6)	349 (3)	362 (2)	345 (2)	358 (35)	}
				450 (10)		-SO$_4^{--}$—ν_2
				463 (6)		
504 (8)	504 (5)	505(6)	503 (14)	500 (6)	499 (5bd)	COO$^-$ rocking
518 (7)	518 (7)					
		540 (2)				O—NO$_2$ bending
		561 (2)				
575 (4)	571 (4)					
587 (3)	584 (3)			587 (3d)	588 (1)	-COO$^-$ wagging
				610		-SO$_4^{--}$—ν_3
				629 (6d)		
665 (3bd)	600 (2d)	689 (3)	686 (4)	665 (6d)	677 (1)	-COO$^-$ bending
				697 (3)	697 (3d)	
878 (18)	873 (13)	869 (4)		870 (10)		-COOH?
890 (12)	889 (8b)	898 (10)	895 (27)	890 (12)	896 (8b)	CCN stretch
924 (−)	913 (3)	924 (4)	924 (−)	902 (8)	925 (3)	OH out of plane bend?
				980 (20)		-SO$_4^{--}$—ν_4
				1009		
1036 (8)	1034 (10)	1053 (5)	1045 (?)	1040 (6d)	1038 (3s)	CCN stretch
			1049 (8)	1092 (3d)		} -SO$_4^{--}$—ν_4
			1104 (6)			
1106 (10)	1104 (12)	1132 (5)		1114 (8)	1112 (2s)	} NH$_3^+$ rocking
1132 (12)	1124 (10)	1144 (3)	1141 (10)	1134 (8)	1140 (3s)	
			1165 (6)	1164 (4d)		
1249 } (5d) 1267	1248 } (3d) 1264					C—OH?
1302 (8)	1301 (12)			1303 (10d)	1320 (6)	CH$_2$ wagging and twisting

† b = broad, d = diffuse, s = sharp.

TABLE I—*continued*

DGCl	DGBr	DGNO$_3$	γ-G	G$_3$S	α-G	Assignment
1330 (16)	1327 (15)	1322 (10)	1326 (25)	1321 (10d)	1330 (10)	
		1339 (12)	1341 (35)			O—NO$_2$
		1346 (12)	1348 (35)			
1394 (6d)	1396 (8d)	1390 (10)	1391 (30)	1375 (3d)	1395 (2)	C—O stretch?
1414 (20)	1412 (17)	1412 (10)	1405 (30)	1414 (15)	1414 (6d)	—C$\overset{\displaystyle O}{\underset{\displaystyle O}{<}}$ valence
			1411 (25)			
1453 (10)	1450 (8)	1443 (10)	1441 (31)	1441 (12)	1441 (4s)	$\Big\}$ CH$_2$ scissoring
1463 (4d)	1460 (5)				1459 (4d)	
		1497 (5)				
1507 (9)	1506 (10)	1512 (3)	1500 (7)	1483 (6)	1506 (3d)	NH$_3^+$ deformation
1599 (7)	1593 (8)	1584 (9)	1586 (10)	1609 (10)	1563 (4d)	
			1607 (5)			
		1625 (5)				O—NO$_2$
1627 (4d)	1610 (5d)	1644 (5)	1629 (5)	1648 (5)	1640 (1)	—C$\overset{\displaystyle O}{\underset{\displaystyle O}{<}}$ valence
1671 (1)	1670 (1)	1675 (4)	1682 (?)	1675 (10)	1668 (2)	C=O ionized carboxyl
1900 (1d)	1910 (0)					
2030 (2d)	2000 (2d)					
2459 $\Big\}$ (2d)				2528 (1d)	2530 (1d)	OH ... O
2553			2546 (3)			
2613 (4d)	2592 (3d)	2620 (2d)	2612 (5)	2651 (3d)	2630 (3d)	N—H hydrogen bonded
		2642 (2d)				
2652 (4d)	2702 (3d)	2707 (3d)	2663 (5)			N—H hydrogen bonded
	2724 (4d)					
				2763 (4d)	2730 (2d)	,,
2713 (3d)	2785 (7d)	2751 (3d)	2733 (8)			,,
2790 (4d)	2874 (7d)	2806 (3d)	2788 (8)	2874 (5d)	2830 (2d)	,,
2853 (5d)	2907 (8d)	2882 (4d)	2876 (11)	2930 (5d)	2895 (2d)	,,
	2917 (7d)					
2974 (19)	2967 (16)	2966 (15)	2964 (41)	2962 (13)	2974 (5d)	CH stretch
2994 (20)	2986 (20)		2995 (35)	2988 (15)		,,
3006 (11)	3002 (13)	3002 (13)		3004	3008 (8)	,,
3040 (8)	3029 (5)	3039		3022 (13)		NH$_3^+$
3066 (3d)	3067 (4d)					,,
3126 (7d)	3122 (7d)	3143 (2d)	3120 (5)	3150 (6d)	3145 (3d)	,,
3229 (2d)	3221 (4d)	3252 (2d)		3230 (5d)		,,
				3270 (4d)		,,
		3339 (1d)				

TABLE II. Infra-red absorption maxima (cm^{-1}) of glycine and its addition compounds†

α-G	DGCl, DGBr	DGNO$_3$	G$_3$S	Assignment
			470	$\nu_2(SO_4^{--})$
505 (s)	507 (s)	504 (s)	504 (s)	COO$^-$ rocking
	516			
		558 (s)		O—NO$_2$ (bend)
609 (w)	587 (w)	611 (w)		COO$^-$ wagging
			618 (s)	$\nu_3(SO_4^{--})$
	641 (w)	644 (w)	645 (w)	
688 (s)	675 (s)	687 (s)		COO$^-$ bending
	875 (m)		866 (m)	COOH (C—OH out of plane bending)
896 (s)	890 (s)	895 (s)	892 (s)	C—CN (sym. stretch)
916 (s)	920 (s)	933 (s)	918 (s)	CH$_2$ rocking
			980 (m)	$\nu_1(SO_4^{--})$
1032	1030	1045	1025	C—CN (asym. stretch)
			1058 1085	$\nu_4(SO_4^{--})$
1110	1105			
1135	1127	1126	1127	NH$_3^+$ rocking
		1149		
	1245		1210	COOH
	1270		1240	C—CH (in plane bending)
	1295			
		1250 (m)		O—NO$_2$ (stretch)
1310				
1335	1330	1333	1310	CH$_2$ twisting
1405	1440	1381	1381	COO$^-$ (sym. stretch)
1450	1445	1428	1403	CH$_2$ scissoring
			1430	
1505	1492	1483	1480	NH$_3^+$ sym. bending
1590	1595		1540	NH$_3^+$ deg. bending
			1585	
		1610		
1615	1625		1625	COO$^-$ (asym. stretch)
			1650	NH$_3^+$ deg. bending
	1725		1725	C=O
	1765		1760	C=O
			1885	
	1990	1980?	1985	O—H...O valence (stretch), combination
2100		2150		
2200		2220		

† s = strong, m = medium, w = weak, vb = very broad.

TABLE II—*continued*

α-G	DGCl, DGBr	DGNO$_3$	G$_3$S	Assignment
		2270		
	2460			
	2620			
2685		2660		N—H$\cdots$O, O—H$\cdots$O
2780	2770	2760		
2860				
	2940	2900		C—H (stretch)
3170 (vb)	3140	3120 (vb)	3125	NH$_3^+$, N—H$\cdots$O,
				O—H$\cdots$O

A. *Glycine*

In this crystal, the glycine units are shown by the present and earlier spectroscopic studies to be in the zwitterion form (NH$_3^+$CH$_2$COO$^-$) with the almost flat molecules lying in the (010) plane and they are held together by hydrogen bonds between the nitrogen and oxygen atoms to form continuous layers in the crystal (Albrecht and Corey, 1939; Marsh, 1957). The four molecules in the unit cell are all parallel to one another; also the presence of a two-fold axis and a plane of symmetry perpendicular to it leads to all the similar chemical bonds being either parallel or antiparallel to one another.

The existence in the Raman and infra-red spectra of broad bands in the region 2500–3000 cm^{-1} indicates the presence of N—H $\cdots$ O bonds; the large number of sub-bands quite possibly arises from an anharmonic interaction of the allowed overtone and summation frequencies (Sheppard, 1959). One also finds that the difference in the crystal structure between α- and γ-glycine and the nature of the hydrogen bonds are reflected in the changes in their Raman spectra in the region 2500–2900 cm^{-1}, and in the change of the NH$_3^+$ frequency (3145 in α-glycine and 3120 in γ-glycine). The C—H stretching frequencies also exhibit a minor variation (2964 and 2999) in γ-glycine and (2974 and 3008) in α-glycine.

An attempt was therefore made to study the orientation of the CH$_2$ groups in α-glycine from Raman effect. The unperturbed CH$_2$ group is characterized by three modes of vibration, a symmetric stretching of frequency $\nu_1 \sim 2960$ cm^{-1}, an antisymmetric stretching of frequency $\nu_2 \sim 3000$ cm^{-1} and a symmetric bending mode of frequency $\nu_3 \sim 1440$ cm^{-1}. The CH$_2$ group has a symmetry C$_{2v}$ (*mm*). Ou is the internal bisector of the angle HĈH and Ov, the external bisector. Ow is taken normal to both Ou and Ov. With respect to this co-ordinate system, the non-vanishing components of the polarizability derivative for the symmetric and the antisymmetric vibrations are

$$[t_s] = \begin{pmatrix} \epsilon_{uu} & 0 & 0 \\ 0 & \epsilon_{vv} & 0 \\ 0 & 0 & \epsilon_{ww} \end{pmatrix} \qquad\qquad [t_a] = \begin{pmatrix} 0 & \epsilon_{uv} & 0 \\ \epsilon_{uv} & 0 & 0 \\ 0 & 0 & 0 \end{pmatrix}$$

Symmetry type A_1 $\qquad\qquad$ Symmetry type B_2

The values of the components will naturally be different in the different vibrations. If the CH_2 groups do not have the symmetry C_{2v}, on account of, say, the two C—H bonds being non-equivalent, then the group will have a symmetry C_s (or m) only and the components other than those indicated in the polarizability derivative may no longer be zero. It has, however, been emphasized by Halford (1946) that such components which arise on account of the perturbing crystalline field will be comparatively small and may be neglected in most cases. Though the values of the polarizability derivatives of the unperturbed CH_2 group are not known directly, one can calculate them from a knowledge of the C—H bond polarizability derivative and the anisotropy derivative. If 2α is the angle HĈH and a and b respectively are the changes in the polarizability along and perpendicular to the bond, then for a symmetric vibration it is easily shown that

$$[t_s] = 2 \begin{pmatrix} a\cos^2\alpha + b\sin^2\alpha & 0 & 0 \\ 0 & a\sin^2\alpha + b\cos^2\alpha & 0 \\ 0 & 0 & b \end{pmatrix}$$

and for an antisymmetric vibration

$$[t_a] = \begin{pmatrix} 0 & 1 & 0 \\ 1 & 0 & 0 \\ 0 & 0 & 0 \end{pmatrix} (a-b)\sin 2\alpha$$

Yoshino and Bernstein (1958), by a study of the intensity of the Raman lines in methane, ethane and neopentane, determined the values of $a(=\partial\alpha_{ZZ}/\partial r_{CH})$ and $b(=\partial\alpha_{XX}/\partial r_{CH})$ to be

$$\left.\begin{aligned} a &= 2{\cdot}44 \times 10^{-16}\ \text{cm}^2 \\ b &= 0{\cdot}34 \times 10^{-16}\ \text{cm}^2 \end{aligned}\right\} \quad \text{or} \quad \left\{\begin{aligned} a &= -0{\cdot}36 \times 10^{-16}\ \text{cm}^2 \\ b &= 1{\cdot}74 \times 10^{-16}\ \text{cm}^2 \end{aligned}\right.$$

The nomenclature used by Yoshino and Bernstein (1958) has been indicated in parenthesis. Since the first set of values are the physically more appropriate ones, they were employed in the present calculation. For a correlation with Raman data obtained from a single crystal of glycine, it is necessary to take into account the orientation of the CH_2 groups with respect to the axes of the refractive index ellipsoid. If there is only one CH_2 group the relation between the tensors $[t_s]$ and $[t_a]$ and those of the crystal $[T_s]$ and $[T_a]$ is straightforward.

But, when there is more than one molecule or ion in the unit cell, then their oscillations will have to be coupled in a manner consistent with the symmetry species for the crystal. The present calculation was carried out using the orientation of the CH_2 group provided by the atomic parameters given by Marsh (1957) and standard transformations were made to evaluate the tensors $[T_s]$ and $[T_a]$ in the crystal. The depolarization factors (ρ) for the antisymmetric vibration of CH_2 (3008 cm^{-1}) can now be easily evaluated for the six possible orientations of experimentation (notation as in Mathieu, 1945) and are shown in Table III below.

TABLE III. Depolarization factors of the symmetric and asymmetric stretching vibrations of $-CH_2-$ in glycine

	Asymmetric (3008 cm^{-1})		Symmetric (2974 cm^{-1})	
	Observed	Calculated	Observed	Calculated
ρ_1	0·6	0·35	0·09	0·104
ρ_2	2·0	1·25	0·64	0·75
ρ_3	0·34	0·42	0·10	0·04
ρ_4	2·5	3·7	0·45	0·39
ρ_5	0·4	0·49	0·20	0·09
ρ_6	0·9	0·67	0·5	0·14

It was however found that the observed and calculated values of ρ_1, ρ_4 and ρ_6 differed appreciably. By trial and error, it was noticed that the agreement improved when the CH_2 groups were rotated by 7° about Ow and 8° about Ov from the positions given by Marsh. The calculated values in Table III refer to this modified orientation. With this new orientation of the $-CH_2-$ groups the depolarization values for the symmetric vibration of glycine (2974 cm^{-1}) were determined and one sees that the agreement of ρ_5 and ρ_6 with the observed values is not very satisfactory. The difference is more than the possible error in photographic photometry and one is therefore forced to conclude that either the polarizability derivatives have changed slightly in the crystal or that the angle 2α is different from the tetrahedral value which has been assumed.

In α-glycine, as only the hydrogen atoms are out of the plane (010), the vibrational modes involving the motion of the hydrogen atoms can lead to a large change of dipole moment along the b axis as well as in the plane (010); on the other hand modes involving a displacement of the skeletal atoms will give rise to changes of moment predominantly in the cleavage plane (010). All these theoretical expectations are fully borne out by our studies on the infra-red absorption in single crystals of glycine and the results agree well with those reported by Robinson and Price (1954) from reflection. The absorption spectrum of the cleavage section (010) was examined with the plane of polarization oriented at 0°, 30°, 60°, 90°, 120° and 150° to the crystallographic c axis and also when it was parallel to the two-fold axis. The absorption band in the neighbourhood of 3170 cm^{-1} is most intense for radiation polarized at an angle of 30° to the c-axis, showing thereby that the symmetry axis of the NH$_3^+$ group is roughly in this direction. The broad and strong absorption in this region for radiation polarized parallel to the b axis is to be attributed to the NH$_3^+$ degenerate stretching mode and also to the fact that the three N—H bonds are no longer equivalent. Attention should also be drawn to the occurrence of absorption in the region below 2600 cm^{-1}, though the N—H $\cdots$ O distances reported are not short enough to account for these.

The Nujol mull and KBr disc spectra of glycine show absorption maxima at 1615 cm^{-1} and 1595 cm^{-1}. Tsuboi *et al.* have assigned the former to COO$^-$ asymmetric stretching and the latter to NH$_3^+$ bending mode. Dodd (1959) has observed only one band at 1600 cm^{-1} and this has been assigned to COO$^-$ asymmetric stretching mode. The polarized infra-red spectrum reveals however some interesting features. The asymmetric COO vibration can be expected to have its transition moment in a direction nearly perpendicular to the c axis in the cleavage plane, whereas the NH$_3^+$ degenerate bending will have components along all the three axes. The spectrum of glycine shows, when the radiation is polarized parallel to the b axis, an intense absorption band at 1615 cm^{-1} while the spectrum of the cleavage section (010) shows a moderate absorption at 1610 cm^{-1} for all orientations. These results can only be explained on the basis of splitting of the NH$_3^+$ bending mode, a fact supported also by the frequency variation for different azimuths of polarization (Table IV).

The absorption at 1615 cm^{-1} is therefore due to the COO$^-$ asymmetric stretching and one component of the NH$_3^+$ bending mode whereas the absorption at 1590 cm^{-1} is to be explained as being due to the other component of the NH$_3^+$ bending vibration. The polarization characteristics of the 1450 cm^{-1} band due to the –CH$_2$ scissoring vibration, 916 cm^{-1} band due to CH$_2$ rocking and the 896 cm^{-1} band due to C—C—N symmetric stretching are not in accordance with the orientation of the transition moments expected on the basis of the simple "oriented gas model". It is necessary to take into account the strong coupling of the CH$_2$ bending and COO$^-$ asymmetric vibration on the one hand and the coupling of the CH_2 rocking and C—C—N symmetric stretching on the other. The frequency variation of the other bands shown in Table IV shows that the coupling of the vibrations of the different ions and consequent splitting needs to be taken into account.

TABLE IV. Frequencies in cm^{-1} for different azimuths of polarization

0°	30°	60°	90°	120°	150°
896	—	888	890	892	896
902	905	910	913	913	913 w
					921 str
1038	1035	1027	1030	1032	1037
1132	1123	1112	1112	1112	1130
1628	1625	1625	1620	1615	1615

B. *DGCl and DGBr*

DGCl and DGBr both belong to the orthorhombic space group $P2_12_12_1$ and the unit cell contains four molecules of the form DGX (X being the halogen atom). According to Buerger *et al.* (1956) and Hahn and Buerger (1957) these structures contain glycine molecules extending perpendicular to the *b*-axis and zig-zag X—X chains along a screw, parallel to the *c*-axis. They have found that one glycine molecule occurs as a zwitterion while the other had a normal glycine configuration with COOH group. A special feature of these two compounds is the occurrence of a very short hydrogen bond in both (DGCl:O—H $\cdots$ O 2·57 Å; DGBr: O—H $\cdots$ O 2·46 Å). DGBr seems to be the first amino acid compound where N—H $\cdots$ Br bonds have been studied in some detail. As expected from the close similarity of structure, their Raman and infrared spectra are very much alike and the frequencies are also nearly the same (Tables I and II). Though their infra-red spectra have been studied in detail with polarized radiation, on account of the glycine units in these crystals being not so simply arranged as in glycine, a theoretical analysis of the orientation of the transition moments has not yet been made. But these data have been qualitatively made use of in the assignment of the bands. The O—H $\cdots$ O bond of 2·57 Å in DGCl would lead us to expect an infra-red absorption band at about 2450 cm^{-1} (Nakamoto *et al.* 1955) and in the neighbourhood of 1800 cm^{-1} in DGBr (O—H $\cdots$ O: 2·46 Å). While one finds an absorption band in DGCl in the expected region, there is no band of appreciable intensity at 1800 cm^{-1} in DGBr. It is probable that because this bond is extremely short it is almost completely covalent in character and is therefore very weak in absorption.

The presence of infra-red absorption bands in the 1725 cm^{-1} region as well as in the neighbourhood of 1600 cm^{-1} is in conformity with results of X-ray structure analysis.

C. $DGNO_3$

This compound crystallizes in the monoclinic system with the space group $P2_1/a$ and the unit cell contains two molecules of diglycine nitrate. In the preliminary report (Pepinsky et al., 1958) on the structure of $DGNO_3$, it has been suggested that on account of the N atoms being at centres of symmetry, the NO_3 groups are either freely rotating or they are disordered in the crystal phase. The absence of the Raman lines at 1050, 720, 1390 and 830 cm^{-1}, which are ordinarily found for NO_3 ions of D_{3h} symmetry or of lower site symmetry C_s, as is the case here, shows that in $DGNO_3$, the NO_3 groups go over to the O—NO_2 configuration of C_{2v} symmetry as in alkyl nitrates. The spectroscopic behaviour suggests therefore that the NO_3 groups are not freely rotating and the final structure should reveal only a disordered arrangement of O—NO_2 groups. Further the presence of an intense absorption band at 1610 cm^{-1} and the absence of any strong absorption at 870 cm^{-1} indicate that all the glycines are in the zwitterion form only.

D. G_3S

Triglycine sulphate is also monoclinic both above and below the Curie point with the space groups $P2_1/a$ and $P2_1$ respectively. There are two molecules in the unit cell and according to Hoshino et al. (1959) out of three glycine molecules in the crystal one has a zwitterion configuration with the NH_3^+ group out of the plane of the other atoms. The remaining two glycines are monoprotonated and planar within experimental error. The evidence for the existence of both forms of glycine from the spectroscopic observations has been well discussed elsewhere and will not be repeated here. The study of the Raman spectrum of G_3S above and below the Curie point was undertaken in the hope that it would enable us to throw light on the exact nature of the switching and hydrogen bond reorientation mechanism responsible for its ferro-electric behaviour. The actual changes noticed however were not as striking as we had hoped for and among the differences found the prominent ones are: (1) the Raman lines 463 and 1092 cm^{-1} due to the SO_4 ions become weaker above the Curie point; (2) the C—H frequency at 2958 cm^{-1} in the ferro-electric phase shifts to 2963 cm^{-1} in the para-electric phase; (3) in the region 2720–2780 cm^{-1}, two bands at 2728 and 2773 cm^{-1} are observed below 47°C, while above this Curie point only one broad Raman line is found at 2741 cm^{-1} and; (4) the Raman lines at 1675 cm^{-1} and 129 cm^{-1} shift to 1682 and 121 cm^{-1} respectively above 47°C. It is worth pointing

12

out that the lines at 2958 and 1675 cm^{-1} behave in a way normally found only during transitions. Ordinarily an increase of temperature leads only to a lowering of frequency, as in the case of the lattice line 129 cm^{-1}; on the contrary, the former two frequencies show an increase with rise of temperature. A similar quantitative study in the infra-red, both above and below the Curie point is therefore highly desirable.

Acknowledgement

We acknowledge here the active participation and collaboration in the study of glycine and its addition compounds by Dr. R. K. Khanna and Mr. K. Balasubramanian.

REFERENCES

Albrecht, G. and Corey, R. B. (1939). *J. Amer. chem. Soc.* **61**, 1087.

Ananthakrishnan, R. (1937). *Proc. Indian Acad. Sci.* **A5**, 200.

Baba, H., Shimanouchi, T. and Mizushima, S. (1949). *J. chem. Soc. Japan, Pure Chem. Sec.* **70, 333.**

Balasubramanian, K. (1961). *Proc. Indian Acad. Sci.* **A53**, 105.

Balasubramanian, K., Krishnan, R. S. and Yoichi Iitaka (1962). *Bull. chem. Soc. Japan* **35**, 1303.

Barnes, R. B., Gore, R. C., Liddel, V., and Williams, V. Z. (1944). *Infrared Spectroscopy.* Reinhold, New York.

Bellamy, L. J. (1954). *The Infrared Spectra of Complex Molecules.* Methuen, London.

Berl, W. G. (1950). *Physical Methods in Chemical Analysis.* Academic Press, New York.

Bernard, M. P. (1961). *C. R. Acad. Sci., Paris* **252**, 2093.

Bhagavantam, S. and Venkatarayudu, T. (1948). *Theory of Groups and its Application to Physical Problems.* Andhra University, Waltair.

Blout, E. R. and Linsley, S. G. (1952). *J. Amer. chem. Soc.* **74**, 1946.

Buerger, M. J., Barney, Y. E. and Hahn, T. (1956). *Z. Kristallogr.* **108**, 130.

Colthup, N. B. (1950). *J. opt. Soc. Amer.* **40**, 397.

Couture, L. (1947). *Ann., phys., Paris* **2**, 5.

Dodd, D. M. (1959). *Spectrochim. Acta* **12**, 1072.

Edsall, J. T. (1936). *J. chem. Phys.* **4**, 1.

Fraser, R. D. B. (1953). *J. chem. Phys.* **21**, 1511.

Hahn, T. and Buerger, M. J. (1957). *Z. Kristallogr.* **108**, 419.

Halford, R. S. (1946). *J. chem. Phys.* **14**, 8.

Hornig, D. G. (1948). *J. chem. Phys.* **16**, 1063.

Hoshino, S., Mitsui, T., Jona, F. and Pepinsky, R. (1957). *Phys. Rev.* **107**, 1255.

Hoshino, S., Okya, Y. and Pepinsky, R. (1959). *Phys. Rev.* **115**, 323.

Kahovec, L. and Kohlrausch, K. W. F. (1936). *Mh. Chem.* **68**, 359.

Klotz, I. M. and Green, D. M. (1948). *J. phys. Chem.* **52**, 961.

Krishnan, R. S. and Balasubramanian, K. (1958a). *Proc. Indian Acad. Sci.* **A42**, 55.

Krishnan, R. S. and Balasubramanian, K. (1958b). *Proc. Indian Acad. Sci.* **A48**, 138.

Lawson, K. E. (1961). *Infrared Absorption of Inorganic Substances*, Reinhold, New York.

Lecomte, J. (1958). *Handbuch der Physik*, XXVI: Light and Matter II.

Lenormant, H. (1952). *J. Chim. Phys.* **49**, 635.

McMurray, H. L. and Thornton, V. (1952). *Analyt. Chem.* **24**, 318.

Marsh, R. E. (1957). *Acta cryst.* **10**, 814.

Mathieu, J. P. (1945). *Spectres de Vibration et Symmetrie des Molecules et des Cristaux.* Herman, Paris.

Mathieu, J. P. (1955). *J. Phys. Radium* **16**, 219.

Mathias, B. T., Miller, C. E. and Remeika, J. P. (1956). *Phys. Rev.* **104**, 849.

Nakamoto, K., Margoshes, M. and Rundle, R. E. (1955). *J. Amer. chem. Soc.* **77**, 6480.

Narayanan, P. S. and Khanna, R. K. (1959). *Proc. Symp. on Raman and Infrared Spectroscopy.* Agra University, Nainital.

Pepinsky, R., Vedam, K. and Okaya, Y. (1958). *Phys. Rev.* **111**, 430.

Randall, H. M., Fowler, R. G., Dangle, J. R. and Fuson, N. (1952). *Infrared Determination of Organic Structures.* Van Nostrand, New York.

Robinson, T. S. and Price, W. C. (1955). *Mol. Spectros. Rept. Congr. Inst. Petroleum*, p. 211. London.

Rousset, A. (1947). *La Diffusion de la Lumière par les Molécules Rigides.*

Sheppard, N. (1959). *Hydrogen Bond* (Hadzi and Thompson, eds.). Pergamon Press, London.

Simon, I. (1951). *J. opt. Soc. Amer.* **41**, 336.

Simon, I. and McMahon, H. O. (1953). *J. Amer. ceram. Soc.* **36**, 130.

Sutherland, G. B. B. M. (1952). *Advances in Protein Chemistry*, Vol. 7. Academic Press, New York.

Taurel, L. *et al.* (1958). *C. R. Acad. Sci., Paris* **246**, 3042.

Tsuboi, M., Onishi, T., Nagakawa, I., Shimanouchi, T. and Mizushima, S. (1958). *Spectrochim. Acta* **12**, 253.

West, W. (1956). *Chemical Applications of Spectroscopy.* Interscience, New York.

Weil-Marchand (1957). *Ann. Phys., Paris* **2**, 881.

Wood, D. L. and Mitra, S. S. (1958). *J. opt. Soc. Amer.* **48**, 537.

Yoshino, T. and Bernstein, H. J. (1958). *J. mol. Spectr.* **2**, 241.

DISCUSSION

T. MIYAZAWA: Have you made vibrational assignments of the low frequency Raman lines of γ- and α-glycine?

R. S. KRISHNAN: Yes. We have given a reasonable assignment to the observed low frequency Raman lines in both γ- and α-glycine. The infra-red spectrum of γ-glycine has also been studied and reported in the *Bulletin of the Chemical Society of Japan* by Dr. Yoichi Iitaka.

T. MIYAZAWA: I find that you have mentioned that both unionized and zwitterion forms are present. Since this is rather unusual, may I know if you have found any other cases such as these?

R. S. KRISHNAN: No. We have examined only the addition compounds of glycine so far.

S. S. MITRA: Have you tried to identify the low frequency Raman spectra with the O—H librational modes, and with multi-phonon interactions?

R. S. KRISHNAN: Yes. We have taken into account the possibility of the O—H librational or bending modes giving rise to Raman lines in this region while assignments were made. Multi-phonon interactions were eliminated by a consideration of the intensity and influence of temperature on these low frequency lines.

S. S. MITRA : Is it not possible to explain the structure observed in the C—H stretching region arising from combination of internal modes with the librational ones? However, it might be useful to have far infra-red spectral data to do such an analysis.

R. S. KRISHNAN : The new features observed are in the region of frequency shifts of 2400–2800 cm^{-1} and the Raman lines due to the internal modes have frequencies up to 1700 cm^{-1} only and the highest observed lattice frequency is about 200 cm^{-1} and I believe therefore that the idea of combinations cannot be used to explain the observed features.

Optical Lattice Vibrations

Shashanka S. Mitra

Physics Research Division, Armour Research Foundation of Illinois Institute of Technology, Chicago, Illinois, U.S.A.

ABSTRACT

Infra-red absorption in ionic crystals is discussed. The different mechanisms explaining the structure observed in the optical lattice absorption or reflection spectra of alkali halides, compound semiconductors and homopolar crystals such as germanium and silicon are reviewed. Different methods of obtaining the values of refractive index and extinction coefficient from observed reflectance data are described. The reststrahlen spectrum of brucite, $Mg(OH)_2$, is analysed to obtain the values of the optical constants. The reflection maxima for both ordinary and extraordinary rays occur at 515 cm^{-1}. The corresponding absorption maxima at 460 cm^{-1} are assigned to the A_{2u} and E_u lattice fundamentals. The Raman active E_g fundamental occurs at 445 cm^{-1}. The secondary reflection and absorption bands are explained as combination tones arising from multiphonon interactions. An effective ionic charge of 0·72 is obtained for $Mg(OH)_2$ from the Szigeti relation, indicating that it is primarily an ionic crystal.

1. Infra-red Absorption in Ionic Crystals

All ionic solids possess infra-red absorption spectra associated with the stimulation of vibrational motion of ions. The interatomic forces in polar compounds are comparable with electronic binding in atoms; however, the optical lattice vibration spectra of solids lie in the infra-red region (10–100 μ) of the electromagnetic radiation, because ions are some 10^4 times heavier than electrons.

A wavelength around 50 μ corresponds to a wave vector,

$$k = \frac{2\pi}{\lambda} \approx 10^3 \, \text{cm}^{-1}.$$

This is extremely small compared with the cut off of the lattice vibrations, $2\pi/a \approx 10^8 \, \text{cm}^{-1}$ (a being lattice spacing). Thus, to a fair approximation, one may consider the wave vector associated with the electromagnetic field in the infra-red region to be essentially zero. In a cubic crystal, like rock salt, having two oppositely charged particles per unit cell, the three normal modes associated with zero wave vector do not contribute to the dipole moment, and are designated as acoustical modes. The remaining three modes belong to the optical branch and correspond to the resonance

347

frequency, ν_0, at $k = 0$. It may be shown (Peierls, 1955) that the infra-red absorption goes through a maximum near this frequency. For the optical branches, the displacements of the positive and negative ions are in opposite directions. The frequency depends on this direction even for very small k, because of the long-range effect of electrostatic forces as shown by Kellermann (1940). For small k, one normal mode is longitudinal, and the others transverse. However, for the longitudinal mode, it may be shown that the transition probability vanishes. In cubic crystals, the transverse modes have the same frequency corresponding to $k = 0$. There is therefore only one absorption maximum at ν_0. It may also be shown that the frequency of the longitudinal mode is larger than that of the transverse ones. Lyddane, Sachs and Teller (1941) have shown that in an isotropic polar crystal the frequency, ν_{L}, for long wavelength (small k) longitudinal vibrations is given by

$$\nu_{\mathrm{L}} = \nu_0 \left(\frac{\epsilon_0}{\epsilon_\infty} \right)^{1/2} \tag{1}$$

where ϵ_∞ and ϵ_0 are respectively the high and low frequency dielectric constants.

For a diatomic linear chain it may be shown (Mitra, 1962) that

$$\nu_0 = \frac{1}{2\pi} \left(\frac{2f}{\mu} \right)^{1/2} \tag{2}$$

where μ is the reduced mass per unit cell and f the nearest neighbour force constant, which is related to the elastic constant c by the relation $c = fa$. Similar approximate relations have been reported (Mitra and Joshi, 1960) for the ionic crystals in terms of the compressibility χ, the lattice constant a, and the reduced mass μ. For crystals of both NaCl and CsCl type

$$\nu_0 = \frac{1}{2\pi} \left(\frac{3a}{\mu\chi} \right)^{1/2} \tag{3}$$

Equation (3) gives the rough estimate, $\nu_0 = 227 \text{ cm}^{-1}$ in the case of rock salt in satisfactory order-of-magnitude agreement with the observed transmission minimum at 164 cm^{-1}.

In the vicinity of this frequency, strong anomalous dispersion is encountered as is always the case near strong absorption lines. The resulting large values of the refractive index lead to high reflection coefficients at a crystal surface. Multiple reflections from such surfaces cause the frequencies near the resonance line to persist while weakening the other components. This is known as the reststrahlen phenomenon, and is the simplest way of experimentally observing the lattice mode. The reflectivity is very high ($\sim 100\%$) at the reststrahlen frequency in ionic crystals. In fact, the amount of maximum reflection is often an approximate measure of ionic character.

Czerny (1930), Barnes and Czerny (1931), Barnes (1932) and others

TABLE I. Principal absorption and reflection maxima
for alkali halide crystals

Crystal	Absorption (μ)	Reflection (μ)
LiF	32·6	26; 17
NaF	40·6	35·8
NaCl	61·1	52·0
NaBr	74·7	—
NaI	85·5	—
KCl	70·7	63·4
KBr	88·3	82·5
KI	102·0	94
RbCl	84·8	73·8
RbBr	114·0	105
RbI	129·5	117
CsCl	102·0	—
CsBr	134·0	125

TABLE II. Effective charge and reflection maxima of
compound semiconductors

Crystal	Reflection max (μ)	Effective charge / Charge on an electron
ZnS	33	0·96
PbS ·	~ 80	0·8
SnS	—	0·7
SiC	12	~ 1·3 (0·94)
AlSb	30·5	0·48
GaAs	36	0·43
GaSb	43·5	0·30
InP	30·7	0·60
InAs	45	0·56
InSb	52	0·34

(Hohls, 1937; Klier, 1958; Heilmann, 1958) have measured the absorption and reflection spectra of a large number of ionic crystals. The positions of the absorption and reflection maxima for a number of alkali halide crystals are given in Table I. Table II gives the reflection maxima for a number of semiconductors.

2. Optical Constants from Reflection Spectrum

The high absorption associated with the fundamental lattice mode makes it necessary to use very thin samples ($< 1\ \mu$) for a suitable transmission spectral measurement. Information on the absorption in such situations may also be available from the reflectivity, which is large because of the large extinction coefficient. Simon (1951) has shown that the extinction coefficient, k, and the refractive index, n, can be calculated from the measurement of reflectivity at two widely separated angles of incidence. Robinson (1952) has modified Simon's method so as to enable one to evaluate k and n in the vicinity of a strong absorption band from the measurement at normal incidence. The quantities n and k are given by

$$n = \frac{1 - r^2}{1 + r^2 - 2r\cos\theta} \qquad k = \frac{-2r\sin\theta}{1 + r^2 - 2r\cos\theta} \qquad (4)$$

The quantity r^2 is the observed reflectivity. The phase difference, θ, between the incident and the reflected waves is solved by a numerical integration:

$$\theta_c = \frac{1}{\pi} \int_0^\infty \frac{\mathrm{d}\ln r}{\mathrm{d}\omega} \ln \left| \frac{\omega + \omega_c}{\omega - \omega_c} \right| \mathrm{d}\omega \qquad (5)$$

Here θ_c is the value of θ at frequency ω_c.

Another method, especially suitable for the far infra-red region, is often used for the determination of optical constants. This, however, needs the knowledge of visible or ultraviolet refractive index and the low-frequency dielectric constant. Drude's dispersion formula (Born and Huang, 1954) can be written as

$$\epsilon(\omega) = \epsilon_\infty + \frac{\epsilon_0 - \epsilon_\infty}{1 - (\omega/\omega_0)^2 + i(\gamma/\omega_0)(\omega/\omega_0)} \qquad (6)$$

where γ/ω_0 represents a damping term and ϵ_∞ and ϵ_0 are high- and low-frequency dielectric constants. $\epsilon(\omega)$ represents a complex dielectric constant

$$\sqrt{[\epsilon(\omega)]} = n - ik \qquad (7)$$

where n and k are respectively refractive index and extinction coefficient. By expressing equation (6) in terms of its real and imaginary components, one gets

$$n^2 - k^2 = \epsilon_\infty + \frac{(\epsilon_0 - \epsilon_\infty)[1 - (\omega/\omega_0)^2]}{[1 - (\omega/\omega_0)^2]^2 + (\omega/\omega_0)^2(\gamma/\omega_0)^2} \qquad (8)$$

$$2nk = \frac{(\epsilon_0 - \epsilon_\infty)(\gamma/\omega_0)(\omega/\omega_0)}{[1 - (\omega/\omega_0)^2]^2 + (\omega/\omega_0)^2(\gamma/\omega_0)^2} \qquad (9)$$

The reflectance, R, is given by

$$R = \frac{(n-1)^2 + k^2}{(n+1)^2 + k^2} \tag{10}$$

Knowing ϵ_0 and ϵ_∞, R is calculated as a function of ω/ω_0 for several γ/ω_0. The inverse of the peak reflectivity is approximately linear with the damping constant (Haas and Ketelaar, 1956). From the observed value of the peak reflectivity a value is obtained for γ/ω_0. n and k are then calculated using equations (8) and (9). For a more accurate evaluation, equations (8), (9), and (10) are fitted to the observed reflection spectrum by a machine programming and the best values of ϵ_0, ϵ_∞ and γ/ω_0 thus obtained are used to calculate n and k. It may be observed here that although the maximum in k occurs very near $\omega/\omega_0 = 1$, it is the conductivity, $nk\omega$ which undergoes (Moss, 1959) the maximum precisely at $\omega = \omega_0$.

3. MULTIPHONON ABSORPTION

The infra-red absorption spectrum of a diatomic ionic cubic crystal is expected, from elementary theory, to consist of a single line associated with the optical lattice mode of essentially zero propagation vector. The resonance absorption in reality, however, is not infinitely sharp but shows the natural line width due to radiation damping. This is caused by the fact that the re-emission of absorbed radiation limits the lifetime of the excited state. The excited state may also, by some coupling mechanism, transform into a state in which two or more different phonons replace the optical one. This process also limits the lifetime of the optical phonon causing a broadening and/or side bands. Such side bands have indeed been observed (Czerny, 1930; Barnes and Czerny, 1931; Barnes, 1932; Hohls, 1937; Klier, 1958; and Heilmann, 1958) on the short wavelength side of the main absorption or reflection bands of alkali halide crystals. Infra-red lattice absorption bands attributed to multiphonon combinations have also been reported for Ge (Brockhouse and Iyengar, 1958), Si (Johnson, 1959), GaP (Kleinman and Spitzer, 1960), InSb (Fray et. al., 1960), SiC (Patrick and Choyke, 1961), GaAs (Cochran et al., 1961) and AlSb (Turner and Reese, 1962).

For polar crystals, the mechanism of interaction of electromagnetic field with phonons in the crystal lattice causing the side bands has been explained (Blackman, 1933; Born and Blackman, 1933; Barnes et al., 1935) as due to the anharmonic part of the potential energy associated with the lattice vibrations. The interaction of the crystal with the incident photon takes place through the dipole moment. Absorption of a photon creates two phonons, neither of which is a fundamental, through an intermediate state in which the fundamental mode is excited. The theory is, however, phenomenological.

12*

In homopolar crystals such as Ge and Si, the factor group fundamental is inactive because of no dipole moment and thus the above mechanism does not hold good. For such systems, Lax and Burstein (1955) have shown that two phonons can interact directly with the radiation through terms in the electric moment of second or higher order in the atomic displacements. The number of phonons involved corresponds to the order of the term in the electric moment. This mechanism thus predicts combination of more than two phonons, and may operate in polar and ionic crystals, as well as in homopolar crystals. The interactions are governed by the conservation of energy and the wave vector of the photon.

Strictly speaking, the combinations should give rise to continuous absorption. Absorption maxima, however, occur because of singularities in the phonon frequency distribution. Such singularities occur where the dispersion curves for the individual branches are flat, which is the case at or near the edge of the Brillouin zone. A given phonon branch can thus be characterized by a single frequency. The broadening of combination bands is explained as due to strong dependence of the energy at the Brillouin zone boundary on the wave vector direction.

Two types of multiphonon combinations are possible. In summation bands, a photon is absorbed and two or more phonons are emitted. In difference bands a photon and one or more low-frequency phonons are absorbed and one or more high-energy phonons are emitted. The two processes have different temperature dependences.

4. OPTICAL LATTICE VIBRATIONS IN BRUCITE

The brucite, $Mg(OH)_2$, crystal is hexagonal and belongs to the space group D_{3d}^3 ($P\bar{3}m$). The unit cell contains only one $Mg(OH)_2$ group. A factor group analysis indicates (Mitra, 1961) that exclusive of the acoustic modes there are ten external modes distributed among two doubly degenerate vibrations of the rotatory type and two non-degenerate and two doubly degenerate modes of the translatory type.

In ionic crystals, the translatory lattice vibrations are so strong that, except for extremely thin samples, they are practically opaque, correspondingly their reflection is very high. The reflection spectra of brucite for the two polarizations are shown in Fig. 1. The maximum reflective power goes up to 75%, and the band is quite broad and is typical of reststrahlen spectra. The reflection maximum occurs at 515 cm^{-1} and is present in both polarizations. Therefore it seems most probable that both the A_{2u} and the E_u translatory lattice modes are excited at nearly the same frequency.

For the calculation of the optical constants, the dielectric constant of brucite was measured at 1 kc/s for electric field parallel to the c axis, giving $\epsilon_0 = 6 \cdot 7$. The corresponding extraordinary refractive index is $1 \cdot 585$, giving $\epsilon_\infty = 2 \cdot 5$. Figure 2 shows calculated reflection spectra for

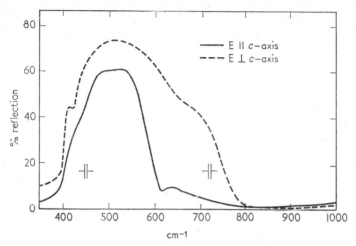

FIG. 1. Reststrahlen spectrum of brucite.

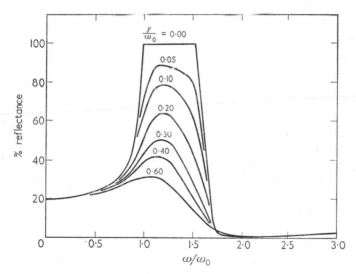

FIG. 2. Reflection spectra of a damped oscillator, with $\epsilon_0 = 6 \cdot 7$ and $\epsilon_\infty = 2 \cdot 5$ (values for the extraordinary ray of brucite).

various damping factors. $1/R_{\max}$ is plotted against γ/ω_0 in Fig. 3. By matching the maximum reflectivity for the extraordinary ray, a value of γ/ω_0 is obtained from Fig. 3. n and k as functions of ω/ω_0 are shown

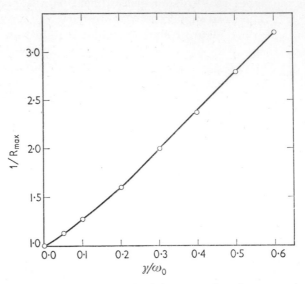

FIG. 3. Inverse of peak reflectivity versus damping constant.

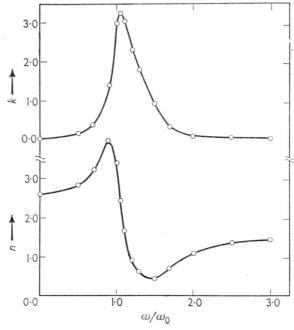

FIG. 4. Optical properties of brucite in the region of fundamental absorption
(E parallel to c-axis).

in Fig. 4. The peak of the absorption given by $4\pi k/\lambda$ occurs at 460 cm^{-1}, corresponding to the A_{2u} fundamental. Since the birefringence in brucite is not very large and the observed reststrahlen peaks occur at the same frequency, the E_u fundamental is also assigned a value of 460 cm^{-1}.

Only one band at 445 cm^{-1} (Mitra, 1957; Krishnamurti, 1959) has been observed in the lattice region of the Raman spectrum. It is difficult to assign this band to any of the modes although the frequency suggests a possible identification with one of the symmetric translational modes.

The low-frequency band at 415 cm^{-1} in the reflection spectrum (a value of 380 cm^{-1} is estimated in transmission) is assigned to the doubly degenerate rotatory mode (E_u), for it is the only band observed in the region and also has the right polarization. It may be mentioned that

TABLE III. Multiphonon combination bands in $Mg(OH)_2$

Observed (cm^{-1})	Assignment	Calculated (cm^{-1})
460	ν_0	—
445	ν_1	—
—	ν_2	190
—	ν_3	125
(590)	$\nu_0 + \nu_3$	590
(650)	$\nu_0 + \nu_2$	650
1010	$2\nu_1 + \nu_3$	1015
1205	$2\nu_1 + \nu_2 + \nu_3$	1205
1383	$3\nu_0$	1380
1412	$\nu_0 + \nu_1 + 2\nu_2 + \nu_3$	1410
1600	$\nu_0 + 2\nu_1 + 2\nu_3$	1600
2000	$2\nu_0 + 2\nu_1 + \nu_2$	2000

while discussing low-frequency vibrations in vibration spectra of molecular crystals Hexter and Dows (1956) have predicted a value of 400 cm^{-1} for the antisymmetric doubly degenerate libration frequency of the hydroxyl ions in brucite.

Since all the infra-red active external modes expected from a factor group analysis have been tentatively assigned, the two unassigned bands at 640 and 700 cm^{-1} observed in the reflection spectra must arise from combinations of the factor group lattice fundamentals with some inter-unit cell phonons. In transmission the positions of these two bands are estimated as 590 and 650 cm^{-1} respectively. Mara (1953) has observed six weak absorption bands between 1000 and 2000 cm^{-1}. Since the only internal modes of brucite are due to the hydroxyl ion and are around $2 \cdot 7 \ \mu$, these bands must also arise from multiphonon combinations. Their high frequency, however, suggests participation of a large number of phonons. With the observed ν_0 at 460 cm^{-1} and the Raman frequency at 445 cm^{-1}, and assuming two optically inactive phonon frequencies at 190 and 125 cm^{-1}, all the observed bands could be explained. Table III shows the assignment.

The ionicity or the effective charge on an ion of brucite is calculated from an equation developed by Szigeti (1949) in which the force constant is expressed in terms of the dielectric constant. The relation is

$$\epsilon_0 = \epsilon_\infty + \left(\frac{\epsilon_\infty + 2}{3}\right)^2 \left(\frac{q^*}{q}\right)^2 \frac{z^2 e^2}{c^2 \pi} \frac{\lambda_0^2}{\overline{m}\overline{v}} \tag{11}$$

where λ_0 is the optical lattice absorption wavelength, $\overline{m}$ and $\overline{v}$ are reduced mass and volume per unit cell and q^*/q is the ionicity or the degree of ionic binding, which ideally should be equal to unity. Although the relation is strictly valid for diatomic cubic crystals, it has been used for such polyatomic crystals as CaF_2 and SiO_2 (Anderson, 1960) and for hexagonal crystals like SiC (Spitzer et. al., 1959). Since in lattice vibrations, the hydroxyl ions move as one unit, the brucite crystal has been regarded as a triatomic crystal. A value of 0·72 is obtained for q^*/q showing that brucite is essentially an ionic crystal, which is also confirmed by the peak value and the band width of the reststrahlen band.

REFERENCES

Anderson, O. L. (1960). *J. Phys. Chem. Solids* **12**, 41.
Barnes, R. B. (1932). *Z. Phys.* **75**, 723.
Barnes, R. B. and Czerny, M. (1931). *Z. Phys.* **72**, 447.
Barnes, R. B., Brattain, R. R. and Seitz, F. (1935). *Phys. Rev.* **48**, 582.
Blackman, M. (1933). *Z. Phys.* **86**, 421.
Born, M. and Blackman, M. (1933). *Z. Phys.* **82**, 551.
Born, M. and Huang, K. (1954). *Dynamical Theory of Crystal Lattices*, p. 121. Oxford University Press, New York.
Brockhouse, B. N. and Iyengar, P. K. (1958). *Phys. Rev.* **111**, 747.
Cochran, W., Fray, S. J., Johnson, F. A., Quarrington, J. E. and Williams, N. (1961). *J. appl. Phys.* **32**, 2102, Supplement.
Czerny, M. (1930). *Z. Phys.* **65**, 600.
Fray, S. J., Johnson, F. A. and Jones, R. H. (1960). *Proc. phys. Soc.* **76**, 939.
Haas, C. and Ketelaar, J. A. A. (1956). *Phys. Rev.* **103**, 564.
Heilmann, G. (1958). *Z. Phys.* **152**, 368.
Hexter, R. M. and Dows, D. A. (1956). *J. chem. Phys.* **25**, 504.
Hohls, H. W. (1937). *Ann. Phys.* **29**, 433.
Johnson, F. A. (1959). *Proc. phys. Soc.* **73**, 265.
Kellermann, E. W. (1940). *Phil. Trans.* **A238**, 513.
Kleinman, D. A. and Spitzer, W. G. (1960). *Phys. Rev.* **118**, 110.
Klier, M. (1958). *Z. Phys.* **150**, 49.
Krishnamurti, D. (1959). *Proc. Indian Acad. Sci.* **A50**, 223.
Lax, M. and Burstein, E. (1955). *Phys. Rev.* **97**, 39.

Lyddane, R. H., Sachs, R. G. and Teller, E. (1941). *Phys. Rev.* **59**, 673.

Mara, R. T. (1953). Dissertation. Ann Arbor, University of Michigan.

Mitra, S. S. (1957). Dissertation. Ann Arbor, University of Michigan.

Mitra, S. S. (1961). *Z. Kristallogr.* **116**, 149.

Mitra, S. S. (1962). *Solid State Physics*, Vol. 13, p. 1. Academic Press, New York.

Mitra, S. S. and Joshi, S. K. (1960). *Physica* **26**, 284, 825.

Moss, T. S. (1959). *Optical Properties of Semiconductors*, p. 17. Academic Press, New York.

Patrick, L. and Choyke, W. J. (1961). *Phys. Rev.* **123**, 813.

Peierls, R. E. (1955). *Quantum Theory of Solids*, p. 54. Clarendon Press, Oxford.

Robinson, T. S. (1952). *Proc. phys. Soc.* **B65**, 910.

Simon, I. (1951). *J. opt. Soc. Amer.* **41**, 336.

Spitzer, W. G., Kleinman, D. and Walsh, D. (1959). *Phys. Rev.* **113**, 127.

Szigeti, B. (1949). *Trans. Faraday Soc.* **45**, 155.

Turner, W. J. and Reese, W. E. (1962). *Phys. Rev.* **127**, 126.

DISCUSSION

S. PANCHARATNAM (University of Mysore, Mysore): I remember that Dr. Krishnamurthy had given a group theoretical analysis of the Raman spectra of magnesium hydroxide in 1959. Does your analysis also agree with his?

S. S. MITRA: Dr. Krishnamurthy, when he wrote his paper, was, I think, not aware of the experimental work done by me in 1957 in the near infra-red and lattice regions. I have discussed those at length in a later article.

The Definition of Antitensors and their Symmetry

I. S. Zheludev

Institute of Crystallography, U.S.S.R. Academy of Science, Moscow, U.S.S.R.

and

Department of Physics, Indian Institute of Science, Bangalore, India

ABSTRACT

The notion of antitensors is given. When co-ordinates are transformed, the signs before combinations of cosines for these antitensors are opposite to the signs of the usual tensors. The signs for the antitensors of the first kind are taken to be minus ($-$) both for rotation and rotation–reflection. The sign for the antitensors of the second kind is taken to be minus ($-$) for rotation and plus ($+$) for rotation–reflection. All the canonical forms of the antitensors of the second rank, of the first and the second kinds are given. It is shown that there are ten groups of complete symmetry for antitensors of the first kind and ten groups of complete symmetry for antitensors of the second kind. The geometrical interpretation of some of these antitensors has also been given.

It is well known that the sign before the combinations of cosines in the formulae for the transformation of co-ordinates for the polar tensor is taken to be plus ($+$) both for a rotation and a rotation–reflection. In the transformation formulae for an axial tensor the positive sign ($+$) is taken only for rotation and the negative ($-$) sign for rotation–reflection. This law (or rule) of signs is written analytically in the form

$$a_{ik} = c_{il} c_{km} a'_{lm}$$

$$a'_{ik} = c_{li} c_{mk} a_{lm} \tag{1}$$

for polar tensors, and in the form

$$A_{ik} = \pm c_{il} c_{km} A'_{lm}$$

$$A'_{ik} = \pm c_{li} c_{mk} A_{lm} \tag{2}$$

for axial tensors.

Let us now introduce quantities for which the formulae of transformation of components are the same as for tensors in Eqs. (1) and (2) but the rules for signs are opposite to the rules in Eqs. (1) and (2), and have the form†

$$b_{ik} = -c_{il} c_{km} b'_{lm}$$

$$b'_{ik} = -c_{li} c_{mk} b_{lm} \tag{3}$$

$$B_{ik} = \mp c_{il} c_{km} B'_{lm}$$

$$B'_{ik} = \mp c_{li} c_{mk} B_{lm} \tag{4}$$

The tensor transformed by Eq. (3) will be called the antitensor of the first kind. The components of this antitensor have a minus sign before the combinations of cosines both for rotation and rotation–reflection. The tensor transformed by formulae (4) will be called an antitensor of the second kind. The components of this antitensor are transformed with the minus sign for a rotation and a plus for a rotation–reflection (see Eq. (4)). We can see that the antitensor of the first kind is opposite to the polar tensor and the antitensor of the second kind is opposite to the axial tensor.

We shall now consider the symmetry of an antitensor of the second rank defined as above. This consideration will be made from the point of view of complete symmetry (Zheludev, 1960a, b, c) using the ideas of the elements of complementary symmetry. By definition, the elements of complementary symmetry are antirotation axes (anti axes) and anti-rotation–reflection axes (antireflection axes). These are denoted by $\underline{1}, \underline{2}, \underline{3}, \underline{4}, \underline{5}, \underline{6}, \ldots \infty$ and $\overline{\underline{1}}, \overline{\underline{2}}, \overline{\underline{3}}, \overline{\underline{4}}, \overline{\underline{5}}, \overline{\underline{6}}, \ldots \overline{\infty}$ respectively. The antireflection axis $\overline{\underline{1}}$, being an antiplane, is denoted by $\underline{m}$; the antireflection axis $\overline{\underline{2}}$ being a symmetry anticentre, is denoted by $\underline{i}$. These elements of anti-symmetry satisfy the following conditions: (a) an antitensor has, as a complementary symmetry element, an antiaxis of any order, if a simple rotation of the system through an angle corresponding to that order causes all components of the antitensor to change sign without change in value; (b) an antitensor has, as a complementary symmetry element, an antireflection axis of any order, if all components of the antitensor change in sign without change in value when the co-ordinate system is trans-formed according to an operation of the rotation–reflection axis. We shall call the group for an antitensor, which includes both the ordinary symmetry operations (rotations and rotation–reflections) as well as the corresponding operations of complementary symmetry (namely antirota-tions and antirotation–reflections), as the "complete" symmetry group of the antitensor.

† The definition of the antitensors here is given by means of the antitensors of the second rank, but it is possible to give the definition generally.

Let us determine, for example, the symmetry of one of the antitensors of the first kind, given by

$$
\begin{array}{ccc}
b_{11} & -b_{12} & b_{13} \\
b_{12} & -b_{11} & -b_{13} \\
-b_{13} & b_{13} & 0
\end{array} \tag{5}
$$

We will prove that this antitensor possesses a two-fold axis that lies in the $X_1 X_2$ plane of the co-ordinate system and is at an angle of $45°$ with the axes X_1 and X_2, a symmetry plane perpendicular to the two-fold axis and an anticentre $\underline{i}$.†

The cosine matrix corresponding to a $180°$ rotation of the co-ordinate system about the above mentioned two-fold axis has the form

$$
\begin{array}{ccc}
0 & -1 & 0 \\
-1 & 0 & 0 \\
0 & 0 & -1
\end{array}
$$

On the basis of transformation formulae (3) for the components of a tensor, we obtain

$$
b'_{11} = b_{11}; \quad b'_{12} = -b_{12}; \quad b'_{13} = b_{13}
$$
$$
b'_{21} = b_{12}; \quad b'_{22} = -b_{11}; \quad b'_{23} = -b_{13}
$$
$$
b'_{31} = -b_{13}; \quad b'_{32} = b_{13}; \quad b'_{33} = 0
$$

which shows that the given axis is a two-fold axis for this antitensor. An analogous situation occurs also for a reflection in a plane which is perpendicular to the two-fold axis, the cosine matrix of which has the form

$$
\begin{array}{ccc}
0 & -1 & 0 \\
-1 & 0 & 0 \\
0 & 0 & 1
\end{array}
$$

Using this matrix it can be shown that this plane is a symmetry plane of the antitensor (5).

In the case of an inversion of the co-ordinate system, which is described by the cosine matrix

$$
\begin{array}{ccc}
-1 & 0 & 0 \\
0 & -1 & 0 \\
0 & 0 & -1
\end{array}
$$

† All the antitensors of the first kind have an anticentre $\underline{i}$ and all the antitensors of the second kind have a centre of symmetry i.

the components of the antitensor (5) will be equal to

$$b'_{11} = -b_{11}; \quad b'_{12} = b_{12}; \quad b'_{13} = -b_{13};$$

$$b'_{21} = -b_{12}; \quad b'_{22} = b_{11}; \quad b'_{23} = b_{13};$$

$$b'_{31} = b_{13}; \quad b'_{32} = -b_{13}; \quad b'_{33} = 0$$

which show that this antitensor has an anticentre $\underline{i}$. It can be shown that (5) has no symmetry elements other than 2, m and $\underline{i}$. Thus, the complete symmetry group of the antitensor (5) can be written in the form $(2:m)$.†

It is not necessary to find in detail all the elements of the complete symmetry for all antitensors to determine their group of total symmetry. For this purpose we can use the complete symmetry of the corresponding tensors (Zheludev, 1960a) and the rule which follows from the rule of signs for the antitensors, namely that every element of symmetry of a tensor must be replaced by the element of antisymmetry of the corresponding antitensor. At the same time, every element of antisymmetry of a tensor must be replaced by the element of symmetry of the corresponding antitensor.

Let us consider two examples. The symmetry group of a scalar, namely

$$\begin{matrix} a_{11} & 0 & 0 \\ 0 & a_{11} & 0 \\ 0 & 0 & a_{11} \end{matrix}$$

is written in the form $\infty/m \cdot \infty : m$. A one-colour sphere has such a symmetry. The total set of the elements of complete symmetry of the scalar can be written in the form‡

$$\infty, \quad \infty 2, \quad m, \quad \infty m, \quad i$$

The corresponding quantity among the antitensors, which can be called the antiscalar, according to the above-mentioned rule, will have the elements of symmetry

$$\underline{\infty}, \quad \infty\underline{2}, \quad \underline{m}, \quad \infty\underline{m}, \quad \underline{i}$$

and its group of complete symmetry can be written in the form $(\underline{\infty}/\underline{m} \cdot \underline{\infty} : \underline{m})$.

---

† We shall denote the group of complete symmetry of an antitensor by enclosing it in parentheses ( ), as distinguished from the group of an ordinary tensor which is written without. In the symbols, only the main elements of symmetry of the group are given. The symbol (:) means that the plane is perpendicular to the axis; the symbol (·) means that the plane is parallel to the axis.

‡ The plane perpendicular to the axis ∞ is written earlier and the planes parallel to it are written next.

We may take another example. The antisymmetrical axial tensor (the polar vector) has the group of the complete symmetry $m \cdot \infty : \underline{m}$ and the set of the elements of complete symmetry

$$\infty, \quad \infty\underline{2}, \quad \underline{m}, \quad \infty m, \quad \underline{i}$$

According to the above-mentioned rule, the antisymmetrical antitensor of the second rank (the polar antivector) will have the elements of complete symmetry

$$\underline{\infty}, \quad \infty 2, \quad m, \quad \infty\underline{m}, \quad i$$

and its group of complete symmetry can be written in the form $(\underline{m} \cdot \infty : m)$.

All the possible groups of complete symmetry for all the canonical forms of the antitensors of the first and second kind are given in Tables I and II.

The geometrical interpretation of scalars, vectors and tensors of the second rank was given in the papers by Zheludev (1957a, b, c). Here, we shall give only the geometrical interpretation of an antiscalar, an antipseudoscalar, a polar antivector and an axial antivector.

As may easily be seen, a sphere shows correctly the symmetry of an antiscalar [group $(\underline{\infty}/m \cdot \infty : \underline{m})$] if the diameters of the sphere are considered to be polar vectors. These vectors are arranged in such a manner that the "positive" ends and the "negative" ends (e.g. the black and the white ends) occur at random on the surface of the sphere. Every plane passing across the centre of the sphere is an antiplane; every axis is an antiaxis and such a sphere will possess an anticentre. A figure containing four polar vectors that are oriented perpendicular to the faces of a regular tetrahedron will represent this sphere as an approximation.

The model of an antipseudoscalar [group $(\infty/m \cdot \infty : m)$] is analogous to the previous sphere, but in this case every diameter is an axial vector.

The polar antivector [group $(\underline{m} \cdot \underline{\infty} : m)$] may be imagined as a cylinder which has one half of all the lines parallel to the axis coloured white and the other half coloured black. All these lines are arranged at random. In the case of an axial antivector [group $(m \cdot \infty : \underline{m})$] these lines are twisted; half of them to the right and the other half to the left. These lines are also arranged randomly.

The geometrical interpretation of antitensors is not as simple as for tensors; but this is to be expected, for the antitensors are rather "strange" quantities. For example they can change sign for a rotation by $360°$ and so on.

TABLE I. Canonical form and complete symmetry of antitensors of the first kind of rank two

Name of the quantity	Canonical form of the antitensor			Complete symmetry group of the antitensor	Orientation of the axes
Antiscalar	b_{11}	0	0	$(\underline{\infty}/\underline{m} \cdot \underline{\infty} : \underline{m})$	Axes oriented arbitrarily
	0	b_{11}	0		
	0	0	b_{11}		
Antitensor of the first kind	b_{11}	0	0	$(\underline{m} \cdot \infty : \underline{m})$	The axis ∞ coincides with the axis $\overline{X}_3$
	0	b_{11}	0		
	0	0	b_{33}		
	b_{11}	0	0	$(\underline{m} \cdot 2 : \underline{m})$	The axes $\underline{2}$ coincide with axes X_1, $\overline{X}_2$, X_3
	0	b_{22}	0		
	0	0	b_{33}		
	b_{11}	0	0	$(\underline{m} \cdot 4 : \underline{m})$	The axis 4 coincides with the axis X_3; the axes $\underline{2}$ coincide with the axes $\overline{X}_1$, X_2
	0	$-b_{11}$	0		
	0	0	0		
Axial antivector	0	$-b_{12}$	0	$(m \cdot \underline{\infty} : \underline{m})$	The axis ∞ of the axial antivector coincides with the axis X_3
	b_{12}	0	0		
	0	0	0		
Combination of an antiscalar and of an axial antivector	b_{11}	$-b_{12}$	0	$(\underline{\infty} : \underline{m})$	The axis ∞ of the antivector coincides with the axis X_3
	b_{12}	b_{11}	0		
	0	0	b_{11}		
Combination of an antitensor of the first kind and of an axial antivector	b_{11}	$-b_{12}$	0	$(\underline{\infty} : \underline{m})$	The axes ∞ of the antitensor of the first kind and the axial antivector coincide with the axis X_3
	b_{12}	b_{11}	0		
	0	0	b_{33}		

TABLE I—*continued*

Name of the quantity	Canonical form of the antitensor			Complete symmetry group of the antitensor	Orientation of the axes
Combination of an anti-tensor of the first kind and of an axial antivector	b_{11}	$-b_{12}$	0	$(\underline{2}:\underline{m})$	The axis ∞ of the antitensor of the first kind coincides with the axis X_1; the axis ∞ of the axial antivector coincides with the axis X_3
	b_{12}	b_{22}	0		
	0	0	b_{22}		
	b_{11}	$-b_{12}$	0	$(\underline{2}:\underline{m})$	The axes $\underline{2}$ of the antitensor of the first kind coincide with the axes X_1, X_2, X_3; the axis ∞ of the axial antivector coincides with the axis X_3
	b_{12}	b_{22}	0		
	0	0	b_{33}		
	b_{11}	$-b_{12}$	0	$(m \cdot \underline{2}:\underline{m})$	The axis 4 of the antitensor of the first kind coincides with the axis X_3; the axis ∞ of the axial antivector coincides with the axis X_3
	b_{12}	$-b_{11}$	0		
	0	0	0		
	b_{11}	$-b_{12}$	b_{13}	$(2:m)$	The axis 4 of the antitensor of the first kind coincides with the axis X_3; the axis ∞ of the axial antivector lies at one of the symmetry planes of the antitensor of the first kind, but does not coincide with the axis X_3
	b_{12}	$-b_{11}$	$-b_{13}$		
	$-b_{13}$	b_{13}	0		
	b_{11}	$-b_{12}$	b_{13}	$(\underline{\bar{2}})$	The axis ∞ of the antitensor of the first kind coincides with the axis X_3; the axis ∞ of the axial antivector does not coincide with any of the axes X_1, X_2, X_3
	b_{12}	b_{11}	$-b_{23}$		
	$-b_{13}$	b_{23}	b_{33}		
	b_{11}	$-b_{12}$	b_{13}	$(\underline{\bar{2}})$	The axes $\underline{2}$ of the antitensor of the first kind coincide with the axes X_1, X_2, X_3; the axis ∞ of the axial antivector does not coincide with any of the axes X_1, X_2, X_3
	b_{12}	b_{22}	$-b_{23}$		
	$-b_{13}$	b_{23}	b_{33}		

TABLE II. Canonical form and complete symmetry of antitensors of the second kind of rank two

Name of the quantity	Canonical form of the antitensor			Complete symmetry group of the antitensor	Orientation of the axes
Anti-pseudo scalar	B_{11}	0	0	$(\underline{\infty}/m \cdot \underline{\infty} : m)$	Axes oriented arbitrarily
	0	B_{11}	0		
	0	0	B_{11}		
Antitensors of the first kind	B_{11}	0	0	$(m \cdot \underline{\infty} : m)$	The axis ∞ coincides with the $\overline{axis}$ X_3
	0	B_{11}	0		
	0	0	B_{33}		
	B_{11}	0	0	$(m \cdot \underline{2} : m)$	The axes 2 coincide with axes $X_1, \overline{X}_2, X_3$
	0	B_{22}	0		
	0	0	B_{33}		
	B_{11}	0	0	$(\underline{m} \cdot 4 : m)$	The axis 4 coincides with the axis X_3; the axes 2 coincide with the axes X_1, X_2
	0	$-B_{11}$	0		
	0	0	0		
Polar antivector	0	$-B_{12}$	0	$(\underline{m} \cdot \underline{\infty} : m)$	The axis $\underline{\infty}$ of the polar antivector coincides with the axis X_3
	B_{12}	0	0		
	0	0	0		
Combination of anti-pseudo-scalar and of a polar antivector	B_{11}	$-B_{12}$	0	$(\underline{\infty} : m)$	The axis $\underline{\infty}$ of the polar antivector coincides with the axis X_3
	B_{12}	B_{11}	0		
	0	0	B_{11}		
Combination of an anti-tensor of the second kind and of a polar antivector	B_{11}	$-B_{12}$	B_{13}	$(\underline{\infty} : m)$	The axes ∞ of the antitensor of the second kind and the polar antivector coincide with the axis X_3
	B_{12}	B_{11}	0		
	0	0	B_{33}		

TABLE II—*continued*

Name of the quantity	Canonical form of the antitensor			Complete symmetry group of the antitensor	Orientation of the axes
Combination of an anti-tensor of the second kind and a polar antivector	B_{11}	$-B_{12}$	0	$(2:m)$	The axis ∞ of the antitensor of the second kind coincides with the axis X_1; the axis ∞ of the polar antivector coincides with the axis X_3
	B_{12}	B_{22}	0		
	0	0	B_{22}		
	B_{11}	$-B_{12}$	0	$(\underline{2}:m)$	The axes 2 of the antitensor of the first kind coincide with the axes X_1, X_2, X_3. The axis ∞ of the polar antivector coincides with the axis X_3
	B_{12}	B_{22}	0		
	0	0	B_{33}		
	B_{11}	$-B_{12}$	0	$(\underline{m}\cdot 2:\underline{m})$	The axis 4 of the antitensor of the second kind coincides with the axis X_3; the axis ∞ of the polar antivector coincides with the axis X_3
	B_{12}	$-B_{11}$	0		
	0	0	0		
	B_{11}	$-B_{12}$	B_{13}	$(2:\underline{m})$	The axis 4 of the antitensor of the second kind coincides with the axis X_3; the axis ∞ of the polar antivector lies at one of the symmetry planes of the antitensor of the second kind, but does not coincide with the axis X_3
	B_{12}	$-B_{11}$	$-B_{13}$		
	$-D_{13}$	B_{13}	0		
	B_{11}	$-B_{12}$	B_{13}	$(\bar{2})$	The axis ∞ of the antitensor of the second kind coincides with the axis X_3; the axis ∞ of the polar antivector does not coincide with any of the axes X_1, X_2, X_3
	B_{12}	B_{11}	$-B_{23}$		
	$-B_{13}$	B_{23}	B_{33}		
	B_{11}	$-B_{12}$	B_{13}	$(\bar{2})$	The axis 2 of the antitensor of the second kind coincides with the axes X_1, X_2, X_3; the axis ∞ of the polar antivector does not coincide with any of the axes X_1, X_2, X_3
	B_{12}	B_{22}	$-B_{23}$		
	$-B_{13}$	B_{23}	B_{33}		

REFERENCES

Zheludev, I. S. (1957a). *Kristallografiya* **2**, 207.
Zheludev, I. S. (1957b). *Kristallografiya* **2**, 334.
Zheludev, I. S. (1957c). *Kristallografiya* **2**, 728.
Zheludev, I. S. (1960a). *Kristallografiya* **5**, 346; English translation *Soviet Physics–Crystallography* **5**, 328 (1960).
Zheludev, I. S. (1960b). *Kristallografiya* **5**, 508; English translation *Soviet Physics—Crystallography* **5**, 489 (1961).
Zheludev, I. S. (1960c). *Izv. Akad. Nauk S.S.S.R.* Ser. Phys. **24**, 1436; not yet translated.

Author Index

Numbers in italics indicate the page on which the reference is listed.

A

Abrahams, S. C., 243, *254*, 285, *291*, 309, *315*
Abrams. M. C., *275*
Adamsky. R. F., 197, 204, *205*
Albrecht, G., 338, *344*
Ananthakrishnan, R., 330, *344*
Anderson, O. L., *356*
Andresen, A. F., 127, *131*
Anzenhofer, K., 51, *65*
Aravindakshan, C., 228, *235*
Arndt, U. W., 127, *131*, *308*
Atoji. M., 272, 273, *275*
Attard, A. E., 118, *121*
Authier, A., 166, *172*
Averbach, B. L., 184, *188*
Azároff, L. V., 110, 112, 113, 115, 117, 118, *121*, *122*

B

Baba, H., 330, *344*
Bacon, G. E., 269, 273, *275*
Bagchi, S. N., 110, *122*
Balasubramanian, K., 330, 331, *344*
Barnes, R. B., 332, *344*, 349, 351, *356*
Barney, Y. E., 342, *344*
Barrett, C. S., 109, *122*
Batterman, B. W., 111, 116, *122*, *143*
Bellamy, L. J., 332, *344*
Berg, W., 109, *122*
Berl, W. G., 332, *344*
Bernal, J. C., 274, *275*
Bernard, M. P., 331, *344*
Bernstein, H. J., 339, *345*
Bertaut, E. F., 43, 47, 49, *50*
Bethe, H. A., 153, *172*, 263, *268*
Beurskens-Kerssen, G., 231, *235*
Bhagavantam, S., 332, *344*
Bhatia, A. B., 322, *327*
Bhide, V. G., 179, *188*
Bijvoet, J. M., 26, *41*, 229, *235*, 243, 244, 247, *254*

Black, P. J., 110, *122*

Blackman, M., 351, *356*
Blout, E. R., 331, *344*
Bokhoven, C., 26, *41*
Bonse, U., 115, *122*, 145, *152*
Borie, B., 184, *188*
Born, M., 158, *172*, 235, *236*, 350, 351, *356*
Borrmann, G., 102, 103, 107, *108*, 109, *122*
Bragg, R. H., 110, 113, *122*
Brattain, R. R., 351, *356*
Brill, R., 110, 116, *122*, 127, *131*
Brockhouse, B. N., 289, *291*, 351, *356*
Brown, P. J., 111, *122*
Buerger, M. J., 4, 6, 11, *14*, 25, *41*, 81, 84, 250, 251, 252, *254*, 342, *344*
Burstein, E., 352, *356*
Busing, W. R., 270, 271, 273, 274, *275*, *276*

C

Chambers, F. W., 140, *143*
Chandrasekaran, K. S., 110, *122*, 127, 129, *131*, 139, *143*, 225, *236*
Chandrasekhar, S., 110, 113, *122*, 125, 126, 129, *131*, 139, *143*
Chatar Singh, 67, 70, 71, *77*
Chidambaram, R., 272, *275*, *276*
Choyke, W. J., 351, *357*
Cochran, W., 49, *50*, 73, *77*, 117, 120, *122*, 351, *356*
Cole, H., 140, *143*
Collin, R. L., 243, *254*, 309, *315*
Colthup, N. B., 332, *344*
Corey, R. B., 338, *344*
Couture, L., 332, *344*
Cowley, J. M., 166, *172*, 177, *188*
Cruickshank, D. W. J., 120, *122*
Curry, N. A., 273, *275*
Czerny, M., 349, 351, *356*

369

D

Dangle, J. R., 332, *345*
Daniel, V., 186, *188*
Darwin, C. G., 109, 110, *122*, 153, 166, *172*
Dasannacharya, B. A., 287, *291*
Dauben, C. H., 119, *122*, 243, *254*
Dayal, B., 321, 322, *327*
Dehlinger, U., 186, *188*
de Launay, J., 322, *327*
De Marco, J. J., 111, *123*
Dickerson, R. E., 26, *41*
Dodd, D. M., 331, 341, *344*
Donnay, G., 182, *188*
Douglas, A. S., 73, *77*
Dows, D. A., 355, *356*

E

Edsall, J. T., 330, *344*
Ehrenreich, H., 120, *122*
Ewald, P. P., 109, *122*, 153, *172*, 235, *236*

F

Fan, Y., 119, *123*
Fankuchen, I., 243, *254*, 309, *315*
Faulkner, T. H., 127, *131*, *308*
Forsyth, J. B., 111, *122*
Fowler, R. G., 332, *345*
Frank, F. C., 179, *188*, 197, *205*
Fraser, R. C., 273, 274, *276*
Fraser, R. D. B., 334, *344*
Fray, S. J., 351, *356*
Freeman, A. J., 111, *122*
Fuchs, K., 321, *327*
Fuson, N., 332, *345*

G

Garrett, B. S., 273, *276*, 285, *291*
Gasilova, E. B., 204, *205*
Gay, P., 115, *122*
Gliky, N. V., 204, *205*
Goetze, G. W., 22, *23*
Gore, R. C., 332, *344*
Green, D. M., 331, *344*
Grimm, H. G., 110, 116, *122*, 127, *131*
Gryder, J. W., 182, *188*
Guinier, A., 109, *122*, 187, *188*

H

Haas, C., 351, *356*
Hägg, G., 184, *188*
Hahn, T., 342, *344*
Halford, R. S., 332, 339, *344*
Hamilton, J. E., 229, 231, *236*
Hamilton, W., 274, *276*
Harada, J., 263, *268*
Hargreaves, M. E., 186, *188*
Harker, D., 20, *23*, 26, *41*
Hartwig, W., 109, *122*
Hashimoto, H., 261, *268*
Hattori, H., 165, 166, *172*
Hauptman, H., 49, *50*, 80, *84*
Heidenreich, R. D., 162, *172*
Heilmann, G., 349, 351, *356*
Hellner, E., 178, 182, *188*
Hendricks, S. B., 178, *188*
Hermann, C., 110, 116, *122*, 127, *131*, 229, *236*
Hexter, R. M., 355, *356*
Hildebrandt, G., 103, 107, *108*
Hirsch, P. B., 113, 115, *122*, 133, 134, *143*, 166, *172*
Hoerni, J. A., 264, *268*
Hohls, H. W., 349, 351, *356*
Honjo, G., 197, 198, *205*
Hoppe, W., 51, 61, *65*
Hornig, D. G., 332, *344*
Hosemann, R., 110, *122*, 182, *188*
Hoshino, S., 330, 343, *344*
Howie, A., 166, 171, *172*
Huang, K., 350, *356*
Huber, R., 51, 61, *65*
Hughes, J. W., 216, *222*
Hull, A. W., 204, *205*
Hume-Rothery, W., 111, *122*
Hunter, L. P., *143*
Hurst, D. G., 282, *291*
Hvoslef, J., 273, *276*

I

Ibers, J. A., 259, 260, 261, 263, *268*
Iitaka, Yoichi, 330, *344*
Irmler, H., 109, *122*
Iyengar, P. K., 287, 290, *291*, 351, *356*

J

Jacobson, R. A., 80, *84*
Jagodzinski, H., 178, 180, 182, 184, *188*, 197, *205*